CURRENT TOPICS IN

DEVELOPMENTAL BIOLOGY

VOLUME 12

CURRENT TOPICS IN
DEVELOPMENTAL BIOLOGY

EDITED BY

A. A. MOSCONA

DEPARTMENTS OF BIOLOGY AND PATHOLOGY
THE UNIVERSITY OF CHICAGO
CHICAGO, ILLINOIS

ALBERTO MONROY

STAZIONE ZOOLOGICA
NAPLES, ITALY

VOLUME 12
Fertilization

1978

ACADEMIC PRESS   New York · San Francisco · London

A Subsidiary of Harcourt Brace Jovanovich, Publishers

ACADEMIC PRESS, INC.
111 Fifth Avenue, New York, New York 10003

United Kingdom Edition published by
ACADEMIC PRESS, INC. (LONDON) LTD.
24/28 Oval Road, London NW1 7DX

LIBRARY OF CONGRESS CATALOG CARD NUMBER: 66–28604

ISBN 0–12–153112–0

PRINTED IN THE UNITED STATES OF AMERICA

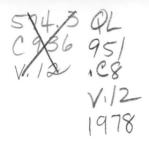

CONTENTS

CHAPTER 1. **Patterns in Metazoan Fertilization**
C. R. AUSTIN

CHAPTER 2. **Biochemistry of Male Germ Cell Differentiation in Mammals: RNA Synthesis in Meiotic and Postmeiotic Cells**
V. MONESI, R. GEREMIA, A. D'AGOSTINO, AND C. BOITANI

CHAPTER 3. **Cell Communication, Cell Union, and Initiation of Meiosis in Ciliate Conjugation**
AKIO MIYAKE

CHAPTER 4. **Sperm–Egg Association in Mammals**
R. YANAGIMACHI

CHAPTER 5. **Sperm and Egg Receptors Involved in Fertilization**
CHARLES B. METZ

CHAPTER 6. **Transformations of Sperm Nuclei upon Insemination**
FRANK J. LONGO AND MEL KUNKLE

CHAPTER 7. **Mechanisms of Activation of Sperm and Egg During
Fertilization of Sea Urchin Gametes**
DAVID EPEL

LIST OF CONTRIBUTORS

Numbers in parentheses indicate the pages on which the authors' contributions begin.

C. R. Austin, *Physiological Laboratory, Cambridge University, Cambridge, England* (1)

C. Boitani, *Institute of Histology and General Embryology, University of Rome, Rome, Italy* (11)

A. D'Agostino, *Institute of Histology and General Embryology, University of Rome, Rome, Italy* (11)

David Epel, *Hopkins Marine Station, Department of Biological Sciences, Stanford University, Pacific Grove, California* (185)

R. Geremia, *Institute of Histology and General Embryology, University of Rome, Rome, Italy* (11)

Mel Kunkle,* *Department of Anatomy, University of Tennessee, Memphis, Tennessee* (149)

Frank J. Longo, *Department of Anatomy, University of Iowa, Iowa City, Iowa* (149)

Charles B. Metz, *Institute for Molecular and Cellular Evolution, University of Miami, Miami, Florida* (107)

Akio Miyake,† *Instituto di Zoologia, Universitá di Pisa, Pisa, Italy* (37)

V. Monesi, *Institute of Histology and General Embryology, University of Rome, Rome, Italy* (11)

R. Yanagimachi, *Department of Anatomy and Reproductive Biology, University of Hawaii School of Medicine, Honolulu, Hawaii* (83)

* Present address: Department of Pharmacology, Baylor College of Medicine, Houston, Texas 77025.

† Present address: Zoologisches Institut der Universität, 4400 Münster, West Germany.

PREFACE

In the past several years the study of Fertilization has moved fast, and important advances have been made. For this reason, we thought it appropriate to collect in this volume of *Current Topics in Developmental Biology* a series of contributions focusing on some of the most relevant aspects of the mechanisms of Fertilization. We thank the contributors for their cooperation and the staff of Academic Press for their efforts to expedite publication.

A. Monroy
A. A. Moscona

ERRATA
Current Topics in Developmental Biology, Volume 11

Page 40   The sentence beginning in line 14 should read:

> In the limiting case of very large r_h, h equilibrates to a near-uniform distribution $\overline{a^2}$.

Line 18 (line following Eq. 4a) should read:

> a has a uniform solution $a = \overline{a} = 1$; this is stable for the mean value $\overline{a}$

Page 53   Line 9 should read:

> (and a returning velocity y) proportional to the deviation. . . .

CHAPTER 1

PATTERNS IN METAZOAN FERTILIZATION

C. R. Austin

PHYSIOLOGICAL LABORATORY
CAMBRIDGE UNIVERSITY
CAMBRIDGE, ENGLAND

Fertilization has been studied in many different ways and in a great assortment of organisms since Van Beneden (1875) and Hertwig (1876) first described pronuclear formation and syngamy in the rabbit and sea urchin. This complex interaction between two specialized cells and the obvious importance of the events involved have captivated the interest of biologists ever since. A multitude of observations and ideas has thus been assembled relating to all levels of organization, and we now know a great deal about fertilization in both plants and animals. This being so, it is not surprising that trends and patterns have become discernible in the accumulated information. These not only have an important bearing on taxonomic and evolutionary relationships, but if aptly interpreted carry predictive value which aids materially in the understanding and interpretation of data on less familiar forms. Devising sound generalizations on structure and function is thus a worthy task, and a brief essay along these lines is presented here. Two distinctive areas in the field of metazoan fertilization are selected for discussion, namely, sperm penetration and the block to polyspermy; these have attracted much attention in recent years and represent major interests for other authors in this book.

I. Sperm Penetration

Basically gamete union is a simple event, involving the fusion of egg and sperm plasma membranes and the formation of a single cell. In the sponges and coelenterates this event remains relatively uncomplicated, but in most metazoans the spermatozoon must penetrate one or more egg investments before starting upon the true process of fertilization. These penetrable coats, which all appear to be in the nature of

1

glycoproteins, are to be distinguished from the impenetrable egg coats of certain insects, cephalopods and fish, which are composed of more resistant material and therefore are necessarily provided with one or more portals (micropyles) permitting sperm entry. Animals having eggs with penetrable coats have spermatozoa with acrosomes. This is consistent with the carriage in the acrosome of an enzyme capable of digesting a passage for the spermatozoon through a penetrable egg investment. Generally speaking, the enzyme in question is released in the course of the acrosome reaction, but in the hamster (Talbot and Franklin, 1974) release may precede the reaction or else the reaction begins in some cryptic manner which as yet has not received ultra-structural description. It would be anticipated that animals having eggs with no coats or impenetrable coats (plus micropyles) would have spermatozoa without acrosomes; and indeed this appears to be true for sponges, coelenterates, teleost fish, and many insects (Baccetti and Afzelius, 1976), but there are exceptions. Some animals (chiefly insects) having eggs with micropyles also possess spermatozoa armed with ac-rosomes. This might seem an anomalous state of affairs, but two points should be noted. First, there seems likely to be in many insect eggs a penetrable coat (a vitelline membrane) additionally investing the cy-toplasmic body of the egg (Perotti, 1975). Second, available evidence indicates that the acrosome reaction is a necessary prelude, not only to egg-coat penetration, but also to sperm-egg fusion. In several non-mammals the acrosome filament, protruded in the acrosome reaction, is evidently alone adapted for the initial step in sperm–egg fusion, in part at least by virtue of its small radius of curvature, which is consid-ered necessary if surfaces are to approach sufficiently closely for fusion to occur (see Austin, 1968). In mammals the reaction seems in some way to condition the postacrosomal plasma membrane so that it be-comes capable of fusion (Yanagimachi and Noda, 1970); here the sur-faces of small radius of curvature are evidently provided by egg mi-crovilli. Accordingly, from the evolutionary point of view, we could argue that enzyme release is of secondary importance, the primary role of the acrosome reaction being the exposure or preparation of a spe-cialized fusion surface on the sperm head.

The realization that the fusion surface is a part of the plasma mem-brane posterior to the acrosome in the mammalian spermatozoon, not part of the inner acrosome membrane as in all animals whose sper-matozoa have acrosomal filaments, came as something of a surprise. It had seemed, from the work on marine invertebrates, that there was something rather special about the inner acrosome membrane (which originates as part of the wall of a cytoplasmic vesicle) that uniquely fitted it for fusion with the egg, and so in the early days there was some expectation that the same circumstance would prove to be true also for mammals. But in fact the mammalian system is in a sense more logical, for here spermatozoa and eggs fuse with homologous membranes. This is true also for the primitive sponges and coelenterates, whose spermatozoa lack acrosomes. In the course of evolution Nature's experiment of presenting the inner acrosome membrane for primary intercourse with the egg evidently represented a new solution to the problem of penetrating egg investments—the mammals have returned to a more ancient device. But how do simpler organisms, lacking acrosomes, manage about preparing a fusible surface on the spermatozoon?

Perhaps such a change can be induced by interaction with substances emanating from the female organism—in the hydroid *Campanularia,* measurable time is absorbed in a supposed interaction of this kind before fertilization takes place (O'Rand, 1971). The idea can be carried further with the assertion that capacitation in mammals has the primary function that it conditions the sperm-head surface for fusion with the egg. In that case, how can one account for the fact that spermatozoa fusing with zona-free eggs have so far always been found to exhibit reacted acrosomes (Yanagimachi and Noda, 1970)? Perhaps it is simply that the reaction in these circumstances is triggered off by the fusion event between sperm and egg plasma membranes.

Another point to be considered here is the possibility that the morphological and other properties of the sperm head have been selected in the course of evolution for the specific task of penetrating egg investments. The idea appealed to early biologists when they contemplated spermatozoa with sharply pointed or hooked heads, which clearly looked designed for penetration; indeed the appelation "perforatorium," which was early applied to a structure at the tip of the rat sperm head (Waldeyer, 1906), testifies to this notion. But the theory is not supported by further observation, for in several species round-headed spermatozoa must penetrate egg investments—as in *Asterias,* for example—and in mammals the suggestively sharp-pointed spermatozoa are distinctly unusual, being found only among the monotremes and the murine and cricetine rodents.

Some order in this apparent chaos was conferred by the classification of spermatozoa into a "primitive" type (with round or oval head and bunched mitochondria) and a "modified" type (with spindle-shaped head and cylindrically arranged mitochondria) (Afzelius, 1972). Both types of spermatozoa have been recorded in different representatives of the same invertebrate phyla, and this is so for seven phyla. Seven other phyla exhibit either one or the other type of spermatozoon. Study of the circumstances in which fertilization takes place in these animals supported the generalization that "primitive" spermatozoa exist in animals that shed their spermatozoa into the surrounding medium, usually seawater, while the "modified" variety belonged to animals that "directed" their spermatozoa in some way, usually through introitus. It was not true to say that the shapes were associated respectively with external and internal fertilization, for in some animals (e.g., tunicates) round-headed spermatozoa take part in internal fertilization. These spermatozoa, however, are not "directed" into the female, for after release in the open water they are carried into the body of the female by currents generated by her feeding mechanism. In most invertebrate phyla, therefore, sperm-head and mitochondrial (midpiece) morphology is related to the manner of sperm delivery and does not show obvious adaptation for egg-coat penetration. Passage of rounded heads through egg coats is made possible by the free release of lytic agents which digest a relatively large penetration hole (e.g., *Hydroides:* Colwin and Colwin, 1961), or by the distortion of the evidently highly plastic sperm head as it passes through a relatively small hole (e.g., *Saccoglossus:* Colwin and Colwin, 1963). [Underlying the functionally significant "primitive" and "modified" aspects of sperm morphology, there are distinct phylogenetic patterns to be seen, and these have been studied by several investigators; this aspect is debated by Baccetti and Afzelius (1976) and by contributors to the book edited by Afzelius (1975).]

Most eutherian mammalian spermatozoa do not conform to the "primitive" versus "modified" classification; delivery into the female tract is certainly "directed," yet the sperm-head form is rather more reminiscent of the "primitive" type than the "modified." The difficulty seems resolvable by the suggestion that the eutherian sperm head is specifically adapted to egg-coat penetration, not to method of delivery (Austin, 1976). Eutherian sperm-head nuclei are roughly oval in one plane (including the hook-shaped ones, after acrosome loss) and are long and narrow in the plane at right angles to the first. They are in fact notably "flat" in shape. In addition, the nucleus is relatively rigid in consistency [owing presumably to rich disulfide cross-linking between DNA molecules (Calvin and Bedford, 1971), and to a strongly oriented lamellar disposition of the chromatin (Koehler, 1970)]. Observations indicate that the hamster spermatozoon moves through the zona with a side-to-side "slicing" action (Yanagimachi, 1966), which is presumably aided by the action of a lytic agent (acrosin?) associated with the inner acrosome membrane. The eutherian sperm head (essentially just the nucleus after the acrosome reaction) would thus seem to be highly adapted for its particular mode of penetrating the zona pellucida. The lytic agent is thought to be stably incorporated in the inner acrosome membrane, for it does not diffuse away from the sperm head (as happens in *Hydroides*) and the spermatozoon leaves behind only a narrow slit as evidence of its passage through the zona pellucida (Austin, 1951).

II. Block to Polyspermy

Polyploidy, we infer, is to be avoided at all cost in metazoan development, for it invariably seems to lead to embryonic anomaly, though it is tolerable, and in many instances favorable, in the vegetable kingdom. Polyploidy can readily arise through polyspermy. With small metazoan eggs, protection against polyspermy is conferred when the fertilizing spermatozoon initiates in the egg surface a propagated reaction which renders that surface, and generally also an overlying investment, opposed to further sperm entry. "Small" as applied to eggs is a relative term, for the frog egg, which is some ten times larger than most eutherian eggs, depends as they do on a propagated surface change (though there is some evidence that frog eggs are preferentially receptive to spermatozoa over a limited area of cortex, i.e., from 60° from the animal pole to the animal–vegetal margin: Elinson, 1975). Feasibility of protection in this way naturally relies also on appropriate limitation in the probability of sperm–egg collision; this probability is restrained by environmental circumstances in animals like frogs with external fertilization, and by reduction of sperm numbers during transport through the female tract in animals like mammals with internal fertilization. With large eggs, such as those of reptiles and birds, it seems reasonable to infer that a propagated change could not pass sufficiently rapidly to confer real protection; large size can be seen as a double handicap, for surface area increases as the square of linear dimension, and both the probability of sperm–egg collision and the time required for completion of a propagated surface change are increased proportionately. Animals with large eggs have accordingly come to depend on either suppression of supernumerary male pronuclei or relegation of these pronuclei to regions beyond the active area of embryogenesis. But "large" like "small" is relative, and urodele eggs, many of which are about the same size as frog eggs, depend on pronuclear suppression rather than a surface change (Werner, 1975). Uniquely, among mammalian eggs, it seems so far, the pig egg employs both a surface block and, when this is incompletely successful, also a suppressive mechanism to deal with extra male pronuclei (Hunter, 1976). It is tempting to think of the behavior of the pig egg as peculiarly atavistic, but really all mammalian eggs deserve this epithet since their protective mechanisms against polyspermy, like their size and general character, hark back to the eggs of marine invertebrates and, except for the monotremes, are quite unlike those of urodeles, reptiles and birds, groups that intervene in the evolutionary series.

The surface block to polyspermy has been found to depend on changes of a related nature in a wide range of animals, from marine invertebrates to mammals. Species for which details are available include several sea urchins such as *Clypeaster* (Endo, 1961), the starfish *Asterias* (Monroy, 1965), the polychaete worm *Nereis* (Fallon and Austin, 1967), several fish (see Yamomoto, 1961), the frog *Rana* (Kemp and Istock, 1967), the toad *Xenopus* (Van Gansen, 1966), and the rat and hamster (Szollosi, 1967). The basic similarity in all these animals lies in the behavior of vesicular bodies that are disposed around the cortex of the egg, in close relation to the plasma membrane, referred to as cortical granules, cortical vesicles, or cortical alveoli. On sperm entry, vesicles in the immediate vicinity react by fusing with the egg plasma membrane and emptying their contents into the perivitelline space, and this response is propagated around the egg cortex. The nature of the propagated message that touches off vesicle evacuation is still unknown. It seems to involve electrical depolarization of charged groups (Jaffe, 1976) presumably associated with the carbohydrate radicals of membrane proteins. This could well lead to loss of the receptors by which spermatozoa become adherent to the egg surface and indeed failure of sperm attachment to the vitellus is an early consequence of fertilization. Such a change could also be expected to permit the close approach between vesicle membrane and plasma membrane that would be necessary for fusion to proceed, since electrostatic charges are implicated in intermembrane forces of repulsion. The propagated change probably corresponds to the "fast partial block" described by Rothschild (1953) in the sea urchin egg. The subsequent evacuation of vesicles is a relatively slow process and in the sea urchin egg presumably underlies the "slow complete block," for it involves elevation of the sperm-impenetrable fertilization membrane. Two blocks to polyspermy could well exist also in other animals that have the cortical vesicle mechanism. Evidence of two in most mammalian eggs was adduced first some years ago (Braden *et al.,* 1954), the second block being the zona reaction. The nature of the change in the zona is still under debate. Some believe that it resides in an alteration in the inherent properties of the zona under the action of the cortical vesicle agent [a "tanning" effect, as Rothschild (1956) termed it] (Barros and Yanagimachi, 1971). Others that it is attributable to infusion into the zona of an enzyme inhibitor from the vesicles which inactivates the sperm zona lysin (Conrad *et al.*, 1971). Others, again, that what infuses from the vesicles into the zona is a protease which destroys the sperm receptors in the zona (Gwatkin *et al.*, 1973). In the rabbit egg, which has cortical vesicles but no zona reaction, it is very tempting to infer that protease from the vesicles destroys sperm receptors on the vitelline surface. Indeed the varying relative effectiveness of the two blocks in different mammals seems most reasonably ascribed to a varying degree of protease action on sperm receptors in vitelline and zona surfaces.

Species differences may well complicate the picture, and are certainly very prominent among the invertebrates. In the trout *Salmo* the perivitelline fluid after cortical vesicle response strongly agglutinates spermatozoa (Ginsburg, 1961). In *Nereis,* vast quantities of jellylike material flow out onto the egg surface when the vesicles evacuate (Fallon and Austin, 1967), forming a layer that spermatozoa cannot penetrate. In the sea urchin, protease released in the reaction is believed to produce a vitelline block to polyspermy by destroying the sperm-binding sites on the egg surface (Vaquier *et al.*, 1973) or, in the sand dollar *Echinarachnius,* by initiating the separation of the fertilization membrane from the egg surface (Summers and Hylander, 1974). In the lamprey the specialized part of the chorion that provides access for spermatozoa becomes thickened and impenetrable (Kille, 1960). In the sturgeon and trout a jellylike material fills the perivitelline space as it forms and apparently prevents further sperm passage (Ginsburg, 1961). In the toad *Xenopus,* the properties of the jelly coat are apparently altered in such a way as to make it impenetrable to spermatozoa (Wyrick *et al.*, 1974). Cortical vesicles, like lysosomes, to which they are evidently closely related (Allison and Hartree, 1969), clearly contain a variety of agents in addition to lytic enzymes, and their range of influence is capable of being equally varied.

In conclusion some comments are due on the underlying relations between the acrosome reaction, sperm–egg fusion, and the block to polyspermy. A homology between the sperm acrosome and the egg cortical vesicle surely exists—in their general structure, their genesis with the Golgi complex, their disposition in close proximity to the plasma membrane and faculty for fusion with it, and in their assorted content of enzymes and mucopolysaccharides. In the spermatozoon and egg, the same organelle has thus been exploited for different ends, but involving identical mechanisms. For both the acrosome reaction and the cortical vesicle response, the crucial step is the closer approximation leading to virtual contact and then fusion between the membranes. In both processes there is the same essential ingredient—a surface curvature of small radius that permits movement against electrostatic repulsive forces—clearly manifest with the cortical vesicle response, and inferred for the acrosome reaction from Wooding's (1975) observations. Sperm–egg fusion is an intercurrent event; it is of the same kind but differs in that it involves external membrane surfaces and alone shows an additional step before fusion, namely adhesion, which is inferred to involve bonding between complementary molecules. This represents a vulnerable point since enzyme action can destroy receptors, thus introducing the possibility of control into the system. In sperm penetration and the block to polyspermy, a remarkable diversity of function has been achieved by modification of comparatively few variables.

REFERENCES

Afzelius, B. A. (1972). *In* "The Genetics of the Spermatozoon" (R. A. Beatty and S. Gluecksohn-Waelsch, eds.), pp. 131–143. Edinburgh.

Afzelius, B. A. (1975). "The Functional Anatomy of the Spermatozoon." Pergamon, Oxford.

Allison, A. C., and Hartree, E. F. (1969). *Res. Reprod.* **1**, 2–3.

Austin, C. R. (1951). *Aust. J. Sci. Res., Ser. B* **4**, 581–596.

Austin, C. R. (1968). "Ultrastructure of Fertilization," p. 141. Holt, New York.

Austin, C. R. (1976). *In* "Reproduction in Mammals" (C. R. Austin and R. V. Short, eds.), Vol. 6, Chapter 5. Cambridge Univ. Press, London and New York.

Baccetti, B., and Afzelius, B. A. (1976). "The Biology of the Sperm Cell." Karger, Basel.

Barros, C., and Yanagimachi, R. (1971). *Nature (London)* **233**, 268–269.

Braden, A. W. H., Austin, C. R., and David, H. A. (1954), *Aust. J. Biol. Sci.* **7**, 391–409.

Calvin, H. I., and Bedford, J. M. (1971). *J. Reprod. Fertil., Suppl.* **13**, 65–75.

Colwin, A. L., and Colwin, L. H. (1961). *J. Biophys. Biochem. Cytol.* **10**, 255–274.

Colwin, L. H., and Colwin, A. L. (1963). *J. Cell Biol.* **19**, 501–518.

Conrad, K., Buckley, J., and Stambaugh, R. (1971). *J. Reprod. Fertil.* **27**, 133–135.

Elinson, R. P. (1975). *Dev. Biol.* **47**, 257–268.

Endo, Y. (1961). *Exp. Cell Res.* **25**, 383–397.

Fallon, J. F., and Austin, C. R. (1967). *J. Exp. Zool.* **166**, 225–242.

Ginsburg, A. S. (1961). *J. Embryol. Exp. Morphol.* **9**, 173–190.

Gwatkin, R. B. L., Williams, D. T., Hartmann, J. F., and Kniazuk, M. (1973). *J. Reprod. Fertil.* **32**, 259–265.

Hertwig, O. (1876). *Morphol. Johrb.* **1**, 347–370.

Hunter, R. H. F. (1976). *J. Anat.* **122**, 43–59.

Jaffe, L. (1976). *Nature (London)* **261**, 68–71.

Kemp, N. E., and Istock, N. L. (1967). *J. Cell Biol.* **34**, 111–122.

Kille, R. A. (1960). *Exp. Cell Res.* **20**, 12–27.

Koehler, J. K. (1970). *In* "Comparative Spermatology" (B. Baccetti, ed.), pp. 515–522. Academic Press, New York.

Monroy, A. (1965). "Chemistry and Physiology of Fertilization." Holt, New York.

O'Rand, M. G. (1971). *Biol. Bull.* **141**, 398.

Perotti, M. E. (1975). In Afzelius (1975).

Rothschild, Lord. (1953). *J. Exp. Biol.* **30,** 57–67.

Rothschild, Lord. (1956). "Fertilization." Methuen, London.

Summers, R. G., and Hylander, B. L. (1974). *Cell Tissue Res.* **150,** 343–368.

Szollosi, D. (1967). *Anat. Rec.* **159,** 431–446.

Talbot, P., and Franklin, L. E. (1974). *J. Exp. Zool.* **189,** 321–332.

Van Beneden, E. (1875). *Bull. Acad. Belg. Cl. Sci.* **40,** 686–736.

Van Gansen, P. (1966). *J. Embryol. Exp. Morphol.* **15,** 355–364.

Vaquier, V. D., Tegner, M. J., and Epel, D. (1973). *Exp. Cell Res.* **80,** 111–119.

Waldeyer, W. (1906). Cited by Wilson (1928).

Werner, G. (1975). "The Functional Anatomy of the Spermatozoon." Pergamon, Oxford.

Wilson, E. G. (1928). "The Cell in Development and Heredity," 3rd ed. Macmillan, New York.

Wooding, F. B. P. (1975). *J. Reprod. Fertil.* **44,** 185–192.

Wyrick, R. E., Nishihara, T., and Hedrick, J. L. (1974). *Proc. Natl. Acad. Sci. U.S.A.* **71,** 2067–2071.

Yamomoto, T.-O. (1961). *Int. Rev. Cytol.* **12,** 361–405.

Yanagimachi, R. (1966). *J. Reprod. Fertil.* **11,** 359–370.

Yanagimachi, R., and Noda, Y. D. (1970). *J. Ultrastruct. Res.* **31,** 486–493.

CHAPTER 2

BIOCHEMISTRY OF MALE GERM CELL DIFFERENTIATION IN MAMMALS: RNA SYNTHESIS IN MEIOTIC AND POSTMEIOTIC CELLS

V. Monesi, R. Geremia, A. D'Agostino, and C. Boitani

INSTITUTE OF HISTOLOGY AND GENERAL EMBRYOLOGY
UNIVERSITY OF ROME
ROME, ITALY

I. Introduction

Spermatogenesis is a highly orderly process that begins with the stem cell and terminates with the release of the mature spermatid into the lumen of the seminiferous tubule.

With cytological methods and [³H]thymidine autoradiography, the kinetics of spermatogenesis has been studied in great detail in several mammals (see, for example, Monesi, 1962; for review articles, see Clermont, 1967, 1972; Courot *et al.,* 1970). In the mouse the total duration of spermatogenesis, from the stem cell to the mature spermatid, is about 34.5 days and is subdivided into three phases: the period of multiplication and maturation of spermatogonia or mitotic phase of spermatogenesis, which lasts about 8 days; meiosis, which lasts 13 days; and spermiogenesis, from the early spermatid to the release of the spermatozoon into the lumen, which is about 13.5 days long.

In any segment of the seminiferous tubule of the mouse four generations of germ cells proceed simultaneously but are separated by one cycle of the seminiferous epithelium (that is by about 8.5 days), thus giving rise to the typical cellular associations found in cross sections of the tubule. This concept is diagrammatically represented in Fig. 1, where the development of the germ cells from the stem cell to the mature spermatid is arranged in four concentric circles. From the duration of the stages of the cycle of the seminiferous epithelium reported in Fig. 1, one can calculate the length of the various phases of spermatogenesis. In the mouse there are six generations of spermatogonia (A_1, A_2, A_3, A_4 spermatogonia, intermediate spermatogonia, and type B spermatogonia) before the beginning of meiosis (Monesi, 1962).

During spermatogonial development the stem cells are renewed. The mechanism of spermatogonial stem cell renewal will not be discussed in this paper. The reader should consult the pertinent literature for this important aspect of regulation of spermatogenesis in mammals (Huckins, 1971a–d; Oakberg, 1971; Clermont, 1972; De Rooij, 1973).

Biochemistry of spermatogenesis is one of the most promising areas of research in developmental biology and mammalian reproduction. The development of germ cell is a field where different experimental approaches—cytology, ultrastructure, cytogenetics, genetics, biochemistry, immunology, endocrinology—can interact in a coordinate view of cell differentiation.

Until very recently the biochemistry of spermatogenesis was studied mainly with autoradiographic methods. The methods now available to separate various classes of germ cells from the mammalian testis open new possibilities for investigating the molecular and metabolic properties of different stages in germ cell development and offer new perspectives for the elucidation of the regulative mechanisms of male germ cell differentiation.

In this paper we shall discuss a few aspects of ribonucleic acid and protein synthesis at different stages of germ cell differentiation in mammals that are relevant to the problem of regulation of spermatogenesis.

II. Inactivation of the XY Bivalent in Meiosis

An interesting feature of chromosome activity in male meiosis is the inactivation of the XY bivalent during meiotic prophase in spermatocytes. In all mammals, as well as in other organisms, the sex chromosomes are condensed (heteropycnotic) throughout meiotic prophase, forming a very prominent body, called sex vesicle, which is applied to the nuclear membrane. It was found that the sex chromosomes are invariably unlabeled with [³H]uridine throughout meiotic prophase in all mammalian species so far studied: mouse (Monesi,

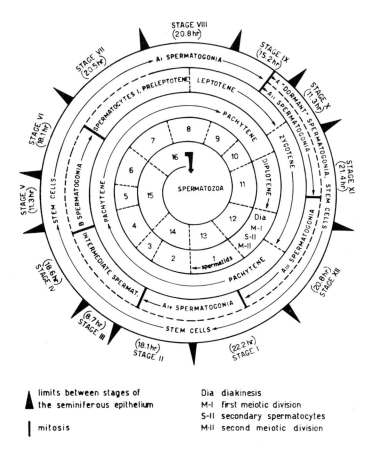

limits between stages of
the seminiferous epithelium

mitosis

Dia   diakinesis
M-I   first meiotic division
S-II secondary spermatocytes
M-II second meiotic division

FIG. 1. Diagram of the dynamics of spermatogenesis in the mouse. Starting from the outer circle at 12 o'clock and following the arrows clockwise, one can complete the development of germ cells, from the stem cell to the spermatozoon, in four concentric turns. Each circle corresponds to one cycle of the seminiferous epithelium. The sectors limited by the spikes represent the stages of the cycle of the seminiferous epithelium and show the cellular composition of each stage from the periphery to the center of the tubule; 1–16 are the various phases of spermiogenesis. In the mouse, in any segment of the seminiferous tubule, which corresponds in this figure to the radii of the circle, four generations of germ cells, separated by a constant interval, develop simultaneously. The durations of the various stages of the cycle of the seminiferous epithelium are those given by Oakberg (1956b). For the description of the sequence of spermatogonial generations before meiosis, see Monesi (1962); for the definition of the stages of the cycle of the seminiferous epithelium, see Leblond and Clermont (1952a,b) and Oakberg (1956a).

1964b, 1965), Chinese hamster (Utakoji, 1966), and rat (Stefanini *et al.*, 1974). The X chromosome, but not the Y chromosome, is also condensed during male meiosis in *Drosophila* (Lifschytz and Lindsley, 1972); condensation of the X chromosome occurs also in spermatocytes of orthopterans (Henderson, 1964).

A biochemical genetic evidence of inactivity of the X chromosome in male meiosis has been obtained by Erickson (1976). The enzyme glucose-6-phosphate dehydrogenase (G6PD), which is coded by an X-linked gene, is probably not synthesized in mouse spermatocytes, but persists through meiosis and spermiogenesis from the premeiotic stages.

A striking feature of the mammalian X chromosome is its opposite state of activity in somatic cells and in germ cells. It is well known that in the female only one X chromosome is functional in the somatic line (Lyon, 1961), whereas both X chromosomes are isopycnotic (Ohno *et al.*, 1961) and genetically active (Epstein, 1969; Gartler *et al.*, 1973; Mangia *et al.*, 1975) in the oocyte. In the male the opposite situation is found; the single X chromosome is isopycnotic and active in somatic cells but becomes heteropycnotic and inactive at a critical stage of spermatogenesis. These observations might suggest that the function of both X chromosomes is needed for the development of female germ cells and, conversely, that the inactivity of the X chromosome is required for normal spermatogenesis at least until the end of meiosis. This view is also supported by many genetic evidences (see, as review articles, Lifschytz and Lindsley, 1972; Lindsley and Lifschytz, 1972; Lyon, 1974): the XO human females are sterile and germ cells are absent; XXY individuals are phenotypically males but are sterile and azoospermic both in human and in the mouse (Cattanach, 1961; Russell and Chu, 1961; Mittwoch, 1967)—it would be interesting to see whether the extra X chromosome in the germ cells of the XXY individuals is isopycnotic and active in transcription, which would substantiate the hypothesis that the presence of a functional X chromosome is incompatible with the complete development of male germ cells; the XX sex-reversed mice are sterile males and germ cells are completely absent but the XO sex reversed animals produce spermatids and few spermatozoa which are, however, unfertile (Cattanach *et al.*, 1971; Cattanach, 1975).

The X chromosome carries a gene (the Tfm locus) (Lyon and Hawkes, 1970) that is concerned with the production of androgen receptors in target organs and with their response to androgen (Ohno, 1971; Bardin *et al.*, 1973; Attardi and Ohno, 1974; Bullock and Bardin, 1974). The discovery that the X chromosome is inactive in spermatocytes should therefore imply that androgen receptors are absent in germ cells at least during first meiosis. This hypothesis has been experimentally tested by Lyon *et al.* (1975) in experiments with mice chimeric for androgen-resistant (Tfm/Y) and normal (+/Y) genotype; the conclusion of this work was that the testicular development and the epididymal maturation of germ cells are not dependent on the androgen responsiveness of the germ cells themselves but are entirely mediated by the somatic cells of the seminiferous tubule (Sertoli cells) and of the epididymis.

III. Ribosomal RNA Synthesis in Spermatocytes

Earlier autoradiographic studies have reported the absence or a very low rate of nucleolar incorporation of RNA precursors in spermatocytes of the Chinese hamster *Cricetulus griseus* (Utakoji, 1966). In a subsequent biochemical study in the same species, it was reported that the ribonucleic acids synthesized in the testis are mostly DNA-like heterogeneous molecules with a rapid turnover and that little synthesis of ribosomal RNA occurs during male meiosis (Muramatsu *et al.*, 1968). Similar results of nucleolar inactivity were obtained in grasshopper spermatocytes (Henderson, 1964) and in maize microsporocytes (Das, 1965). These data led to the suggestion that a selective inhibition of ribosomal RNA synthesis occurs in male germ cells during meiotic prophase.

This general conclusion proved to be erroneous on the basis of more recent autoradiographic (Stefanini *et al.*, 1974; Kierszenbaum and Tres, 1974a,b; Tres, 1975) and biochemical studies (D'Agostino *et al.*, 1976; Söderström and Parvinen, 1976; Geremia *et al.*, 1977b) in the mouse and the rat.

In cytological preparations of mouse spermatocytes a large nucleolus attached to the sex bivalent is visible. This cytological observation of the proximity of the nucleolus to the XY pair led to the conclusion that the sex chromosomes carry the nucleolus organizer in the mouse and that the autosomes do not participate in nucleolar formation (Ohno *et al.*, 1957). Besides the main nucleolus, other smaller nucleoli associated with the autosomes were described with the electron microscope (Solari and Tres, 1967; Solari, 1969). In a recent electron microscopic and autoradiographic study of the evolution of nucleoli during male meiosis in the mouse, Kierszenbaum and Tres (1974a,b) showed that the nucleolar organizers in mouse spermatocytes are close to the paracentromeric heterochromatin of several bivalent autosomes and that, during formation of the nucleolus, nucleolar masses originating from these chromosomal regions become secondarily associated with the sex chromosomes. The conclusive evidence that the nucleolus organizer in the mouse is not associated with the sex chromosomes was provided by DNA–RNA hybridization experiments in cytological preparations; this study demonstrated that in the mouse the ribosomal RNA cistrons are located in the nucleolus organizer region of three autosomes, 15, 18, and 19 (Henderson *et al.,* 1974). By using the same technique, the ribosomal cistrons were identified in the autosomes 3, 11, and 12 of the rat genome (Kano *et al.,* 1976) and in the acrocentric autosomes of the D and G groups (chromosomes 13, 14, 15, 21, and 22) of the human genome (Henderson *et al.,* 1972; Evans *et al.,* 1974).

In previous autoradiographic studies (Monesi, 1965) it was difficult to assess the activity of the nucleolus in mouse spermatocytes, since this organelle is not easily visible in standard cytological preparations. In subsequent investigations employing more sophisticated cytological procedures (semithin sections) and electron microscopy autoradiography, it was clearly demonstrated that the nucleoli do incorporate radioactive RNA precursors during male meiosis both in the mouse (Kierszenbaum and Tres, 1974a,b), in the rat (Stefanini *et al.,* 1974) and in man (Tres, 1975). The pattern of nucleolar labeling at different meiotic stages suggests that during male meiosis there is a stepwise increase in the rate of ribosomal RNA (rRNA) transcription to a peak in mid-pachytene followed by a progressive decline up to a complete arrest in the most advanced stages (Stefanini *et al.,* 1974). The inactivation of rRNA transcription in diplotene spermatocytes is revealed at the ultrastructural level by the segregation of the fibrillar and the granular components, which is considered to be a morphological expression of nucleolar inactivity (see Busch and Smetana, 1970).

By using a quasi-homogeneous population of spermatocytes at the pachytene stage, we have obtained clear biochemical evidence of synthesis of ribosomal RNA during male meiosis in the mouse (D'Agostino *et al.,* 1976; Geremia *et al.,* 1977c). Seminiferous tubules were labeled in culture with [^{3}H]uridine and then fractionated into several cell types by velocity sedimentation at unit gravity (Lam *et al.,* 1970; Meistrich, 1972) as described in detail below and in the legend to Fig. 2. The RNA was extracted with phenol–chloroform from the cell fraction composed of middle-late pachytene spermatocytes and centrifuged in a linear sucrose gradient (see legend to the figure for methods). Figure 2 shows the sedimentation profile of RNA extracted from middle–late pachytene spermatocytes labeled for 3 hours with [^{3}H]uridine (a) or for 3 hours with the radioactive precursor followed by a 5-hour chase with cold uridine (b). It is clearly evident that 18 S and 28 S ribosomal RNA are synthesized in this cell type. It is noteworthy that the ratio between the amounts of radioactivity incorporated into 18 S and 28 S RNA is altered with respect to the normal 1:2 ratio even after a 5-hour chase, suggesting that the maturation of the rRNA precursors or the transfer to the cytoplasm of the ribosomal subunits is slowed down as compared to other systems. A similar slow rate of maturation kinetics of the rRNA precursors has been described in *Lilium longiflorum* microsporocytes (Parchman and Lin, 1972) and in *Paracentrotus lividus* oocytes (Sconzo *et al.*, 1972).

Kierszenbaum and Tres (1974a) have reported that the organization of the nucleolus during male meiosis in the mouse begins with the appearance of the fibrillar component at zygotene stage followed by the development of the granular moiety at early pachytene. This delayed appearance of the granular component of the nucleolus during the early stages of meiotic development is probably a reflection of a decreased rate of maturation of ribosomal RNA precursors during male meiosis.

IV. Nonribosomal RNA Synthesis in Spermatocytes

The pattern of RNA synthesis at different stages of spermatogenesis in the mouse was investigated formerly with autoradiographic methods (Monesi, 1964b, 1965, 1967, 1971) and more recently with biochemical procedures (Geremia *et al.*, 1976a, 1977c).

Using autoradiography, we have seen that the synthesis of RNA on the autosomes follows a well-defined pattern during meiosis, which is diagrammatically summarized in Fig. 3 (Monesi, 1964b, 1965, 1971). The rate of incorporation of [³H]uridine is very low during leptotene, zygotene, and early pachytene stages, rises rapidly to a peak in middle–late pachytene, and then declines again during diplotene and diakinesis to stop completely during metaphases and anaphases I and II. Between the two meiotic divisions resting secondary spermatocytes show a low level of incorporation. It is noteworthy that the rate of incorporation is much higher during diplotene than in leptotene or zygotene. The amino acid incorporation into cytoplasmic and nuclear proteins follows a similar temporal pattern but also early and late meiotic stages show a high level of nuclear and cytoplasmic labeling (Fig. 3). A similar pattern of RNA synthesis was described in the Chinese hamster (Utakoji, 1966), in orthopterans (Henderson, 1964; Muckenthaler, 1964), and in the rat (Söderström and Parvinen, 1976) and was recently confirmed in the mouse by Moore (1971) and Kierszenbaum and Tres (1974a,b).

This pattern of RNA synthesis during male meiosis is related to the

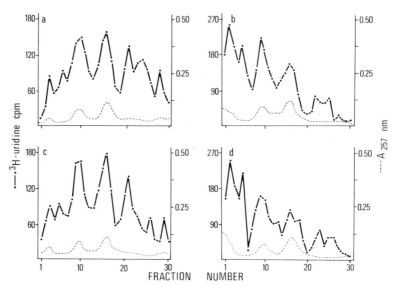

F$_{IG}$. 2. Sedimentation profiles and radioactivity distribution of RNA extracted from middle-late pachytene spermatocytes (a,b) and from round spermatids (steps 1 to 8 of spermiogenesis) (c,d) labeled in culture with [³H]uridine for 3 hours (a,c) or for 3 hours with [³H]uridine followed by a 5 hour chase with cold precursor (b,d).

Homogeneous cell fractions were prepared as previously described (Geremia *et al.*, 1976a). C57BL/Casaccia mice were given two X-ray doses 4 days apart (300 and 100 R) and sacrificed 24 hours after the last radiation exposure. The seminiferous tubules, mechanically dissociated from interstitial tissue under a dissecting microscope and washed twice by sedimentation in Dulbecco's phosphate-buffered saline (PBS) were cut into 1–2 mm fragments with a razor blade. Fragments from 4 testes, after two washings by sedimentation in PBS to discard damaged cells, were placed in a Falcon dish and incubated in 4 ml of MEM with Earle's BSS, containing per milliliter 100 μCi of [³H]5-uridine (NEN, spec. act. 26 Ci/mmole) at 32°C with 5% CO_2 in air; the culture medium was supplemented with 1 mM sodium pyruvate, 0.1 mM nonessential amino acids, and 4 mM L-glutamine (Microbiological Associates) (Steinberger and Steinberger, 1970). The incubation was carried on for 3 hours or for 3 hours followed by a 5-hour chase with 0.4 mg of cold uridine per milliliter. The seminiferous tubules were then washed by sedimentation in PBS and incubated with 0.1% trypsin (1 : 250, Difco) and 0.005% DNase (crude, Worthington) in PBS for 30 minutes at room temperature to release the germ cells. The germ cell suspension was filtered through an 80-μm mesh nylon screen; 40×10^6 cells, in 0.2% Ficoll (Pharmacia) in PBS, were layered over a PBS-buffered Ficoll gradient (25 ml 0.5%, 250 ml 1%, 250 ml 3%) and allowed to sediment for 3 hours at 4°C (Lam *et al.*, 1970).

Germ cells sedimenting at 4.5 mm/hour (spermatid steps 1 to 8) and at 9 mm/hour (middle-late pachytene spermatocytes) were collected by unloading the gradient chamber from the bottom, washed by centrifugation (20 min at 500 g), and lysed in 25 mM Tris-HCl pH 7.5, 25 mM NaCl, 5 mM $MgCl_2$ with 0.5 mg heparin sodium salt (Calbiochem) per milliliter and 0.05% Triton X-100. The postmitochondrial supernatant (20 minutes at 27,000 g) was extracted with sodium dodecyl sulfate–phenol–chloroform

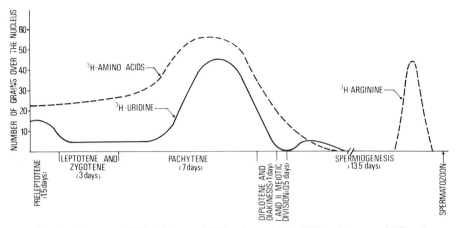

FIG. 3. Pattern of [³H]uridine and [³H]amino acids (L-[³H]arginine; DL-[³H]leucine; DL-[³H]lysine; L-[³H]tyrosine; DL-[³H]β-phenylalanine; L[³H]histidine) incorporation into RNA and nuclear proteins, respectively, 1 hour after intratesticular administration of radioactive precursors. From Monesi (1971).

lampbrush organization of the chromosomes in middle-late meiotic prophase (Nebel and Coulon, 1962; Monesi, 1965; Kierszenbaum and Tres, 1974b; Glätzer, 1975).

In the spermatocyte, as well as in the oocyte nucleus (for review articles, see Callan, 1969; Miller and Hamkalo, 1972; Hamkalo and Miller, 1973), the lateral loops projecting from both sides of the chromosomal axis are the sites of RNA transcription in meiosis; this has been demonstrated with light microscopy autoradiography indicating that the [³H]uridine labeling at pachytene stage is more concentrated along the margin than over the core of the chromosomes (Monesi, 1965) and more recently with the "spreading" technique of whole-mount meiotic chromosomes examined under the electron microscope showing that the lateral loops of mouse and *Drosophila* pachytene spermatocytes are associated with nascent RNA chains of

(Palmiter, 1974) and precipitated with ethanol. Several preparations (4 to 6) were pooled in order to have enough radioactive RNA to run a sucrose gradient; the material was loaded on a 12-ml 5 to 20% linear sucrose gradient in 10 mM NaCl, 1 mM Na EDTA, 10 mM Tris-HCl pH 7.5. Gradients were centrifuged in a SW 41 rotor (Beckman) at 285,000 g for 3 hours at 4° and fractionated with continuous optical density recording. The trichloroacetic acid-precipitable material in each fraction was collected on Millipore filters, and the radioactivity incorporated was determined in toluene-based scintillation fluid.

variable length (Kierszenbaum and Tres, 1974b; Meyer and Hennig, 1974; Hennig *et al.*, 1974; Glätzer, 1975) and become labeled with [³H]uridine (Hennig, 1967; Kierszenbaum and Tres, 1975).

A remarkable feature of the RNA produced in meiosis is its stability. Biochemical analyses performed on whole testis of the Chinese hamster (Muramatsu *et al.*, 1968) or on isolated seminiferous tubules of the rat (Söderström and Parvinen, 1976) have indicated that the ribonucleic acids synthesized in germ cells are mostly DNA-like heterogeneous molecules of high molecular weight with an intranuclear turnover and a remarkable stability as compared to the high-molecular-weight nuclear RNA (HnRNA) of somatic cells. Using autoradiography we have seen (Monesi, 1964b, 1965, 1971) that a large fraction of the RNAs synthesized by the autosomes during meiosis in the mouse is not immediately transferred into the cytoplasm but remains associated with the chromosomes for a very long time. A part of this labeled RNA undergoes a slow process of breakdown within the nucleus or is slowly released into the cytoplasm, but a large fraction of it remains in the nucleus until diakinesis or prometaphase, when is rapidly shed into the cytoplasm. The cytoplasmic RNA present in spermatids is mostly of meiotic origin (see below). These observations were confirmed in the Chinese hamster by Utakoji (1966) and in the mouse by Kierszenbaum and Tres (1974a). A similar pattern of RNA metabolism was described for the Y chromosome in *Drosophila* spermatocytes (Meyer, 1972), which pass through a lampbrush stage comparable to that of the oocyte, in amphibian (Callan, 1969), and in mammalian (Baker, 1971) diplotene oocytes; both in oocytes and in spermatocytes ribonucleoprotein particles accumulate in the loops of the chromosomes for a considerable time, forming the loop matrix, before they are released into the cytoplasm or break down. From the current evidence it appears therefore that the synthesis of nuclear RNA that accumulates in the chromosomes is a common feature of the activity of the lampbrush chromosomes during both oogenesis and spermatogenesis.

We have approached biochemically the problem of RNA synthesis and metabolism in spermatogenesis by using a technique of cell separation by velocity sedimentation at unit gravity (Lam *et al.*, 1970; Meistrich, 1972; Meistrich *et al.*, 1973). With this technique several cell fractions of sufficient homogeneity can be obtained; of these the most homogeneous ones were those composed of middle-late pachytene spermatocytes, of early or round spermatids (steps 1 to 8 of spermiogenesis), of late or elongated spermatids (steps 13 to 16 of spermiogenesis). However, the first two cell fractions are contaminated by spermatogonia and the fraction composed of early spermatids is also contaminated by early meiotic cells (preleptotene, leptotene, and zygotene spermatocytes).

In order to eliminate the contaminating cells, we have exposed the mice to a low dose of X-rays, which kills spermatogonia without affecting the other germ cell stages (Oakberg, 1955) and killed the animals 5 days after radiation exposure to allow preleptotene spermatocytes and early meiotic cells to develop to more mature stages (Geremia et al., 1976b). In most experiments the animals were exposed to two doses of X-rays (300 and 100 R) 4 days apart and used 1 day after the second exposure. The second X-ray treatment is needed to kill the spermatogonia originating from the surviving stem cells in the 4 day interval. After the X-ray treatment the seminiferous tubules were freed from the interstitial tissue either by mechanical manipulation or by collagenase digestion and dispersed into single cells by trypsin treatment; these were fractionated into several cell classes by sedimentation at unit gravity in a Ficoll gradient, as previously described (Geremia et al., 1976a). The cellular composition in the middle-late pachytene spermatocyte and round spermatid fractions was tested both morphologically and by [³H]thymidine labeling kinetics. Morphological analysis has shown that these two cell fractions were 90% homogeneous. The 10% contaminating cells were early and intermediate spermatid symplasts in the spermatocyte fraction and intermediate and late spermatids in the round spermatid fraction; somatic cells and spermatogonia were completely absent (Geremia et al., 1976a).

For the study of RNA synthesis, the testes were either labeled in vivo by injecting [³H]uridine intratesticularly or in vitro by incubating the seminiferous tubules in a culture medium containing the radioactive precursor. The analysis of the [³H]uridine radioactivity incorporated into acid-insoluble material has shown that the middle-late pachytene stage is the meiotic phase of maximum synthetic activity, confirming previous autoradiographic results (Monesi, 1965). For the analysis of the RNA classes synthesized in meiosis, seminiferous tubules were labeled in culture for 3 hours with [³H]5-uridine alone or with [³H]5-uridine and [³H]2-adenosine; after cell separation the RNA was extracted with sodium dodecyl sulfate (SDS)–phenol–chloroform from the postmitochondrial supernatant and analyzed in a 5 to 20% linear sucrose gradient (Fig. 2) or in a poly(U)–Sepharose column by affinity chromatography (Table I) (D'Agostino et al., 1976; Geremia et al., 1977c).

From Fig. 2a it can be seen that the radioactive RNA extracted from middle-late pachytene spermatocytes labeled for 3 hours with

[³H]uridine is distributed heterodispersely; however, as mentioned before, discrete peaks of radioactivity are clearly identifiable in the 4 S, 18 S, and 28 S regions of the gradient as well as in the heavier part of the sedimentation gradient. The labeled HnRNA classes correspond probably to nuclear RNA molecules, including rRNA precursors, leaked from the nucleus. After a 5-hour chase with cold uridine (Fig. 2b) the faster sedimenting labeled RNA molecules decrease in quantity, and the 18 S and 28 S radioactive peaks become more pronounced. As already mentioned, the ratio between the peaks of radioactivity associated with the 18 S and 28 S regions of the gradient is altered with respect to the normal 1 : 2 absorbancy ratio of the two classes of rRNA molecules; this finding suggests that the process of maturation of the rRNA precursors is slowed down in this system.

Since a poly(A) sequence at the 3′ terminus is a characteristic of most messenger RNA (mRNA) molecules (Darnell *et al.*, 1971; Lee *et al.*, 1971; Milcarek *et al.*, 1974), the detection of polyadenylated RNA is taken as evidence for the presence of mRNA molecules. The poly(A)-containing RNA molecules can easily be detected by affinity chromatography on a poly(U)–Sepharose column. For this analysis, the seminiferous tubules free of interstitial tissue were labeled in culture for 3 hours with [³H]5-uridine and [³H]2-adenosine, middle-late pachytene spermatocytes were separated by sedimentation at unit gravity as described (Geremia *et al.*, 1977a), and the RNA was extracted with phenol–chloroform from the postmitochondrial supernatant, and analyzed in a poly(U)–Sepharose column. From Table I it can be seen that pachytene spermatocytes actively synthesize polyadenylated RNA molecules. The percentage of radioactivity bound to the poly(U)-column is, however, an overestimate of the actual rate of synthesis of poly(A)-containing RNA relative to the total RNA synthesis since the cells were labeled with both [³H]uridine and [³H]adenosine.

V. Haploid Gene Activity in Spermatogenesis and Preservation of Meiotic RNA in Spermatids

A fundamental problem in the genetics of spermatogenesis is whether the phenotype of the spermatozoon is dependent upon the diploid genotype of the organism (diploid control) or upon the haploid genotype of the spermatid nucleus itself (haploid control). The diploid effect on spermatid differentiation can operate through the synthesis and accumulation in the primary spermatocyte of stable RNA molecules that are translated during spermiogenesis (meiotic control).

TABLE I

ANALYSIS BY AFFINITY CHROMATOGRAPHY ON POLY(U)–SEPHAROSE COLUMN OF
POLYADENYLATED RNA LABELED WITH [³H]URIDINE AND [³H]ADENOSINE

RNA	Activity unbound to the column (cpm/cell, × 10⁻³)	Activity bound to the column (cpm/cell, × 10⁻³)	Percentage of bound activity
RNA from postmitochondrial supernatant of pachytene spermatocytes[a]	2.5	1.4	36
RNA from postmitochondrial supernatant of round spermatids[a]	0.33	0.16	33
Polysomal RNA from spermatids[b]	0.01	0.005	33

[a] RNA from postmitochondrial supernatant was extracted from pachytene spermatocytes and round spermatids separated in a Ficoll gradient after labeling the seminiferous tubules for 3 hours, as described in the legend to Fig. 2. The labeling was performed with 100 μCi of [³H]5-uridine (NEN, spec. act. 26 Ci/mmole) and 100 μCi of [³H]2-adenosine (NEN, spec. act. 11 Ci/mmole) per milliliter. The RNA was extracted with phenol–chloroform and solubilized in CSB (0.7 M NaCl, 50 mM Tris-HCl pH 7.5, 10 mM EDTA) with 25% deionized formamide and chromatographed on poly(U)–Sepharose column (Pharmacia). RNA unbound to the column was washed with 25% formamide in CSB; polyadenylated RNA was eluted with 90% formamide in EB (10 mM potassium phosphate pH 7.5, 10 mM EDTA, 0.2% SDS) (Lindberg and Persson, 1972). The RNA present in each fraction from the column was precipitated with TCA, and the radioactivity was determined in toluene-based scintillation liquid.

[b] Polysomal RNA was obtained from spermatids prepared by the following procedure. Groups of 15 mice were exposed to three doses of X-rays (300, 100, and 100 R) 6 days apart in order to deplete the testes of spermatogonia and all meiotic cells, injected 30 hours after the last X-ray exposure with 20 μCi of [³H]uridine and 20 μCi of [³H]adenosine per testis, and sacrificed 24 hours later. Seminiferous tubules were freed from interstitial tissue by means of a 15-minute treatment with 0.1% collagenase (Worthington) in phosphate-buffered saline (PBS) at room temperature, washed twice by sedimentation in PBS, and cut into 1–2-mm fragments with a razor blade. The fragments were washed twice by sedimentation in PBS and gently pipetted several times in order to release the spermatids without removing the somatic cells of the tubule. The morphological examination by phase contrast microscopy has demonstrated that the cell suspension thus obtained was composed almost exclusively of round and elongated spermatids; somatic cells, spermatogonia, and meiotic cells were absent. Polysomes were obtained by MgCl₂ precipitation of postmitochondrial supernatant and fractionated in a 0.5 to 1.5 M linear sucrose gradient (Palmiter, 1974). The RNA was extracted with phenol–chloroform from the pooled fractions corresponding to the polysome region of the gradient, precipitated with ethanol, and analyzed on a poly(U)–Sepharose column as described above.

An alternative mechanism of diploid control of spermiogenesis is that the RNA molecules (or the protein products) synthesized postmeiotically are freely exchanged between the four daughter spermatids arising from the two meiotic divisions through the cytoplasmic bridges connecting them (Dym and Fawcett, 1971) (postmeiotic diploid effect). This mechanism can therefore prevent the phenotypic expression of the haploid genotype.

The numerous genetic, cytological, and autoradiographic studies on animal gametogenesis have provided conflicting evidence as to the meiotic or the haploid control of spermatid differentiation.

With few exceptions, most of the genetic evidence argues against a haploid effect in mammalian spermatogenesis (as review articles, see Beatty, 1970, 1972). However, well documented genetic evidence in favor of the expression of the haploid genotype in spermatogenesis was obtained from the studies on recessive mutants at the T locus in the mouse (as a review, see Bennett, 1975). This complex chromosomal region contains genes specifying cell surface components, present only in sperm and early embryo, which are essential for early embryonic development and possibly for sperm differentiation (Bennett *et al.*, 1972; Yanagisawa *et al.*, 1974; Artzt *et al.*, 1973; Fellous *et al.*, 1974; Artzt and Bennett, 1975). The transmission ratio of the *t* allele from heterozygous males (T/t or $+/t$) is distorted in favor of the *t* mutation, whereas segregation from heterozygous females is completely normal. Not all *t* alleles, however, produce a distortion of the transmission ratio. It was clearly shown that the mechanism responsible for the segregation distortion of the *t* allele is not an abnormal chromosomal segregation in meiosis resulting in a differential production of + and *t* spermatozoa, but must reside in the haploid expression of the *t* mutation and its normal allele, which confers some advantage in fertilization to the *t*-bearing spermatozoa (Braden, 1958; Yanagisawa *et al.*, 1961; Erickson, 1973; Hammerberg and Klein, 1975).

Although the T-locus data can be explained only by assuming that this chromosomal region is expressed after meiosis, there are data concerning sterility in animals carrying two *t* alleles which suggest that the diploid genotype can somehow influence the haploid gene function (Bennett and Dunn, 1967, 1971).

Biochemical and cytological studies have provided wide experimental evidence of meiotic control of spermatid differentiation, but support also the possibility of a haploid gene action during the early phase of spermiogenesis. Earlier autoradiographic studies in the mouse (Monesi, 1965, 1971) and more recent biochemical studies in our laboratory (Geremia *et al.*, 1977a) have indicated that RNA synthesis in the autosomes is very active in primary spermatocytes, with a peak in middle-late pachytene, ceases completely during metaphases and anaphases I and II, resumes again in early or round spermatids (steps 1 to 8 of spermiogenesis), but stops completely in elongating spermatids (steps 9 to 16) and mature spermatozoa (Fig. 3). No haploid gene action is therefore possible after the beginning of nuclear elongation in spermatids. These results have been confirmed in the mouse by Moore (1971) and Kierszenbaum and Tres (1974b, 1975), in the rat by Söderström and Parvinen (1976), and in the ram by Loir (1971).

Protein synthesis in spermatids follows a well defined pattern. Cytoplasmic protein labeling occurs throughout spermiogenesis, whereas protein labeling in the nucleus is detected only at certain stages (Fig. 3). It is present, at a low level, during early spermiogenesis, then stops completely in spermatid stages 8 or 9 to resume again from spermatid steps 11 to 14. After this burst in late spermiogenesis, nuclear protein synthesis stops completely in the mature (steps 15 and 16) spermatid (Monesi, 1965). The nuclear labeling in late spermiogenesis of mammals reflects the well known synthesis of the "sperm histone" (Monesi, 1964a, 1965; Lam and Bruce, 1971; Coelingh *et al.*, 1972; Monfoort *et al.*, 1973; Marushige and Marushige, 1974, 1975; Bellvé *et al.*, 1975; Geremia *et al.*, 1976b) which persists in the nucleus until the time of fertilization (Kopečný, 1970; Kopečný and Pavlok, 1975; Ecklund and Levine, 1975).

As already said above, autoradiographic experiments with [³H]uridine have demonstrated that a considerable proportion of the RNA synthesized in pachytene spermatocytes is preserved during further cell development until the end of spermiogenesis when it is eliminated from the cell within the residual bodies (Monesi, 1964b, 1965, 1971). As mentioned above, recent biochemical studies in the rat have added new information on the turnover of nuclear RNA synthesized in meiosis. These studies have demonstrated that the RNA synthesized by pachytene spermatocytes is mostly heterogeneous HnRNA which shows a remarkable stability as compared to that of somatic tissues (Söderström and Parvinen, 1976; Söderström, 1976). This HnRNA may include precursors of long-lived mRNA molecules required for directing protein synthesis during late spermiogehesis, when RNA transcription stops completely.

The dependence of spermatid differentiation on the activity of meiotic chromosomes has been clearly demonstrated in *Drosophila*. Contrary to the mouse, in *Drosophila* the Y chromosome is devoid of male-determining genes (the X/O individuals are phenotypically males but sterile) but contains male-fertility factors that are indispensable for the development of functional sperm. Many cytological and autoradiographic studies have clearly demonstrated that these fertility factors located on the Y chromosome are active exclusively during meiosis and that their activity governs the postmeiotic development of germ cells. In *Drosophila* the Y chromosome exhibits during meiosis an extensive lampbrush organization (Hess, 1968; Hennig, 1968; Meyer, 1972; Meyer and Hennig, 1974), is very active in RNA synthesis, and synthesizes specific RNA molecules which are restricted to the male germ line (Hennig, 1967, 1968). Deficiencies of the Y chromosome determining the disappearance of the loop pairs in the spermatocyte cause disturbances of spermiogenesis and consequently sterility in the carrier males (Hess, 1967; Meyer, 1968). These observations indicate that the male-fertility factors are located within the loop-forming sites of the Y chromosome and that the process of spermiogenesis is directed by stable gene products synthesized on the Y chromosome during spermatocyte development and stored until the time of spermateliosis. This conclusion does not, however, exclude the possibility that, in addition to the meiotic control, spermiogenesis is also regulated by gene products transcribed postmeiotically.

We have recently approached biochemically the problem of a haploid versus a meiotic regulation of germ cell differentiation by using quasi-homogeneous populations of pachytene spermatocytes and round spermatids separated from the seminiferous tubules of the mouse with the technique of velocity sedimentation at unit gravity (Lam *et al.*, 1970; Meistrich *et al.*, 1973) after X-irradiation (Geremia *et al.*, 1976a). We have shown that the rate of RNA synthesis per DNA content is about the same in round spermatids and pachytene spermatocytes (Geremia *et al.*, 1976a, 1977a), that round spermatids synthesize both ribosomal RNA and polyadenylated RNA which is engaged in polysomes (presumably mRNA) (D'Agostino *et al.*, 1976; Geremia *et al.*, 1977c), and finally that a considerable fraction of the ribosomal and polyadenylated RNA produced by pachytene spermatocytes is preserved until late spermiogenesis (unpublished data).

A. Rate of RNA Synthesis in Meiotic and Postmeiotic Cells

As mentioned above, in our studies animals exposed to two X-ray doses of 300 and 100 R 4 days apart were used. With this procedure the testis becomes depleted of spermatogonia and early meiotic cells which cosediment in a velocity sedimentation gradient with pachytene spermatocytes and round spermatids. After the X-ray treatment the seminiferous tubules were freed from the interstitial tissue by means of mechanical manipulation or collagenase digestion, dispersed into single cells by trypsin treatment, and these were fractionated into several cell classes by sedimentation at unit gravity in a Ficoll gradient, as mentioned above and described in more detail previously (Geremia *et al.*, 1976a).

The first approach to the problem of RNA synthesis at various stages of spermatogenesis was to study the distribution of [³H]uridine radioactivity in the various cell fractions separated by velocity sedimentation from the mouse testis. For this study the animals were injected intratesticularly with 20 μCi of [³H]5-uridine per testis or intraperitoneally with 50 μCi per gram body weight. Figure 4 shows the distribution of acid-precipitable radioactivity in the various germ cell fractions separated from the seminiferous tubules. It can be seen that [³H]uridine incorporation into RNA occurs in three cell fractions—i.e., middle-late pachytene spermatocytes; round spermatids (steps 1 to 8 of spermiogenesis); early pachytene and II spermatocytes—and that there is no RNA synthesis in intermediate and late spermatids (steps 9 to 16 of spermiogenesis), thus confirming previous autoradiographic results (Monesi, 1965).

The experiments designed to study the rate of RNA synthesis in pachytene spermatocytes and in round spermatids were performed *in vitro* by incubating seminiferous tubules in culture with [³H]uridine for 3 hours (see, for experimental details, Geremia *et al.*, 1977a). This

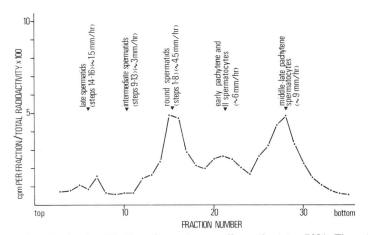

FIG. 4. Distribution in a Ficoll gradient of germ cells synthesizing RNA. The radioactivity per fraction is plotted as the percentage of the total radioactivity in the gradient. Mice were X-irradiated twice 4 days apart, as described in the text, to deplete the testis of spermatogonia and early meiotic cell, injected intratesticularly with 20 μCi of [³H]uridine per testis 24 hours after the second X-ray dose, and killed 24 hours after labeling. From Geremia *et al.* (1977a).

interval of incubation was chosen since a preliminary experiment had indicated that the precursor in the culture medium takes a minimum of 2 hours to equilibrate with the intracellular [³H]uridine pool.

To evaluate the rate of RNA synthesis by using radioactive precursors, it is necessary to know the specific activity of the intracellular precursor pool. This parameter, which cannot be measured directly in our system, can be evaluated by expanding the endogenous uridine pool to the point that the specific activity of the precursor within the cell becomes virtually the same as that in the medium (Berg and Mertes, 1970; epstein and Daentl, 1971; Epstein and Smith, 1973). This can be achieved by measuring the precursor incorporation into RNA at increasing concentrations of the precursor in the medium; the curve should rise rapidly until a plateau is reached. At the plateau value the endogenous uridine pool makes a minimal contribution to the intracellular specific activity, and this can be considered to be effectively the same as that in the medium. In these conditions the actual rate of RNA synthesis can be calculated.

Figure 5 shows the results of the pool expansion experiments. Although a true plateau of incorporation was not reached in this system, it is clear that at precursor concentrations in the medium higher than 50 μM the ratio of incorporation in middle-late pachytene spermatocytes and in round spermatids keeps a constant value of 4:1. The

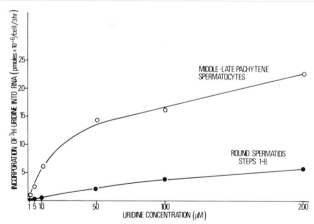

FIG. 5. Incorporation of [³H]uridine into RNA in middle-late pachytene spermatocyte and round spermatid fractions at different precursor concentrations in the medium. Seminiferous tubules from X-irradiated mice were incubated for 3 hours with increasing concentrations of the precursor, the germ cell suspensions were fractionated by velocity sedimentation in a Ficoll gradient, and the uridine radioactivity incorporated in the two cell types was evaluated. From Geremia et al. (1977a).

conclusion should therefore be drawn that the rate of RNA synthesis per DNA content is about the same in these two cell stages.

B. RNA CLASSES SYNTHESIZED IN EARLY SPERMATIDS

The next step in the analysis of RNA transcription in meiotic and postmeiotic cells was to study the classes of RNA synthesized by middle-late pachytene spermatocytes and round or early spermatids.

Seminiferous tubules were labeled in culture for 3 hours with [³H]5-uridine alone (100 μCi/ml) or with [³H]5-uridine (100 μCi/ml) and [³H]2-adenosine (100 μCi/ml) at 32°C in an atmosphere of 5% CO_2 in air. In few experiments a 5-hour chase with the cold precursor was performed after labeling. After labeling, the germ cells, released from the seminiferous tubules as already described, were fractionated by velocity sedimentation in a Ficoll gradient. The middle-late pachytene spermatocyte fraction, the round spermatid (steps 1–8 of spermiogenesis) fraction and the intermediate-late spermatid (steps 9–16) fraction were collected, the RNA was extracted with SDS–phenol–chloroform from the postmitochondrial supernatant and analyzed in a 5 to 20% linear sucrose gradient (Fig. 2) or in a poly(U)–Sepharose column by affinity chromatography (Table I) (Geremia et al., 1977c).

The results of the sucrose-gradient analysis of the RNA extracted from the postmitochondrial supernatant indicate that round spermatids, as well as pachytene spermatocytes, synthesize 4 S, 18 S, and 28 S RNA (Fig. 2 c, d). The labeled RNA in the heavier part of the sucrose gradient corresponds probably to nuclear RNA molecules, including ribosomal RNA precursors, leaked from the nucleus. These faster sedimenting labeled RNA molecules decrease greatly in quantity after a 5-hour chase with cold uridine, while the 18 S and 28 S radioactive peaks become more pronounced (Fig. 2d).

The analysis of the synthesis of poly(A)-containing RNA by affinity chromatography on poly(U)–Sepharose column is shown in Table I. The data reported in the first two rows of the table indicate that round spermatids, as well as pachytene spermatocytes, actively synthesize polyadenylated RNA molecules. The percentage of the radioactivity bound to the poly(U) column is, however, an overestimate of the actual rate of synthesis of poly(A)-containing RNA relative to the total RNA synthesis, since the cells were labeled with both [³H]uridine and [³H]adenosine.

From the data reported in Table I it appears that the rate of incorporation of the radioactive precursors into nonpolyadenylated and into polyadenylated RNA is about 8-fold lower in spermatids than in spermatocytes; the labeling of poly(A)-containing RNA relative to the total labeled RNA is about the same in the two cell types. The rate of incorporation at the precursor concentrations used in these experiments does not, however, reflect the actual rate of RNA synthesis, since previous pool expansion experiments in our laboratory (Geremia *et al.*, 1977a) have indicated that it is necessary to use very high concentrations of the precursors in the medium in order to attain the same specific activity of the intracellular pool in round spermatids and in pachytene spermatocytes. In these conditions the ratio of incorporation in spermatocytes and in round spermatids is about $4:1$ ($1:1$ if expressed per DNA content). The conclusion should therefore be drawn that pachytene spermatocytes and round spermatids synthesize about an equal amount of poly(A)-containing RNA as well as of non-polyadenylated RNA per DNA content.

The RNA extracted from intermediate and late spermatids was completely unlabeled. This excludes the possibility that the radioactive ribosomal and polyadenylated RNA detected in round spermatids arise from fragments of Sertoli cell cytoplasm still attached to the spermatids and cosedimenting with these cells in the Ficoll gradient.

The subsequent step in the analysis of the genetic activity of germ cells was to see whether the newly synthesized poly(A)-containing RNA detected in spermatids was mRNA rather than polyadenylated nuclear RNA leaked from the nucleus. This type of study requires the analysis of the RNA extracted from polysome preparations. Preliminary experiments have demonstrated that it is difficult to perform this analysis in cell fractions separated by velocity sedimentation since the amount of polysomal RNA obtainable is not sufficient to run a poly(U) column. Therefore the analysis of the radioactivity incorporated into polysomal RNA was performed in the following way (see legend to Table I for experimental details). The animals were exposed to three doses of X-rays (300, 100, and 100 R) 6 days apart in order to deplete the testes of spermatogonia and all meiotic cells, injected 30 hours after the last X-ray exposure with 20 μCi of [³H]uridine and 20 μCi of [³H]adenosine per testis, and sacrificed 24 hours later. The histological examination of these irradiated testes has demonstrated that the only germ cells present in the seminiferous tubules were spermatids. Fragments of seminiferous tubules were gently pipetted several times in order to release the spermatids without removing the somatic cells of the tubule. Morphological examination by phase-contrast microscopy has demonstrated that the cell suspension thus obtained was composed almost exclusively of round and elongated spermatids; somatic cells, spermatogonia, and meiotic cells were absent. The RNA was extracted with phenol–chloroform from the polysomes and analyzed in a 5 to 20%

linear sucrose gradient and in a poly(U)–Sepharose column, as described in detail in the legend to Table I.

The results obtained showed that polysomes extracted from this material contain both radioactive ribosomal RNA (data not shown) and radioactive poly(A)-containing RNA (Table I, third row), suggesting that spermatids synthesize mRNA molecules.

C. PRESERVATION OF MEIOTIC RNA UNTIL SPERMIOGENESIS

As mentioned above, an important problem in the study of germ cell differentiation is whether the development of spermatids is dependent solely on the activity of the haploid genome or whether it is also regulated by stable RNA molecules produced in meiosis and translated during spermiogenesis. This is particularly important in middle-late spermiogenesis, when RNA transcription ceases completely.

An initial approach to this problem is to see whether the RNA produced in meiosis is preserved during further cell development. Groups of animals, depleted of spermatogonia and early meiotic cells by means of the X-irradiation schedule described above, were injected intratesticularly or intraperitoneally with [³H]uridine and killed at several postlabeling intervals from 1 to 19 days. The germ cells were separated into different cell classes by velocity sedimentation, as already described (Geremia et al., 1976a), and the TCA-precipitable radioactivity was determined in each cell fraction. The results indicated that a considerable proportion of the RNA synthesized by middle-late pachytene spermatocytes is preserved for as long as 17 days during further cell development until late spermiogenesis, when it is shed from the cell within the residual bodies (Geremia et al., 1977a), thus confirming previous autoradiographic experiments (Monesi, 1965).

In order to exclude the possibility that the labeled RNA detected at long postlabeling intervals arises from a continuous reincorporation of [³H]uridine from the intracellular pool, the PCA (perchloric acid)-soluble intracellular radioactivity was determined at various intervals after injection of the radioactive precursor. The results showed that the soluble intracellular radioactivity drops to 50% and 10% of the initial radioactivity 16 hours and 3 days after labeling, respectively, and becomes undetectable after 4 days. This experiment indicates, therefore, that the labeled RNA found in germ cells later than 4 days after labeling is not a product of a new synthesis from the intracellular pool, but represents stable RNA molecules preserved from the preceding stages (Geremia et al., 1977a).

The labeled cytoplasmic RNA preserved from meiosis until spermiogenesis has been analyzed in a linear sucrose gradient and in a poly(U)–Sepharose affinity chromatography column. The results obtained indicated that the stable RNA molecules produced in meiosis and preserved during spermatid development include both ribosomal RNA and polyadenylated RNA (presumptive mRNA). Some of these stable poly(A)+RNA molecules preserved from the diploid to the haploid phase of spermatogenesis have a lifetime as long as 14 days, since we have detected labeled poly(A)-containing RNA molecules in intermediate and late spermatids as late as 14 days after labeling.

D. CONCLUDING COMMENTS

The results described provide clear evidence for gene expression during the haploid phase of spermatogenesis in the mouse; the transcriptional activity during early spermiogenesis involves both polyadenylated RNA (presumptive mRNA) and rRNA. This latter finding was quite unexpected in view of previous autoradiographic and electron microscopic observations of nucleolar inactivity in mouse spermatids (Kierszenbaum and Tres, 1975). The rate of synthesis per DNA content of nonpolyadenylated and of polyadenylated RNA in round spermatids is comparable to that of primary spermatocytes at middle-late pachytene, which is the stage of maximum RNA synthetic activity in meiosis (Monesi, 1965, 1971). The presence of cytoplasmic bridges connecting groups of synchronously developing spermatids (Dym and Fawcett, 1971) precludes, however, a definite conclusion as to the effect of the haploid genotype on the phenotype of the mature gamete.

The results of the labeling kinetics experiments indicate, furthermore, that a great proportion of the polyadenylated RNA (presumably mRNA) and of the nonpolyadenylated RNA transcribed in middle-late pachytene spermatocytes is preserved through spermatid development until late spermiogenesis. This evidence does not, however, necessarily imply that this meiotic RNA is translated in the spermatid cytoplasm. Experiments are in progress in our laboratory to see whether the labeled RNA synthesized in meiosis and detected in the spermatid cytoplasm is present in polysomes. Another approach to the problem of whether the meiotic RNA includes molecules that codify for proteins synthesized postmeiotically is to see whether the mRNA extracted from pachytene spermatocytes can be translated in a cell-free system into sperm-specific proteins. This is probably the most crucial experiment to answer the question whether the differentiation of spermatozoa is exclusively dependent on haploid transcription or whether a meiotic regulation through the synthesis and storage in spermatocytes of stable mRNA molecules can also play a role.

ACKNOWLEDGMENTS

This work was supported by Grant No. 7600300.85 (research project Biology of Reproduction) from the National Council of Research and by Grant No. 730.0208 from the Ford Foundation.

REFERENCES

Artzt, K., and Bennett, D. (1975). *Nature (London)* **256**, 545–547.
Artzt, K., Dubois, P., Bennett, D., Condamine, H., Babinet, C., and Jacob, F. (1973). *Proc. Natl. Acad. Sci. U.S.A.* **70**, 2988–2992.
Attardi, B., and Ohno, S. (1974). *Cell* **2**, 205–212.
Baker, T. G. (1971). *Adv. Biosci.* **6**, 7–23.
Bardin, C. W., Bullock, L. P., Sherins, R. J., Mowszowicz, I., and Blackburn, W. R. (1973). *Recent Prog. Horm. Res.* **29**, 65–109.
Beatty, R. A. (1970). *Biol. Rev. Cambridge Philos. Soc.* **45**, 73–119.
Beatty, R. A. (1972). *In* "Edinburgh Symposium on the Genetics of the Spermatozoon" R. A. Beatty and S. Gluecksohn-Waelsch, eds.), pp. 97–115. Edinburgh Univ. Press, Edinburgh.
Bellvé, A. R., Anderson, E., and Hanley-Bowdoin, L. (1975). *Dev. Biol.* **47**, 349–365.
Bennett, D. (1975). *Cell* **6**, 441–454.
Bennett, D., and Dunn L. C. (1967). *J. Reprod. Fertil.* **13**, 421–428.
Bennett, D., and Dunn, L. C. (1971). *Immunogenet. H-2 Syst., Proc. Symp., 1970* pp. 90–103.
Bennett, D., Goldberg, E., Dunn, L. C., and Boyse, E. A. (1972). *Proc. Natl. Acad. Sci. U.S.A.* **69**, 2076–2080.
Berg, W. E., and Mertes, D. H. (1970). *Exp. Cell Res.* **60**, 218–224.
Braden, A. W. H. (1958). *Nature (London)* **181**, 786–787.
Bullock, L. P., and Bardin, C. W. (1974). *Endocrinology* **94**, 746–756.
Busch, H., and Smetana, K. (1970). "The Nucleolus." Academic Press, New York.
Callan, A. G. (1969). *In* "Handbook of Molecular Cytology" (A. Lima-de-Faria, ed.), pp. 540–552. North Holland Publ., Amsterdam.
Cattanach, B. M. (1961). *Genet. Res.* **2**, 156–158.
Cattanach, B. M. (1975). *Early Dev. Mamm., Symp. Br. Soc. Dev. Biol., 2nd, 1974* pp. 305–317.
Cattanach, B. M., Pollard, C. E., and Hawkes J. G. (1971). *Cytogenetics* **10**, 318–337.
Clermont, Y. (1967). *Arch. Anat. Microsc. Morphol. Exp.* **56**, 7–60.
Clermont, Y. (1972). *Physiol. Rev.* **52**, 198–236.
Coelingh, J. P., Monfoort, C. H., Rozijn, J. H., Gevers Leuven, J. A., Schiphof, R., Steyn-Parvé, E. P., Braunitzer, G., Schrank, B., and Ruhfus, A. (1972). *Biochim. Biophys. Acta* **285**, 1–14.
Courot, M., Hochereau-de Reviers, M. T., and Ortavant, R. (1970). *In* "The Testis" (A. D. Johnson, W. R. Gomes, and N. L. Van Demark, eds.), Vol. 1, pp. 339–432. Academic Press, New York.
D'Agostino, A., Geremia, R., and Monesi, V. (1976). *Arch. Ital. Anat. Embriol.* **81** Suppl., 35.
Darnell, J. E., Wall, R., and Tushinski, R. J. (1971). *Proc. Natl. Acad. Sci. U.S.A.* **68**, 1321–1325.
Das, N. K. (1965). *Exp. Cell Res.* **40**, 360–364.

De Rooij, D. G. (1973). *Cell Tissue Kinet.* **6**, 281–287.

Dym, M., and Fawcett, D. W. (1971). *Biol. Reprod.* **4**, 195–215.

Ecklund, P. S., and Levine, L. (1975). *J. Cell Biol.* **66**, 251–262.

Epstein, C. J. (1969). *Science* **163**, 1078–1079.

Epstein, C. J., and Daentl, D. L. (1971). *Dev. Biol.* **26**, 517–524.

Epstein, C. J., and Smith, S. A. (1973). *Dev. Biol.* **33**, 171–184.

Erickson, R. P. (1973). *Nature (London) New Biol.* **243**, 210–212.

Erickson, R. P. (1976). *Dev. Biol.* **53**, 134–137.

Evans, H. J., Buckland, R. A., and Pardue, M. L. (1974). *Chromosoma* **48**, 405–426.

Fellous, M., Gachelin, G., Buc-Caron, M., Dubois, P. H., and Jacob, F. (1974). *Dev. Biol.* **41**, 331–337.

Gartler, S. M., Liskay, R. M., and Gant, N. (1973). *Exp. Cell Res.* **82**, 464–465.

Geremia, R., Galdieri, M., D'Agostino, A., Boitani, C., Proietti, F., Ferracin, A., and Monesi, V. (1976a). *Boll. Zool.* **43**, 139–149.

Geremia, R., Goldberg, R. B., and Bruce, W. R. (1976b). *Andrologia* **8**, 147–156.

Geremia, R., Boitani, C., Conti, M., and Monesi, V. (1977a). *Cell Differ.* **5**, 343–355.

Geremia, R., D'Agostino, A., Boitani, C., Ferracin, A., and Monesi, V. (1977b). *Boll. Zool.* (in press).

Geremia, R., D'Agostino, A., and Monesi, V. (1977c). *Exp. Cell Res.* (in press).

Glätzer, K. H. (1975). *Chromosoma* **53**, 371–379.

Hamkalo, B. A., and Miller, O. L. (1973). *Annu. Rev. Biochem.* **42**, 379–396.

Hammerberg, C., and Klein, J. (1975). *Nature (London)* **253**, 137–138.

Henderson, A. S. (1964). *Chromosoma* **15**, 345–366.

Henderson, A. S., Warburton, D., and Atwood, K. C. (1972). *Proc. Natl. Acad. Sci. U.S.A.* **69**, 3394–3398.

Henderson, A. S., Eicher, E. M., Yu, M. T., and Atwood, K. C. (1974). *Chromosoma* **49**, 155–160.

Hennig, W. (1967). *Chromosoma* **22**, 294–357.

Hennig, W. (1968). *J. Mol. Biol.* **38**, 227–239.

Hennig, W., Meyer, G. F., Hennig, I., and Leoncini, O. (1974). *Cold Spring Harbor Symp. Quant. Biol.* **38**, 673–683.

Hess, O. (1967). *Genetics* **56**, 283–295.

Hess, O. (1968). *Mol. Gen. Genet.* **103**, 58–71.

Huckins, C. (1971a). *Anat. Rec.* **169**, 533–558.

Huckins, C. (1971b). *Cell Tissue Kinet.* **4**, 139–154.

Huckins, C. (1971c). *Cell Tissue Kinet.* **4**, 313–334.

Huckins, C. (1971d). *Cell Tissue Kinet.* **4**, 335–349.

Kano, Y., Maeda, S., and Sugiyama, T. (1976). *Chromosoma* **55**, 37–42.

Kierszenbaum, A. L., and Tres, L. L. (1974a). *J. Cell Biol.* **60**, 39–53.

Kierszenbaum, A. L., and Tres, L. L. (1974b). *J. Cell Biol.* **63**, 923–935.

Kierszenbaum, A. L., and Tres, L. L. (1975). *J. Cell Biol.* **65**, 258–270.

Kopečný, V. (1970). *Z. Zellforsch. Mikrosk. Anat.* **109**, 414–419.

Kopečný, V., and Pavlok, A. (1975). *J. Exp. Zool.* **191**, 85–96.

Lam, D. M. K., and Bruce, W. R. (1971). *J. Cell Physiol.* **78**, 13–24.

Lam, D. M. K., Furrer, R., and Bruce, W. R. (1970). *Proc. Natl. Acad. Sci. U.S.A.* **65**, 192–199.

Leblond, C. P., and Clermont, Y. (1952a). *Am. J. Anat.* **90**, 167–215.

Leblond, C. P., and Clermont, Y. (1952b). *Ann. N.Y. Acad. Sci.* **55**, 548–573.

Lee, S. Y., Mendecki, J., and Brawerman, G. (1971). *Proc. Natl. Acad. Sci. U.S.A.* **68**, 1331–1335.

Lifschytz, E., and Lindsley, D. L. (1972). *Proc. Natl. Acad. Sci. U.S.A.* **69**, 182–186.
Lindberg, U., and Persson, T. (1972). *Eur. J. Biochem.* **31**, 246–254.
Lindsley, D. L., and Lifschytz, E. (1972). *In* "Edinburgh Symposium on the Genetics of the Spermatozoon" (R. A. Beatty and S. Gluecksohn-Waelsch, eds.), pp. 203–211. Edinburgh Univ. Press, Edinburgh.
Loir, M. (1971). *C.R. Hebd. Seances Acad. Sci., Ser. D* **271**, 1634–1636.
Lyon, M. F. (1961). *Nature (London)* **190**, 372–373.
Lyon, M. F. (1974). *In* "Physiology and Genetics of Reproduction, Part A" (E. M. Coutinho and F. Fuchs, eds.), pp. 63–71. Plenum, New York.
Lyon, M. F., and Hawkes, S. G. (1970). *Nature (London)* **227**, 1217–1219.
Lyon, M. F., Glenister, P. H., and Lynn Lamoreux, M. (1975). *Nature (London)* **258**, 620–622.
Mangia, F., Abbo-Halbasch, G., and Epstein, C. J. (1975). *Dev. Biol.* **45**, 366–368.
Marushige, Y., and Marushige, K. (1974). *Biochim. Biophys. Acta* **340**, 498–508.
Marushige, Y., and Marushige, K. (1975). *J. Biol. Chem.* **250**, 39–45.
Meistrich, M. L. (1972). *J. Cell. Physiol.* **80**, 299–312.
Meistrich, M. L., Bruce, W. R., and Clermont, Y. (1973). *Exp. Cell Res.* **79**, 213–227.
Meyer, G. F. (1968). *Z. Zellforsch. Mikrosk. Anat.* **84**, 141–175.
Meyer, G. F. (1972). *In* "Edinburgh Symposium on the Genetics of the Spermatozoon" (R. A. Beatty and S. Gluecksohn-Waelsch, eds.), pp. 387–404. Edinburgh Univ. Press, Edinburgh.
Meyer, G. F., and Hennig, W. (1974). *In* "The Functional Anatomy of the Spermatozoon" (B. A. Afzelius, ed.), pp. 69–75. Pergamon, Oxford.
Milcarek, C., Price, R., and Penman, S. (1974). *Cell* **3**, 1–10.
Miller, O. L., and Hamkalo, B. A. (1972). *Int. Rev. Cytol.* **33**, 1–25.
Mittwoch, U. (1967). "Sex Chromosomes." Academic Press, New York.
Monesi, V. (1962). *J. Cell Biol.* **14**, 1–18.
Monesi, V. (1964a). *Exp. Cell Res.* **36**, 683–688.
Monesi, V. (1964b). *J. Cell Biol.* **22**, 521–532.
Monesi, V. (1965). *Exp. Cell Res.* **39**, 197–224.
Monesi, V. (1967). *Arch. Anat. Microsc. Morphol. Exp.* **56**, Suppl. 3–4, 61–74.
Monesi, V. (1971). *J. Reprod. Fertil., Suppl.* **13**, 1–14.
Monfoort, C. H., Schiphof, R., Rozijn, T. H., and Steyn-Parvé, E. P. (1973). *Biochim. Biophys. Acta* **322**, 173–177.
Moore, G. P. M. (1971). *Exp. Cell Res.* **68**, 462–465.
Muckenthaler, F. A. (1964). *Exp. Cell Res.* **35**, 531–547.
Muramatsu, M., Utakoji, T., and Sugano, H. (1968). *Exp. Cell Res.* **53**, 278–283.
Nebel, B. R., and Coulon, E. M. (1962). *Chromosoma* **13**, 272–291.
Oakberg, E. F. (1955). *Radiat. Res.* **2**, 369–391.
Oakberg, E. F. (1956a). *Am. J. Anat.* **99**, 391–413.
Oakberg, E. F. (1956b). *Am. J. Anat.* **99**, 507–510.
Oakberg, E. F. (1971). *Anat. Rec.* **169**, 515–532.
Ohno, S. (1971). *Nature (London)* **234**, 134–137.
Ohno, S., Kaplan, W., and Kinosita, R. (1957). *Exp. Cell Res.* **13**, 358–364.
Ohno, S., Kaplan, W., and Kinosita, R. (1961). *Exp. Cell Res.* **22**, 535–544.
Palmiter, R. D. (1974). *Biochemistry* **13**, 3606–3614.
Parchman, L. G., and Lin, K.-C. (1972). *Nature (London), New Biol.* **239**, 235–237.
Russell, L. B., and Chu, E. H. (1961). *Proc. Natl. Acad. Sci. U.S.A.* **47**, 571–575.
Sconzo, G., Bono, D., Albanese, I., and Giudice, G. (1972). *Exp. Cell Res.* **72**, 95–100.
Söderström, K.-O. (1976). *Exp. Cell Res.* **102**, 237–245.

Söderström, K.-O., and Parvinen, M. (1976). *Mol. Cell. Endocrinol.* **5,** 181–199.

Solari, J. (1969). *J. Ultrastruct. Res.* **27,** 289–305.

Solari, J., and Tres, L. L. (1967). *Exp. Cell Res.* **47,** 86–96.

Stefanini, M., De Martino, C., D'Agostino, A., Agrestini, A., and Monesi, V. (1974). *Exp. Cell Res.* **86,** 166–170.

Steinberger, A., and Steinberger, E. (1970). *In* "The Testis" (A. D. Johnson, W. R. Gomes, and N. L. Van Demark, eds.), Vol. 2, pp. 363–391. Academic Press, New York.

Tres, L. L. (1975). *Chromosoma* **53,** 141–151.

Utakoji, T. (1966). *Exp. Cell Res.* **42,** 585–587.

Yanagisawa, K., Dunn, L. C., and Bennett, D. (1961). *Genetics* **46,** 1635–1644.

Yanagisawa, K., Bennett, D., Boyse, E. A., Dunn, L. C., and Dimeo, A. (1974). *Immunogenetics* **1,** 57–67.

CHAPTER 3

CELL COMMUNICATION, CELL UNION, AND INITIATION OF MEIOSIS IN CILIATE CONJUGATION

*Akio Miyake**

ISTITUTO DI ZOOLOGIA
UNIVERSITÀ DI PISA
PISA, ITALY

I. Introduction

For ciliate cells, conjugation is an exceptionally social occasion. During this time, cells of complementary mating types first communi-

---

* Present address: Zoologisches Institut der Universität, 4400 Münster, West Germany.

cate by mating signals, gain the capacity to unite, and temporarily form bicellular conjugant pairs. In the united cells, a series of nuclear changes including meiosis, exchange, and fusion of gametic nuclei, is set in motion. Then cells separate, returning to their unicellular phase, but developmental changes continue. The fertilization nucleus repeatedly divides mitotically, and the division products differentiate into somatic and germ nuclei, which eventually replace the preexisting nuclear system. Certain cortical structures are also reconstructed. Thus, ciliate conjugation encompasses two important features of fertilization, namely, karyogamy and initiation of development.

Since each ciliate cell can be regarded as an individual, it may be asked whether conjugation is fertilization or mating. Perhaps it is both. But in this chapter such a question is bypassed and attention is focused on the component processes of conjugation, particularly cell communication, cell union, and initiation of meiosis.

These processes all commonly occur in fertilization and in related phenomena in many organisms, but some of the characteristics of ciliate conjugation appear to provide unique investigative opportunities. Like fertilization in Metazoa, conjugation is regularly induced by mixing two types of cells, but unlike eggs and sperms the two types of ciliate cells must interact for an hour or even longer before they form conjugant pairs. Such a relatively long "preconjugant cell interaction" provides an opportunity to study the details of how cells interact and gain the capacity to unite. The reversibility of the cell union in conjugation makes it possible to study the formation and termination of cell union in the same material. Since meiosis starts soon after the cells unite, the study of meiosis-initiating mechanisms is feasible.

In order to apply the results of these studies to general problems of cellular regulation, conjugation is most profitably investigated at the molecular level, because it is at this level that the uniformity of life has been most clearly demonstrated. Therefore, such investigations will be preferentially presented. A more general treatment of cell interaction in ciliates will be found in a recent review by Nanney (1977).

II. Cell Communication

That two cell types (mating types) are needed for conjugation in ciliates was first demonstrated by Sonneborn (1937) in *Paramecium aurelia*. He mixed cells of two different cultures under appropriate conditions; a burst of conjugation occurred within a few hours, while unmixed cells remain unpaired (for methods, see Sonneborn, 1950, 1970).

In some ciliates, e.g., *Paramecium,* the mixing of the two types of cells is immediately followed by a ciliary agglutination between them, whereas in others, e.g., *Blepharisma, Tetrahymena,* any characteristic physical association of cells becomes visible only after 1–2 hours of the "waiting period" (Fig. 1). However, in spite of such apparent diversities among different groups of ciliates, one thing is consistent: that is, there is always a time lag ranging from one to a few hours between the mixing of the two types of cells and the appearance of "conjugant pairs" (Fig. 2), in which cells firmly unite with a direct contact of cell bodies. In order to distinguish the union of cells with a direct contact of cell bodies from the union of cells by ciliary agglutination, only the former will be called cell union; the latter will be termed ciliary union or ciliary agglutination in this chapter.

The requirement of two types of cells and the regular presence of a time lag between the mixing of cells and the appearance of cell union leads to the important generalization that communication between the two types of cells is necessary for the formation of cell union in conjugation. For a communication to occur, a signal of cellular origin (conjugation signal) and a recognition mechanism for this signal are needed.

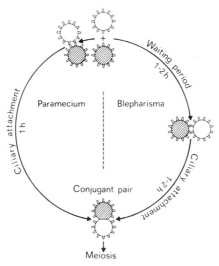

FIG. 1. Two types of preconjugant cell interaction classified on the basis of the presence or the absence of a waiting period. Complementary mating types are differently shaded. In *Paramecium,* conjugation signals are cell-bound, whereas in *Blepharisma,* they are excreted in the medium. Ciliary attachment is mating-type-specific in *Paramecium,* but not in *Blepharisma.* For a unifying view on such different types of interaction, see Sections II, H and III, A.

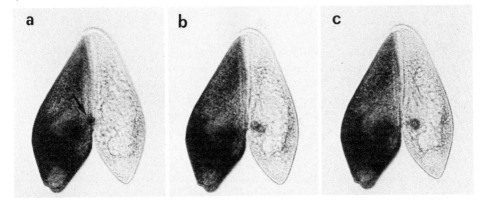

FIG. 2. Conjugant pairs of *Blepharisma japonicum* at the time of karyogamy. *Left:* Red-pigmented (wild type) cell, mating type II. *Right:* albino cell, mating type I. Cells unite along the whole length of the oral groove. At this stage of conjugation, the red pigment tends to accumulate at the posterior end of the cell and also at the vicinity of the micronuclei, making gametic nuclei visible without staining. (a) The migratory gametic nucleus of the red cell (arrow) is at the border of the united cells. Gametic nuclei in the albino cell are invisible because of the lack of pigment. (b) The same pair as in (a), 31 minutes later. The migratory gametic nucleus of the red cell has entered the albino cell. This nucleus has brought in pigment, which also surrounds the stationary gametic nucleus of the albino cell. (c) The same pair as in (b), 6 minutes later. The two gametic nuclei have fused to form a fertilization nucleus. Photographs of living, unstained cells. ×210.

Studies on such signals and recognition mechanisms will be described first.

A. CONJUGATION SIGNALS IN *Blepharisma*

In *B. japonicum,**** complementary mating types I and II communicate by conjugation signals or "gamones" excreted into the medium, as diagrammatically shown in Fig. 3 (Miyake, 1968a; Miyake and Beyer, 1973). Type I cells excrete gamone 1 (step 1). This gamone gives specific information to type II cells (step 2) and transforms them so that they can unite (step 3), at the same time inducing them to excrete gamone 2 (step 4). This gamone gives specific information to type I cells (step 5) and transforms them so that they can unite (step 6). The transformed cells unite to form pairs (step 7).

The union between transformed cells can occur in any combination of mating types. Therefore, in the mixture of the two cell types, both heterotypic pairs (type I–type II) and homotypic pairs (type I–type I,

---

* *Blepharisma intermedium* (Bhandary, 1962), on which most of the studies on conjugation signals of *Blepharisma* were carried out, was recently reassigned to *B. japonicum* var. *intermedium* (Hirshfield *et al.*, 1973).

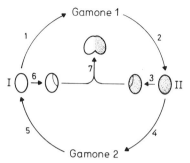

FIG. 3. Diagram of preconjugant cell interaction in *Blepharisma japonicum*. I: Mating type I cell. II: Mating type II cell. Modified from Miyake and Beyer (1973).

type II–type II) are formed. If cells of only one type are treated by gamone of the other type, homotypic pairs are formed. Using this cellular response, gamone can be detected and assayed.

The excretion of gamone 1 autonomously begins when type I cells are suspended in a nutrient-free medium. The rate of excretion reaches a maximum after 1 day and then declines, but the excretion continues for a week or even longer until cells die out from starvation. During this time of reduced excretion, gamone 2 can enhance the excretion. Therefore, the reaction chain consisting of steps 1, 2, 4, and 5 in Fig. 3 is a positive feedback cycle.

Some cultures of type II cells (*non-augex* form) do not autonomously excrete gamone 2. They excrete gamone 2 only when gamone 1 is present. Others (*augex* form) autonomously excrete gamone 2. Like the gamone 1 excretion by type I cells, gamone 2 excretion by *augex* changes according to nutritive conditions. At the time of diminished excretion, gamone 1 enhances the excretion.

Gamone 2 was isolated first, identified as calcium-3-(2'-formyl-amino-5'-hydroxybenzoyl) lactate (Fig. 4) (Kubota *et al.*, 1973) and chemically synthesized (Tokoroyama *et al.*, 1973). Pure gamone 2 (blepharismone) at a concentration of 1 ng/ml can induce homotypic pairs in type I cells suspended at a density of 500–1000 cells/ml. At 4 ng/ml, it can induce pairs in nearly all cells in about 2 hours under the same conditions. Synthetic blepharismone is approximately half

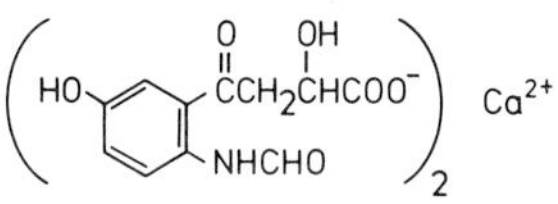

$$\left(HO{-}\underset{NHCHO}{\underset{\displaystyle \bigcirc}{}}{-}\overset{\overset{\displaystyle O}{\parallel}}{C}CH_2\overset{\overset{\displaystyle OH}{\mid}}{C}HCOO^- \right)_2 Ca^{2+}$$

FIG. 4. Blepharismone, gamone 2 of *Blepharisma japonicum*.

as active as the natural compound. This is explained by assuming that one of the enantiometric forms (L-) is several times more biologically active than the other form (D-). This assumption is supported by the finding that L-isomers of gamone 2 inhibitors are more effective than their D-isomers (see Section II, D). The chemical structure of the gamone 2 molecule suggests that a precursor of this gamone is tryptophan (Kubota *et al.*, 1973) (see Fig. 21). Indeed, type II cells incorporate [^{14}C]tryptophan into gamone 2 (Miyake, 1974a; unpublished).

In the isolation of the more unstable gamone 1, the finding that serum albumin is a potent protector of this gamone played a critical role. Thus all the processes of concentration and purification were carried out in the presence of bovine serum albumin until albumin was removed in the last step of purification (Miyake and Beyer, 1974). Gamone 1 was identified as a glycoprotein with a molecular weight of 20,000 (Miyake and Beyer, 1973, 1974). It has characteristically high contents of tyrosine, aspartic acid, threonine, and serine (13, 26, 17, and 19 residues, respectively, among the total 175 amino acids excluding tryptophan), a low content of glutamic acid (7 residues), and 5% of sugars (3 glucosamine, 3 mannose) (Braun and Miyake, 1975). Purified gamone 1 (blepharmone) at a concentration of 0.06 ng/ml can induce homotypic pairs in type II cells suspended at a density of 500–1000 cells/ml.

When type II cells *(non-augex)* were treated by gamone 1, they started producing gamone 2 after a time lag of 1–2 hours (Miyake and Beyer, 1973). If the gamone 1 treatment was discontinued after 1, 1.5, or 2 hours by washing the cells, gamone 2 production began at nearly the same time and continued for 3–4 hours at the same rate as in the control, which was continuously exposed to gamone 1 (A. Miyake, unpublished) (Fig. 5). Induction was achieved also by a shorter treatment, though the gamone 2 production never reached the level of the control. The results indicate that gamone 1 induces a gamone 2-producing mechanism in 1–2 hours and that the mechanism, once induced, continues functioning for hours even after gamone 1 is removed from the medium. This suggests that gamone 1 induces an enzyme system that converts tryptophan to gamone 2. In the induction of gamone 1 by gamone 2, a time lag of 1–2 hours was also observed (Miyake and Beyer, 1973), but this phenomenon has not been further analyzed.

Blepharmone and blepharismone are the only conjugation signals so far isolated in ciliates. Comparative studies on 4 species of the genus *Blepharisma* indicate that they all share blepharismone as gamone 2, while each species has species-specific gamone 1 (Miyake and Bleyman, 1976). The significance of a striking chemical difference be-

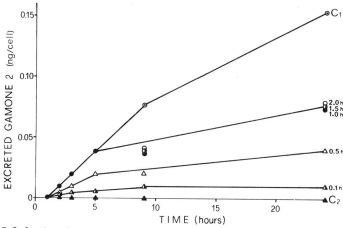

FIG. 5. Induction of gamone 2 by a pulse treatment with gamone 1 (5×10^3 U/ml) in *Blepharisma japonicum*, mating type II, *non-augex* form (5×10^3 cells/ml). Gamone 1 was added at time 0 and removed after different times as indicated, except in the two controls, C_1 and C_2, which were incubated for 24 hours with and without gamone 1, respectively.

tween a pair of gamones that provoke similar responses in target cells is discussed elsewhere (Miyake and Beyer, 1974; Miyake and Bleyman, 1976; Nanney, 1977).

B. CONJUGATION SIGNALS IN *Paramecium*

In contrast to *Blepharisma*, no signal activity has been detected in cell-free fluids of *Paramecium* (Sonneborn, 1937; for review, see Metz, 1954; Hiwatashi, 1969; Miyake, 1974a) suggesting that the conjugation signals of this ciliate are cell-bound and function through direct contact of the two types of cells. In fact cells of complementary mating types of *Paramecium* begin ciliary agglutination with each other (mating reaction) as soon as they are mixed together under appropriate conditions (Fig. 1). There is no lag time for mating reaction, since the two types of cells may agglutinate at the first casual contact after the mixing. Mating reaction continues for approximately an hour until the cells unite in conjugant pairs.

Killed cells (Metz, 1947; Hiwatashi, 1949), isolated cilia (Miyake, 1964; Fukushi and Hiwatashi, 1970; Cronkite, 1972, 1974; Byrne, 1972; Takahashi *et al.*, 1974) and the membranous fraction of isolated cilia (Kitamura and Hiwatashi, 1976) of one mating type induce conjugation in living cells of the complementary mating type. Since killed cells without cilia have no such signal activity (Kitamura and Hiwatashi, 1976), the signal appears to be localized on the cilia (see also Section III, A). In these experiments the ability to induce conjugant pairs was always associated with the ability to agglutinate with living cells of the complementary mating types. These results are generally consistent with the hypothesis (Metz, 1948, 1954) that the material basis of agglutination also functions as the cell union-inducing signal.

Conjugation signals of *Paramecium* have not yet been isolated, but the effect of heat, enzymes, and protein synthesis inhibitors on the signal activity or on the agglutinability suggest that they are proteins (for review, see Metz, 1954; Hiwatashi, 1969).

As in *Paramecium,* cells of the two complementary mating types of *Chlamydomonas moewusii,* a unicellular alga, agglutinate with each other (with flagella instead of cilia) when they are mixed together. The agglutination continues until cells unite by a direct contact of cell bodies and fuse. Substances participating in the agglutination were purified and identified as large glycoproteins. One of them, gynogamone, has a molecular weight of the order of 10^8 (Förster *et al.,* 1956). The glycoprotein of one mating type induces agglutination in living cells of the other mating type, but not the fusion of cells (Wiese, 1961). This suggests that in addition to these glycoproteins, other factors might participate in the induction of cell fusion. The mechanism of agglutination and cell fusion in *Chlamydomonas* has been investigated further (for review, see Crandall, 1977). It may be profitable to consider the cell communication in *Paramecium* in the light of the results obtained in *Chlamydomonas* and vice versa.

C. CONJUGATION SIGNALS IN OTHER CILIATES

Excretion of mating-type-specific signals participating in conjugation were reported in *Euplotes patella* (Kimball, 1939, 1942; Katashima, 1961), *E. eurystomus* (Katashima, 1959), *Dileptus anser* (Vinnikova and Tavrovskaya, 1973; Tavrovskaya, 1974), *Oxytricha bifaria* (Ricci *et al.,* 1975; Esposito *et al.,* 1976), and *Tokophrya* (T. M. Sonneborn, personal communication, cited in Miyake, 1974a). The chemical nature of these signals is unknown, but these examples suggest that a number of ciliates use excreted signals for preconjugant communication.

On the other hand, in *E. crassus* (Heckmann, 1964; Miyake and Nobili, 1974) and *Tetrahymena pyriformis* (Takahashi, 1973) any mating-type-specific signals have not been detected in the medium, indicating that they are cell bound as in *Paramecium*. Cell fractions, including killed cells, with the signal activity have not yet been obtained. The chemical nature of the signal can only be guessed at from indirect evidence (McCoy, 1972; Allewell *et al.*, 1976; Dini and Miyake, 1977, 1978; see also Section II, G).

D. RECEPTORS FOR CONJUGATION SIGNALS

In *B. japonicum,* the induction of cell union in type I cells by gamone 2 is competitively inhibited by structurally related amino acids, particularly 5-hydroxytryptophan and tryptophan. L-Isomers are 4 times more effective than D-isomers in this inhibition (Beyer and Miyake, 1973; Miyake, 1974a). These compounds have no comparable effect on the induction of cell union in type II cells by gamone 1 (A. Miyake, unpublished). This result indicates that type I cells have a mechanism for the recognition of the structural characteristics of the gamone 2 molecule. The material basis of this recognition mechanism, a receptor molecule for gamone 2, may be postulated by the analogy with receptors for hormones and neurotransmitters. In view of the functional similarity between gamones 1 and 2, a receptor for gamone 1 may also be postulated.

Other evidence for a gamone 2 receptor was obtained by Revoltella *et al.* (1976). They demonstrated that ^{125}I-labeled gamone 2 binds to type I cells fixed by formaldehyde and glutaraldehyde and that this binding is inhibited by unlabeled gamone 2. Unfortunately, however, the mating type specificity of this binding was not tested by contrasting type I and type II cells. Ricci *et al.* (1976) showed that phytohemagglutinin W, concanavalin A (Con A) and antitubulin antibodies inhibit the induction of homotypic union by gamone 2 only when suboptimal concentrations of gamone 2 are used. This result indicates that the receptor site for gamone 2 is distinct from the binding site of these ligands.

The possibility that gamones 1 and 2 might function as receptors for each other is unlikely, since these gamones do not interact with each other: The activities of gamone 1 (7.5×10^3 U/ml) and of gamone 2 (1.6×10^4 U/ml) are not appreciably changed by mixing with gamone 2 (1.6×10^4 U/ml) and gamone 1 (10^6 U/ml), respectively (Miyake, 1974a; unpublished).

In *T. pyriformis,* conjugation is inhibited by Con A (Klein *et al.*, 1975; Ofer *et al.*, 1976; Frisch *et al.*, 1977), polylysine, metal chelators (Ofer *et al.*, 1976), trypsin (McCoy, 1972), cycloheximide (see Section III, F, 1), tunicamycin (Frisch *et al.*, 1976—a specific inhibitor of glycoprotein synthesis (Kuo and Lampén, 1974; Tkacz and Lampén,

1975)—colchicine, theophylline, dithiothreitol, and caffeine (Allewell *et al.,* 1976). These results are suggestive, but they still fall short in drawing any definite conclusion about the nature of conjugation signals, signal receptors, and the reaction between them.

Although the presence of gamone receptors has not yet been proved, the hypothesis that a gamone induces conjugation through a specific binding with its receptor is attractive. The confirmation of this hypothesis would be a step toward generalization and simplification that would make ciliate conjugation more amenable to molecular analysis.

E. POSITIVE FEEDBACK IN PRECONJUGANT CELL COMMUNICATION

As described above, mating types I and II of *B. japonicum* show positive feedback in gamone production. In this way, the first subtle sign of the presence of potential mates triggers the production of more and more conjugation signals until cells are stimulated to the point where they are inescapably engaged. A similar positive feedback was also reported in *Oxytricha* (Esposito *et al.,* 1976).

The occurrence of positive feedback in preconjugant communication was first suggested by Heckmann and Siegel (1964) in their work on *E. crassus.* In this ciliate, the mixing of complementary mating types is usually followed by a 1- to 2-hour waiting period. After this period, cells start agglutinating and eventually form conjugant pairs. Heckmann and Siegel assumed that the amount of agglutination substances on the surface of the cells is too small to cause a visible agglutination at the beginning, but the substances react at the initial casual contact of cells and induce the production of the same substances so that later the agglutination becomes strong enough to be visible. This hypothesis is supported by the finding that the mixing of highly reactive cells of complementary mating types is immediately followed by a weak but distinctive agglutination that becomes stronger later (Miyake and Nobili, 1974). It is also supported by recent work indicating the presence on unmixed cells of protein factors for preconjugant interaction (Dini and Miyake, 1977, 1978).

Similar positive-feedback mechanisms might be widely seen in ciliate conjugation in which amplification of a subtle initial interaction appears to be advantageous.

F. CHEMOTACTIC COMMUNICATION

In many ciliates, the first contact between potential mates appears to be by chance, as in many animal gametes. However, chemotaxis in conjugation is known in *Tokophrya* and *Blepharisma.*

In *Tokophrya,* a sessile ciliate, complementary mating types placed within a certain distance orient and stretch toward each other (T. M. Sonneborn, personal communication cited in Miyake, 1974a). The chemical nature of the attractant is unknown.

In *B. japonicum*, gamone 2 attracts type I cells (Honda and Miyake, 1975). Gamone 2 concentration as low as $3 \times 10^{-12} M$ attracted type I cells under the experimental conditions used. This sensitivity is comparable with that found in chemotaxis of a water mold *Allomyces*, in which male gametes are attracted to sirenine concentration of $10^{-10} M$ (Carlile and Machlis, 1965). Only starved blepharismas, which can also respond to this gamone by cell union, are attracted. The treatment of cells with 20 μg of cycloheximide per milliliter, which completely inhibits protein synthesis and hence also induction of cell union (Section III, F), does not affect the ability of cells to be attracted by gamone 2. Type II cells are not attracted by gamone 1. The attraction is therefore unidirectional in spite of the fact that both types of cells are equally motile. This may be compared with the fact that in many organisms only one of the two sexes attracts the other with a pheromone.

G. COMPETENCE FOR PRECONJUGANT CELL COMMUNICATION

Since Maupas (1889) concluded that "une riche alimentation endort l'appétit conjugant, le jeune, au contraire, l'éveille et l'excite," the necessity of food deprivation for conjugation has long been known. In *T. pyriformis*, logarithmically growing cells take 2 hours in a nutrient-free medium to gain the competence to undergo preconjugant cell interaction (Bruns and Brussard, 1974). The process is reversible. Thus competent cells fail to conjugate if mixed in a synthetic culture medium (Allewell *et al.*, 1976). It appears that a cellular switch for conjugation is turned on or off according to the nutritive condition.

However, this interesting switching mechanism has been investigated only to a limited extent (Bruns and Palestine, 1975; Allewell *et al.*, 1976). For further analysis, it would be important to find out which component of the preconjugant communication is affected by nutrition. Well fed cells of mating type I in *B. japonicum* do not produce, or only poorly produce, gamone 1 (Miyake and Beyer, 1973). Such cells also do not respond to gamone 2 (Honda and Miyake, 1975). Well fed cells of *Paramecium* that lack the ability to undergo mating reaction do not respond to chemical induction of conjugation in spite of the fact that the chemical induction does not require the mating reaction (Section III, B). These results indicate that more than one specific component of preconjugant cell interaction is affected by nutrition. Because the occurrence of communication may be blocked by inhibiting any of the components, the problem will be tackled more effectively by investigating the effect of nutritive conditions on individual components such as gamone, gamone receptor, and the processing mechanism of gamone receptor reaction, rather than by investigating the effect on the communication itself, or worse, the end result of the communication, conjugation.

In some ciliates, e.g., *P. bursaria* (Ehret, 1953), *P. aurelia,* syngen 3 (Karakashian, 1968), *P. multimicronucleatum,* syngen 2 (Barnett, 1966), and *E. crassus* (Miyake and Nobili, 1974), competence for the mating reaction rhythmically changes daily and the rhythm is "circadian." If the adaptive significance of these phenomena is difficult to understand, they might simply indicate that the control mechanism of the mating reaction tends to be linked with a hypothetical general clock mechanism of the cell.

The phase of the cell cycle also appears to be a regulatory factor for mating competence. In *T. pyriformis,* only cells in macronuclear G_1 can conjugate (Wolfe, 1973). In *E. crassus* and two other hypotrichs, only cells in G_1 and in a very early stage of S phase conjugate (Luporini and Dini, 1975). Wolfe (1973) discusses this phenomenom in relation to cellular differentiation, whereas Nanney (1977) discusses it in relation to a need for coordination between conjugating cells.

In *T. pyriformis,* syngen 7, Phillips (1971) reported that a small number of cells excrete into the medium a heat-stable factor that makes other cells competent to undergo preconjugant communication. The effect of this factor is not mating-type specific.

Finally, in those ciliates that have an immature period in their clonal life history, the competence for conjugation appears only after this period is over. Such temporal regulations in ciliates have been reviewed by Bleyman (1971) and Nanney (1974). The length of the immature period is more accurately measured by cell divisions rather than real time (Kroll and Barnett, 1968; Miwa and Hiwatashi, 1970; Takagi, 1970), although other factors might also be involved (Miwa, 1973; Miwa and Hiwatashi, 1970; Takagi, 1970). Recently, Miwa *et al.* (1975) reported experimental reversion of mature cells to immaturity by the injection of the cytoplasm of immature cells. The effective factor appears to be in the soluble fraction of immature cells and to have the properties of heat-labile macromolecules.

H. DISCUSSION

The survey of preconjugant cell communication described above indicates a considerable diversity among ciliates. However, it should be pointed out that since the role of preconjugant cell communication is in guiding cells to accomplish conjugation, each ciliate may control the former according to its specific ecological need as to when and how to conjugate. Thus each group of ciliates may exploit available cellular mechanisms to meet this need. What results are dazzling arrays of diversity in genetic and epigenetic control of mating types and mating reactivity (capably reviewed by Nanney, 1977), as well as in chemotaxis, positive feedback, solubility of mating signals, ciliary agglutination, etc.

On the other hand, once competent potential mates come very close to each other, the situation appears to be similar in all ciliates. What is left for them to do is mainly to gain the capacity to undergo cell union and then actually unite to form conjugant pairs. Apparently the same contrasting diversity followed by uniformity is seen in fertilization of Metazoa. Although different groups of Metazoa express arrays of diversity in determination and expression of sex, in the formation of gametes, and in the way eggs and sperms are brought together, fertilization itself is remarkably similar. Therefore, in the next section, on cell union, I will treat different groups of ciliates together.

III. Cell Union

A. INTRODUCTION

The physical association of cells in conjugation may begin with a subtle contact of cilia, but the association soon becomes more intimate, eventually turning into a tight cell union with cytoplasmic bridges. The morphological aspects of this process are briefly presented here as a background for later discussions.

In *Paramecium,* cells of complementary mating types immediately begin the mating reaction when they are brought together. Only the cilia on the oral side of the cell participate in this agglutination (Hiwatashi, 1961; Cohen, 1964). Cilia at the anterior part of the cell then degenerate and a union is formed there (Hiwatashi, 1955b; Miyake, 1966) by a direct contact of cell bodies (holdfast union). The united area is very small at the beginning, but it extends posteriorly to the end of the oral groove where the mouth opens. The union is particularly tight near the mouth (paroral union) and gametic nuclei are exchanged there. Cytoplasmic bridges may be only 1 μm wide in *P. multimicronucleatum* (Inaba *et al.,* 1966) or as wide as 10 μm in *P. aurelia* (Schneider, 1963).

In *Blepharisma,* the ciliary agglutination begins only after a 1–2-hour waiting period. Unlike that of *Paramecium,* the agglutination is not mating type specific and cells may agglutinate in any combination

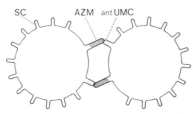

Fig. 6. Diagrammatic illustration of the ciliary union in *Blepharisma japonicum* (cross section). AZM: adoral zone of membranelle, antUMC: cilia anterior to undulating membrane; SC: somatic cilia. Between AZM and antUMC is the oral groove. Modified from Honda and Miyake (1976).

of mating types. Yet this ciliary union is formed by a specific adhesion between the adoral zone of membranelle (AZM) and a row of cilia anterior to the undulating membrane (antUMC) (Honda and Miyake, 1976) (Fig. 6). These two surface structures run nearly parallel to each other on the left and right side of the oral groove, respectively, and are spatially separated so that they can unit only with complementary surfaces of other cells. Thus two cells unite "face-to-face" by two AZM–antUMC bondings forming a pair that looks very much like a conjugant pair. This is another contrast to the ciliary agglutination in *Paramecium,* in which cells tend to form large irregular clumps. After another 1–2 hours, the cell union is formed by a direct contact of cell bodies at the anterior part of the oral groove, which is always devoid of cilia (Ototake, 1969). The degeneration of cilia briefly mentioned by Miyake and Beyer (1973) was not confirmed by recent electron microscopic observations (Bedini *et al.,* 1978). In heterotypic pairs, the cell union enlarges posteriorly to the end of the oral groove where the mouth opens. Cytoplasmic bridges near the mouth are 10–16 μm wide (Ototake, 1969; K. Miyake, 1970; Bedini *et al.,* 1978). Homotypic pairs are formed in the same way, but the cell union extends less extensively. Cytoplasmic bridges as wide as 3 μm are formed (Bedini *et al.,* 1978).

In *Euplotes,* a waiting period generally precedes ciliary agglutination, which is followed by the union of cells by a direct contact of cell bodies. Cytoplasmic bridges as wide as 5 μm were reported by Nobili (1967), who observed the ultrastructural changes of cell union from the beginning to the end.

In *Tetrahymena,* a distinct waiting period exists, but the process of pair formation has not been observed in detail. It appears, though, that the first visible union is ciliary. Cytoplasmic bridges are about 0.2 μm wide (Elliott and Tremor, 1958).

The diversity among these four groups of ciliates is largely due to the variation in ciliary agglutination. As will be described below, the ciliary agglutination can be totally bypassed or greatly reduced experimentally, at least in some ciliates, suggesting that it might be the mechanism for specific recognition of cell types and for facilitating the occurrence of cell union rather than an indispensable process for cell union. If so, the essential processes for the formation of conjugant pairs are (1) reaction between conjugation signals and cells; (2) acquisition by the cell of the capacity to form cell union; (3) formation of cell union, i.e., uniting of cells by a direct contact of cell bodies; and (4) formation of cytoplasmic bridges.

Regardless of the validity of this working hypothesis, the simplicity of the system to be dealt with is imperative for the future analysis of cell union. Although ciliate conjugation is already simple, involving only two types of cells at one time, it can be made even simpler by replacing one of the cell types by nonliving agent. So far three such systems have been established as described below.

B. INDUCTION OF CELL UNION BETWEEN CELLS OF ONE MATING TYPE

1. Induction of Conjugation by Cell Fractions in Paramecium

Metz (1947) killed mating reactive cells of *P. aurelia* by formalin, washed, and mixed them with live cells of the complementary mating type. Live cells agglutinated with killed cells. After 1–2 hours, pairs were formed between live cells. Although cell union was limited to the anterior part of the cells, they underwent meiosis and other nuclear changes of conjugation except cross fertilization. The same method was successfully applied to *P. caudatum* by Hiwatashi (1949), who also reported nuclear reorganization in paired cells. Since the occurrence of nuclear reorganization requires paroral union in this species (Hiwatashi, 1955a), it appears that paroral union was also induced.

The system was simplified when killed cells were replaced by isolated cilia. In *P. multimicronucleatum* (Miyake, 1964), *P. caudatum* (Fukushi and Hiwatashi, 1970; Takahashi *et al.*, 1974) and *P. aurelia* (Cronkite, 1972, 1974; Byrne, 1972), a properly prepared ciliary fraction of one mating type induces apparently normal conjugation in live cells of the complementary mating type. Further simplification was achieved when cilia were replaced by membrane vesicles obtained from isolated cilia of *P. caudatum* (Kitamura and Hiwatashi, 1976).

2. Chemical Induction of Conjugation in Paramecium

In several species of *Paramecium,* certain chemical treatments induce conjugation in cells of one mating type or between cells that are not complementary mating types (Miyake, 1958, 1968b; Hiwatashi, 1959; for review, see Hiwatashi, 1969; Miyake, 1974a; for methods, see Sonneborn, 1970). Although the details of the method vary from species to species, the essential feature of the "chemical induction" is to expose cells to any of the ions—K^+, Rb^+, Cs^+, Mg^{2+}, Mn^{2+}, Co^{2+}— acriflavine, heparin, EDTA, or their combinations under Ca-poor conditions. KCl (4–12 mM) and KCl (4–32 mM) + acriflavine (0.1–0.8 mg/100 ml) have been most commonly used. Certain organic compounds, including urea and acetamide, enhance the induction.

Holdfast union is induced in approximately 1 hour after the beginning of the chemical treatment. The subsequently occurring processes are essentially the same as those in normal conjugation, although some abnormalities, including a lower rate of cross-fertilization (Miyake, 1968b) and a tendency to form chains of conjugating cells (Miyake, 1958), were reported.

Chemical induction is effective only in moderately starved mature cells (Takagi, 1971). These physiological conditions are exactly the same as those required for mating reactivity, i.e., the ability to undergo mating reaction. Moreover, mating reaction and chemical treatment are synergistic. If subthreshold concentrations of isolated cilia and conjugation-inducing chemicals are combined, conjugation can be induced (A. Miyake, unpublished) (Table I). For another kind of additivity between the two inductions, see Section III, D and E. These results indicate that chemicals and conjugation signals both induce conjugation by a similar mechanism.

However, chemical induction is not affected by trypsin at 4 mg/100 ml, which completely destroys the mating reactivity and the signal activity (Miyake, 1969a) indicating that the mating reactivity itself is not required for chemical induction. Indeed, irrespective of the presence or absence of trypsin, the ciliary agglutination comparable to the mating reaction does not occur in chemical induction. Thus chemical induction not only reduces the number of participating cell types to the minimum one, but also eliminates the participation of ciliary union, making the system remarkably simple. Possible mechanisms of chemical induction have been discussed elsewhere (Miyake, 1968b, 1969a, 1974a; Cronkite, 1974, 1975, 1976).

Genes controlling chemical induction were discovered by Cronkite (1974, 1975) in *P. aurelia,* syngen 8. Unlinked recessive genes *kau-1* and *kau-2* both prevent chemical induction but not natural conjugation. *Su(kau-2)* is a dominant partial suppressor of *kau-2*. It permits chemical induction by $MgCl_2$ + acriflavine, but not by KCl + acriflavine.

TABLE I

Synergism between Cilia and Chemical Agents in the Induction of Conjugation in *Paramecium multimicronucleatum*, Syngen 2, Mating Type IV[a]

Chemical agents	Percent conjugation								
	Cilia suspension (dilution)								
	0	2^{10}	2^9	2^8	2^7	2^6	2^5	2^4	2^3
KCl, 8 mM	0	0	0	0	0	0	8	71	83
KCl, 16 mM	0	0	0	0	0	20	64	—[b]	—[b]
KCl, 12 mM; acriflavine, 0.2 mg/100 ml	0	0	0	1	10	35	74	82	91
KCl, 10 mM; acriflavine, 0.4 mg/100 ml	0	1	2	5	23	77	83	82	92

[a] Cells were simultaneously treated with chemical agents and cilia of mating type III. Percent conjugation was obtained by observing macronuclear fragmentation characteristic to exconjugants in 100 cells 1 day after the beginning of the treatment.

[b] Not counted, as some cells were found dead.

Fig. 7. Ring of homotypically united cells of *Blepharisma japonicum*. Eleven doublet cells of mating type II, treated by gamone 1 (10^4 U/ml), unite side by side; 8.5 hours after beginning of gamone treatment. Further explanation in the text (see also Section IV, B). Photograph of living, unstained cells. ×115.

3. Induction of Cell Union by Gamones in Blepharisma

As described above (Section II, A), in *B. japonicum* purified gamone of one mating type induces homotypic union in cells of the other mating type, a striking example of cell union induced by a single specific substance of cellular origin (Fig. 7). A characteristic feature of this union is the absence of the nuclear changes of conjugation. Homotypic cell union (see Fig. 13) is ultrastructurally similar to the heterotypic union (Bedini *et al.*, 1974, 1978) (Section III, G) and may persist for 1 day or even longer, but meiosis and the other nuclear changes of conjugation, which regularly occur in heterotypic unions, never occur, as if conjugation is arrested at the stage of the formation of cell union. This provides an unique opportunity to investigate cell union under the condition where it is effectively separated from the other processes of conjugation.

Another characteristic feature of gamone-induced homotypic union lies in the way ciliary union is formed. Ciliary union and cell union are induced in sequence with an interval of 1–2 hours. As in heterotypic pairs, the ciliary union in homotypic pairs is formed by a specific adhesion between AZM and antUMC (Fig. 6). This provides an interesting example where two cells unite by the complementarity of their surfaces yet both cells are identical (Honda and Miyake, 1976).

Both ciliary and cell unions are prevented by mechanical stirring. If the stirring of gamone-treated cells is stopped at or after the time at which cells in the control (withoug stirring) start forming cell unions, the formation of ciliary unions immediately begins, quickly followed by the formation of cell unions. In this way the interval between the occurrence of ciliary union and that of cell union can be greatly reduced, suggesting that ciliary union could be bypassed in the induction of cell union (Honda and Miyake, 1976).

C. REQUIREMENT OF CONTINUOUS STIMULATION FOR CELL UNION

In *P. multimicronucleatum,* homotypic conjugation of mating type IV cells can be induced either by isolated cilia of mating type III (ciliary induction) or by KCl + acriflavine (chemical induction). For each induction, a specific inhibitor is known. Trypsin (4 mg/100 ml) stops the mating reaction between cilia and living cells within 1 minute and inhibits the ciliary induction of conjugation, while it has little effect on chemical induction. On the contrary, $CaCl_2$ (1 mM) inhibits only chemical induction (Miyake, 1969a).

In ciliary induction, trypsin completely inhibits the formation of cell union if added at any time between the beginning of induction and the appearance of holdfast union, except for the last one-fifth of the period. Similarly, in chemical induction, $CaCl_2$ completely inhibits the formation of cell union if added at any time between the beginning of induction and the appearance of holdfast union, except for the last one-sixth of the period (Miyake, 1969a, 1974a). Even when trypsin or $CaCl_2$, added at the last fifth or sixth of the induction period, permits the formation of cell union, the number of holdfast pairs induced is much less than in the control without inhibitors. It may be concluded that in both inductions the inducer must be present nearly all the time until the cell union is formed.

A similar result was obtained in *B. japonicum* (Miyake and Beyer, 1973; Miyake and Honda, 1976). In the induction of homotypic unions by gamone, a precocious removal of gamone during the waiting period prevented cells from forming pairs. Even after pairs were formed, cells soon separated if placed in a gamone-free medium. This is in sharp contrast to the induction of gamone 2 excretion by gamone 1, in which the production of gamone 2 is induced by a brief exposure of type II cells to gamone 1 and continues for many hours after gamone 1 is removed (Fig. 5). Unfortunately, these observations were made before the distinction between ciliary and cell union was appreciated in this species. Since ciliary union regularly appears before cell union, the result may be applied more directly to ciliary union than to cell union.

D. Summation of Subliminal Stimuli in the Induction of Cell Union

The requirement of the continuous presence of inducers for the induction of cell union suggests that the effect of subliminal stimuli accumulates during the induction. This hypothesis was tested by the following experiments.

The induction of cell union in *P. multimicronucleatum* was initiated with isolated cilia. After time T_m, the induction was blocked by tryspin. At this moment, the induction was "taken over" by chemicals, and the time needed to induce cell union by this second induction, T_c, was measured. As T_m increased, T_c linearly decreased to zero (Miyake, 1969a) (Fig. 8A). When the induction was initiated by chemicals, blocked by $CaCl_2$ and then taken over by isolated cilia, a similar result was obtained (A. Miyake, unpublished) (Fig. 8B). Thus sequentially applied two subliminal stimuli are additive. Results of similar experiments carried out on *P. aurelia* (Cronkite, 1972, 1974) are consistent with this conclusion. The linear relationship between T_m and T_c is suggestive, but it does not necessarily indicate that the effect of the stimulus accumulates at a constant rate. Further analysis is needed to deduce the time course of the accumulation.

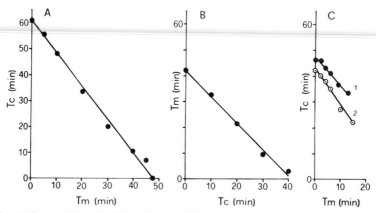

Fig. 8. Summation of subliminal stimuli for conjugation. Two kinds of stimulants, chemical agents, and cilia of mating type III, were sequentially given to mating type IV cells of *Paramecium multimicronucleatum*, syngen 2. Abscissa: Duration of the first stimulus. Ordinate: Duration of the second stimulus needed to induce cell union in conjugation. T_c: time of chemical stimulus. T_m: time of ciliary stimulus. Chemical agents: 20 mM KCl + 0.4 mg/100 ml acriflavine in (A) and (B), 20 mM KCl + 0.8 mg/100 ml acriflavine for experiment 1 in (C), 24 mM KCl + 0.8 mg/100 ml acriflavine for experiment 2 in (C). Further explanation is given in the text. (A) Modified from Miyake (1969a).

That a stimulus as short as a few minutes is also additive (Fig. 8C) (A. Miyake, unpublished) indicates that the unit of the accumulable stimulus is very small. It may be concluded that the effect of a stimulus continuously accumulates during the induction of cell union.

E. BREAKDOWN OF THE EFFECT OF THE SUBLIMINAL STIMULUS

The stability of the accumulated effect of a subliminal stimulus for the induction of cell union was investigated by introducing a recess time between the two inductions in the summation experiment described above. Induction was carried out with cilia for T_m, and then it was blocked by trypsin. After a recess time, induction was resumed with chemicals and the time needed to induce cell union by this second induction, T_c, was measured. As the recess time increased, T_c decreased first, remained unchanged for a while, and then increased until it reached the time required for chemical induction of cell union without any previous treatment (Fig. 9) (Miyake, 1969a). The first decrease is consistent with the fact described above (Section III, C) that ciliary

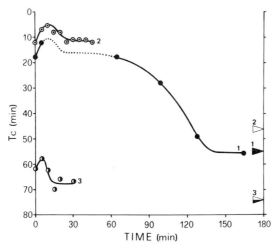

FIG. 9. Transition of the activated state of cells, induced by a subliminal stimulus for conjugation, after blocking of the stimulus. Mating type IV cells of *Paramecium multimicronucleatum,* syngen 2 were treated with cilia of mating type III for 35 minutes in experiment 1 (curve 1), for 30 minutes in experiment 2 (curve 2) and for 5 minutes in experiment 3 (curve 3) before cilia were inactivated by 4 mg/100 ml trypsin at time 0. After the recess time (abscissa), chemical induction of conjugation was started and the time needed to induce cell union by this induction, T_c (ordinate), was measured. Triangles: Time of chemical induction needed to induce the cell union without any previous treatment in the experiment indicated by the number. Further explanation is given in the text. Curves 1 and 2: modified from Miyake (1969a).

induction continues to some extent after trypsin is added. The last increase of T_c indicates the breakdown of the accumulated effect of cilia. Curve 1 of Fig. 9 indicates that the effect of the ciliary induction accumulated during the previous 35 minutes totally breaks down 2–3 hours after the stimulus is blocked. The material basis of this accumulated effect could be complex, but for the sake of simplicity it will be regarded as a single factor.

The process of induction of cell union that emerges from these results (Section III, C–E) is as follows. A conjugation signal induces in target cells the production of a factor that is labile but may persist for a few hours. While the signal is present, the factor is continuously produced. When the accumulation of the factor reaches a certain threshold, cells gain the capacity to form cell union.

F. CELL UNION AND PROTEIN SYNTHESIS

1. Inhibitors of Protein Synthesis and Cell Union

Previous work almost unanimously indicates that inhibitors of protein synthesis prevent conjugation, although Beisson and Capdeville (1966) reported no inhibiting effect of puromycin (100 μg/ml) on conjugation (but not on autogamy, see Section IV, C). Earlier studies were mainly concerned with the inhibition of mating reactivity in *Paramecium* (Nobili, 1963; Nobili and Kotopolus De Angelis, 1963; Bleyman, 1964; Cohen, 1965), but Miyake (1969a) showed that puromycin (250–500 μg/ml) also inhibits the chemical induction of conjugation. More recently, inhibition of conjugation by cycloheximide has been reported in *T. pyriformis* (Tyler and Wolfe, 1972; Flickinger and Murrary, 1974; Bruns and Palestine, 1975; Allewell *et al.*, 1976; Ofer *et al.*, 1976), *O. bifaria* (Esposito and Ricci, 1975), *E. crassus* (Dini and Miyake, 1977, 1978), and *B. japonicum* (Beyer and Miyake, 1973). These studies all indicate the necessity of protein synthesis for the occurrence of cell union in conjugation. However, cell union is an end result of preconjugant cell interaction, which may last 1 hour or even longer and consists of component steps that may include positive feedback in the production of conjugation signals. Since all these experiments except the one on *B. japonicum* and the one using chemical induction, were carried out on the mixture of two complementary types of cells, they tend to fall short of indicating in which step or steps protein synthesis is involved. In addition, in order to conclude that protein synthesis is necessary for conjugation, it must be demonstrated that the inhibitor prevents conjugation by inhibiting protein synthesis. Although the inhibition of amino acid incorporation by cycloheximide was shown along with the inhibition of conjugation by some workers (Tyler and Wolfe, 1972; Ofer et al., 1976; Dini and Miyake, 1978), a closer correlation between the two inhibitions was not demonstrated.

These difficulties were reduced by simultaneously examining the effect of various concentrations of cycloheximide both on the ^{14}C-labeled amino acid incorporation and on the induction of homotypic pairs by gamone in B. japonicum (Miyake and Honda, 1976) (Fig. 10A). At 0.25 μg/ml, cycloheximide inhibited neither lysine incorporation nor induction of pairs. At 0.5 μg/ml, both were only slightly inhibited. At 1 μg/ml, the incorporation was considerably reduced, pairs were induced, but in fewer cells (5% versus more than 50% in the control) with a delay. At 2 μg/ml, incorporation was further reduced and pairs were never induced. Such a close correlation between the two inhibitions is a strong indication that cycloheximide inhibits the induction of homotypic pairs by inhibiting protein synthesis. Moreover, only gamone and one type of cell are involved in this experiment, eliminating possible complications due to the interaction between two types of cells. Thus it was concluded that protein synthesis is needed for the induction of homotypic pairs by gamone. A shortcoming in this experiment is that ciliary and cell unions were not clearly distinguished, making it difficult to apply the result to each of the unions individually.

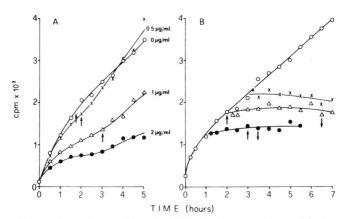

Fig. 10. Effects of cycloheximide on the [14C]lysine incorporation and on the induction of cell pairs in mating type I of Blepharisma japonicum treated by gamone 2 (1.6 × 10² U/ml). [14C]Lysine and gamone 2 were added at time 0. (A) Cycloheximide of indicated concentrations were added at time 0. (B) Cycloheximide (10 μg/ml) was added 1 hour (●——●), 2 hours (△——△) and 3 hours (×——×) after the beginning of gamone treatment. ○——○; No cycloheximide; ↑, appearance of pairs; ↓, disappearance of pairs. From Miyake and Honda (1976).

Cycloheximide at 10 μg/ml stopped the amino acid incorporation almost immediately (Fig. 10B). If added 1 hour after beginning of gamone treatment, very few pairs were formed, and they soon separated. If added 2 and 3 hours later, pairing continued to increase in the same way as in the control for 0.5 and 1 hour, respectively, before it started decreasing. The last pair separated 4.5 and 5 hours, respectively, after addition of cycloheximide. The fact that united cells separated in spite of the presence of gamone indicates that protein synthesis is needed for the maintenance of the pair. On the other hand, the fact that pairing continued to increase about 1 hour after protein synthesis stopped may indicate that a process other than protein synthesis also participates in the induction of pairs. This process might be the transportation of the protein needed for cell union to the specific site, as suggested by Miyake and Honda (1976).

2. Gamone-Induced Protein Synthesis

In order to warrant the conclusion that protein synthesis participates in the induction of cell union, it is also necessary to demonstrate the occurrence of a specific protein synthesis during the induction. Therefore, the ^{14}C-labeled amino acid incorporation by gamone-treated and nontreated cells were compared in *B. japonicum* (Miyake and Honda, 1976).

Very starved cells (but still having the ability to respond to gamone and unite) were used to reduce the "background incorporation," which may overshadow the induced incorporation. To obtain a cpm value high enough to make the experiment reproducible, a large amount of cells

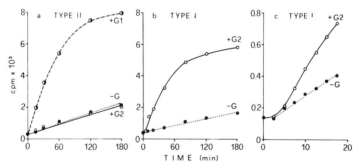

Fig. 11. Gamone-induced amino acid incorporation in *Blepharisma japonicum*. Gamones (10^4 U/ml for gamone 1, 1.6×10^2 U/ml for gamone 2) were added at time 0. [14C]Amino acid was added at time 0 in (a) and (c), 30 minutes before time 0 in (b). (a) Mating type II cells, [14C]leucine. (b) Mating type I cells, [14C]leucine. (c) Mating type I cells, [14C]lysine. +G1: Gamone 1; +G2: gamone 2; −G: no gamone. From Miyake and Honda (1976).

was used for each measurement. Special precautions were also taken to remove bacterial interference. Under these conditions, it was clearly shown that gamones 1 and 2 specifically increase the amino acid incorporation in type II and type I cells, respectively (Fig. 11). The induced incorporation was detectable about 5 minutes after the beginning of gamone treatment (Fig. 11c) and lasted for about 2 hours before becoming undetectable (Fig. 11a, b).

If cells were washed after 2 hours of labeling, a small but rapid drop of cpm during the washing (about 20 minutes) was followed by a slower but steady decrease of cpm both in gamone-treated and nontreated cells irrespective of the presence or the absence of gamone after the washing. The speed of the decrease in cpm was similar in both groups during the 6 hours of measurement. The fact that an increase of the incorporation was not seen after washing indicates that ^{14}C-labeled amino acid does not remain free in detectable amount in washed cells.

Separation of the labeled proteins by SDS-electrophoresis indicates that gamone induces many proteins of molecular weight greater than 3×10^4 during the first 2 hours of gamone treatment (Fig. 12a), while no such specific induction occurs in the following 2 hours (Fig. 12b). Although the overall separation patterns of labeled proteins of the gamone-treated cells and those of the nontreated cells are distinctly different in Fig. 12a, the difference is much less remarkable if the comparison is limited only to proteins of molecular weight greater than 3×10^4. This suggests that many of the gamone-induced proteins are also synthesized in the control cells, though to a lesser extent. Comparing the result of agarose chromatography and that of the density gradient centrifugation of cell fractions of gamone-treated and nontreated labeled cells, it was deduced that some of the gamone-induced proteins are associated with lipid-containing particles larger than M_r 10^6.

Based on these results, Miyake and Honda (1976) concluded that gamone induces protein synthesis and suggested that the induced proteins might be membrane proteins. Since only one type of cell is involved in the induction of cell union by gamone and since the induced cell union is the homotypic union in which no further changes of conjugation occur, it is likely that these proteins mainly participate in the uniting of cells, whether it be the ciliary union, the cell union, or both.

G. Cell Union and Ultrastructural Changes

Electron microscopical observations on early stages of ciliate conjugation are still few and fragmental, but they appear to provide promising clues to the mechanism of cell union.

In growing cells of *T. pyriformis,* smooth-surfaced saccules scatter

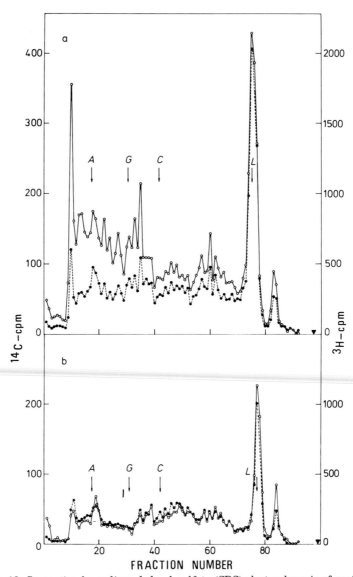

FIG. 12. Separation by sodium dodecyl sulfate (SDS)-electrophoresis of proteins of mating type I cells of *Blepharisma japonicum* incubated with and without gamone 2 $(1.6 \times 10^2\,\text{U/ml})$ and labeled by [^{14}C]leucine and [^{3}H]leucine, respectively. (a) Labeled for 2 hours, starting at the beginning of the gamone treatment. (b) Labeled for 2 hours, starting 2 hours after the beginning of the gamone treatment. ○——○, ^{14}C; ● · · · · ●, ^{3}H. Fractions 1–9, spacer gel; ▼, front. Standard proteins: A, bovine serum albumin (M_r 68,000); G, glyceraldehyde-3-phosphate dehydrogenase (M_r 36,000); C, chymotrypsinogen A (M_r 25,700); L, lysozyme (M_r 14,300). From Miyake and Honda (1976).

in the cytoplasm at the oral region. In starved cells these saccules are aligned in stacks. When such cells of complementary mating types are mixed, saccules swell, elongate, and apparently pinch off small vesicles. This activity of saccules begins as early as 5 minutes after the mixing of two cell types and continues until cell union is completed (Elliot and Zieg, 1968). The activity is inhibited by cycloheximide (10 μg/ml), but not by actinomycin (30 μg/ml), whereas conjugation is inhibited by both agents (Flickinger and Murray, 1974).

Elliot and Zieg (1968) suggested that these saccules might produce a substance participating in conjugation. Their suggestion is particularly interesting if considered together with the result that in *B. japonicum* gamone-induced protein synthesis begins within 5 minutes after beginning of gamone treatment and that it continues until cells start to unite (Section III, F). However, Flickinger and Murray (1974) point out the possibility that the observed changes of saccules might be simply a result of the decreased feeding activity accompanying mating behavior, e.g., the reduced rate of food vacuole formation, which brings about a decline in the demand for replacement of pharyngeal membrane causing the accumulation of unused materials.

In starved cells of the same species, mixed with cells of the complementary mating type, fingerlike projections were found at the presumptive site of cell union. During the initial stages of conjugation, these projections attach to a cuplike structure of the partner cell (Elliot, 1973). These structures may be comparable with "mating structure" in *Chlamydomonas* (Friedman *et al.*, 1968; Goodenough and Weiss, 1975).

In early stages of the heterotypic union of *B. japonicum,* cell membranes of the united cells are juxtaposed with a distance of about 200 Å. This arrangement is interrupted in some places by vacuoles and small cytoplasmic bridges (Ototake, 1969; K. Miyake, 1970; Bedini *et al.,* 1978). These observations generally conform to those in *Paramecium* (Vivier and André, 1961; Inaba *et al.,* 1966; Jurand and Selman, 1969) and *Tetrahymena* (Elliot, 1973). However, microtubules running perpendicular or oblique to the united surface have been reported only in *B. japonicum* (Ototake, 1969; Bedini *et al.,* 1978). These microtubules are unique not only because they are present only in conjugating cells, but also because they are perpendicularly associated with the cell membrane without any evident connection with kinetosomes. They will be called PACM (perpendicularly associated to the cell membrane) microtubules. In addition, vesicles, which are always found throughout the cytoplasm, tend to be more abundant near the united region. Several hours later, PACM microtubules disappear and cytoplasmic bridges broaden at the posterior part of the oral groove where gametic nuclei are exchanged.

The homotypic union is very similar to the heterotypic union in early stages (Bedini *et al.*, 1974, 1978). However, in the former, this early condition is maintained for a long time, apparently until cells start separating. As a result, PACM microtubules are clearly visible for 10 hours or even longer (Fig. 13). This result is consistent with the previous assumption that in the homotypic union conjugation is arrested at the stage of the formation of cell union (Section III, B, 3). The result also indicates that PACM microtubules participate in the very early processes of conjugation, including the formation of cell union.

This hypothesis is supported by the following two observations (Miyake *et al.*, 1978): (1) PACM microtubules are formed also at the presumptive site of cell union in single cells that are individually

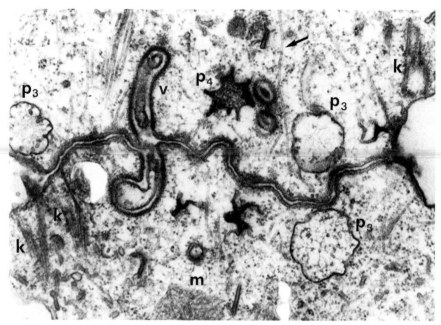

Fig. 13. Cross section at the united region of a homotypic pair of *Blepharisma japonicum* (albino, mating type I), 10 hours after beginning of gamone 2 treatment (1.6×10^2 U/ml). The cell union of each cell starts in the vicinity of the antUMC and then extends on the oral groove toward AZM. The antUMC can be located by its kinetosomes (k), which are arranged in two longitudinal rows, only one of which bears cilia in this region. No kinetosomes are present in the oral groove. The regular juxtaposition of cell membranes is interrupted by one large vacuole (v) and a cytoplasmic bridge in the process of formation. Arrow: one of the PACM microtubules (see text); p_3 and p_4, type 3 and type 4 pigment granules, characteristic to the albino cell (Kurita, 1968); m, mitochondrion. ×31,400. Courtesy of C. Bedini, A. Lanfranchi, R. Nobili and A. Miyake.

treated by gamone; (2) if a doublet cell (see Section IV, B, Fig. 15B) is treated by gamone and unites homotypically with one of its oral grooves leaving the other one free, PACM microtubules are found at both oral grooves. In these observations, the accumulation of vesicles mentioned above was also seen at the free oral grooves along with PACM microtubules. Some pictures (Fig. 14) suggest that vesicles might be carried by PACM microtubules to the site of cell union and that vesicles might become incorporated into the cell membrane. Many small bodies apparently derived from the vesicles are seen outside the cell at the presumptive site of cell union.

These results clearly indicate that both the formation of PACM microtubules and the accumulation of vesicles are responses of cells to gamone treatment, not the result of the cell union. This conclusion,

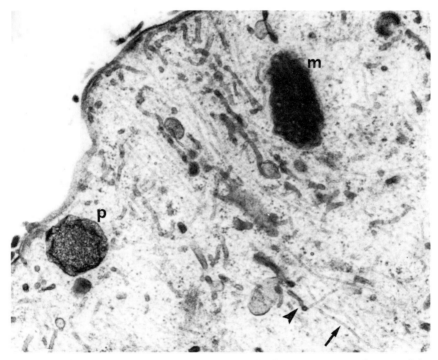

FIG. 14. Cross section at the presumptive site of cell union, i.e., anterior part of the oral groove, of a doublet cell of *Blepharisma japonicum* (mating type II) treated by gamone 1 (10^4 U/ml) for 7 hours. The cell is at the terminus of a homotypic chain of four doublet cells, thus having one free oral groove shown in this figure. Arrow, one of the PACM microtubules; arrowhead, one of the vesicles supposedly carrying gamone-induced proteins (see Section III, H); *p*, pigment granule; *m*, mitochondrion. Further explanation is given in the text. ×30,000. From Miyake *et al.* (1978).

together with the timing and the place of microtubule formation and vesicle accumulation, strongly suggests that PACM microtubules and vesicles are devices for cell union.

Whether these structural changes occur also in early stages of conjugation in other ciliates is still to be examined, but the formation of microfilaments has been demonstrated in conjugation of *Chlamydomonas* (Goodenough and Weiss, 1975). Bedini *et al.* (1978) described the following similarities between the cell union in conjugation of *Blepharisma,* particularly the homotypic union, and the desmosome-bearing cell union in multicellular organisms: regular juxtaposition of cell membranes at a distance of about 200 Å, the presence of tufts of filamentous structures emanating from the united surfaces, the persistence of the union for hours or days without total fusion of cells, and the reversibility of the cell union. Crandall (1977), reviewing observations related to the process of cell union in many different systems, pointed out the strong similarities between them.

H. HYPOTHESIS ON THE MECHANISM OF CELL UNION

Studies in *Paramecium* at the cellular level demonstrate that a conjugation signal induces a factor, the accumulation of which to a certain threshold is required for the formation of cell union (Section III, C–E). Biochemical studies in *Blepharisma* demonstrate that protein synthesis is needed for the induction of cell union and that gamone induces proteins (Section III, F). The factor and the induced proteins both increase only while inducers are present, and both slowly breakdown when inducers are removed or inactivated. If the difference between *Paramecium* and *Blepharisma* is momentarily disregarded, it may be concluded that the accumulable factor is protein and therefore that the accumulation of the induced proteins to a certain threshold is needed for the occurrence of cell union. Further biochemical studies in *Blepharisma* suggest that induced proteins might be membrane proteins associated with large particles (Section III, F). This is consistent with the effect of ficin and lipase on conjugation. These enzymes strongly inhibit the formation of cell union in chemical induction of conjugation in *P. multimicronucleatum* even if they are added just before cells unite (Miyake, 1969a). Similar effect of lipase was reported also in *O. bifaria* (Ricci *et al.,* 1975).

Studies in *Blepharisma* at the ultrastructural level demonstrate that gamone induces microtubules perpendicular to the cell surface at the site of cell union and also an accumulation of vesicles in the same area (Section III, G). These vesicles might be particles with which gamone-induced proteins are associated. The microtubules might serve as a device to transport them to the presumptive site of cell union.

Observations on the specific activity of saccules in mating cells of *Tetrahymena* (Section III, G) are consistent with these assumptions.

These experimental results and considerations lead me to a hypothesis that the conjugation signal induces a rapid synthesis and accumulation of membrane materials at a localized area of the cell surface, thus providing the cell with the capacity to form a cell union in this region (Miyake and Honda, 1976). The validity of this hypothesis is to be experimentally tested.

IV. Initiation of Meiosis

A. NUCLEAR SYSTEMS, SEXUAL REPRODUCTION, AND MEIOSIS IN CILIATES

In most ciliates, the nucleus differentiates into the diploid micronucleus and the macronucleus, which may contain many times more DNA than the micronucleus. In asexual life, only the macronucleus is indispensable. In sexual reproduction, the micronucleus undergoes meiosis producing gametic nuclei, which then fuse to form a fertilization nucleus (Fig. 2) from which the nuclear system of the new generation develops, while the old macronucleus degenerates. Thus the micronucleus and the macronucleus of ciliates can be compared with the nuclei of germ cells and those of somatic cells in multicellular organisms.

Sexual reproduction in ciliates consists of conjugation, autogamy, and their modifications. In autogamy, which is practiced only by some ciliates, single cells begin and complete all the nuclear changes of conjugation except the exchange of gametic nuclei between cells.

Genetic analyses (for review, see Sonneborn, 1947, 1974a,b) and cytochemical studies on DNA content (Pieri, 1965; Pieri *et al.*, 1968) indicate that meiosis in ciliates is essentially the same as meiosis in multicellular organisms. Studies on the cytological details of ciliate meiosis have been hampered by the fact that the chromosomes of many ciliates are small and numerous. Peculiarities were reported in earlier studies (for review, see Raikov, 1972), but in *T. pyriformis* ($n = 5$), the chromosomal behavior in meiosis is similar to that of metazoa (Ray, 1956; Sugai and Hiwatashi, 1974). It is currently believed that meiosis in ciliates corresponds to the classical scheme of the metazoan meiosis (Raikov, 1972).

B. MEIOSIS-INITIATING FACTOR

Factors controlling meiosis are known in some organisms. Thus in frog and starfish, progestrone (for review, see Smith and Ecker, 1970) and 1-methyladenine (for review, see Kanatani, 1973), respectively, induce maturation of the oocyte in which the nucleus, arrested at meiotic prophase, resumes meiosis. Both inducers act on the cell surface from the outside and activate the nucleus by means of intracellular messengers (Kanatani, 1973; Wasserman and Masui, 1976). These results suggest that other steps of meiosis as well as its initiation are also regulated by specific substances.

Such substances, particularly meiosis-initiating substances, might be profitably investigated in ciliates in which meiosis is initiated soon after cells unite in conjugation or when cells begin autogamy. Since the meiosis-initiating factor is most clearly demonstrated by recent work on *Blepharisma,* it will be presented first.

In homotypic pairs of *B. japonicum,* meiosis and other nuclear changes of conjugation do not occur, whereas they regularly occur in heterotypic pairs (Section III, B). This provides an opportunity to investigate the mechanism of meiosis by comparing homotypic and heterotypic pairs. The first indication of the presence of a meiosis-initiating factor which is transferable from cell to cell was obtained by observing conjugation between a chain of homotypically united "doublet" cells (mating type II) and a "singlet" cell (mating type I) (Miyake, 1975). A doublet is a morphological mutant possessing two sets of oral structures (Fig. 15B). A singlet is the wild type with one set of structures (Fig. 15A). Since cell union in conjugation occurs at the oral region, each cell of a doublet can conjugate with two cells. If doublet cells are treated with gamone of the complementary mating type, they unite side by side, forming chains that often close, producing rings

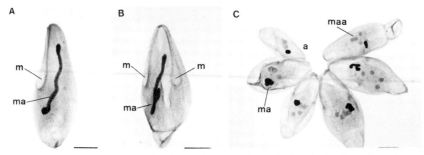

Fig. 15. Singlet, doublet, and a chain of conjugating cells in *Blepharisma japonicum.* (A) Singlet cell. (B) Doublet cell. (C) Conjugation between an albino singlet cell of mating type I (a) and a homotypic chain consisting of 5 red doublet cells of mating type II, 36 hours after mixing singlets and homotypic chains induced by gamone. m, Mouth; ma in (A) and (B), normal macronucleus; ma in (C), degenerating macronucleus; maa, macronuclear anlage. Fixation: Schaudinn's fixative. Staining: Feulgen's stain and Light Green. Scale: 50 μm. From Miyake (1975).

Fig. 16. Conjugation between an albino cell of mating type I and a homotypic chain consisting of 5 red doublet cells of mating type II in *Blepharisma japonicum*, 18 hours after the albino united to the chain. The albino cell is receiving a migratory gametic nucleus (arrow) from the red partner. Two dark spots in each red doublet cell except the one farthest from the albino are micronuclei at the stage near karyogamy. See also explanation of Fig. 2. Photograph of living, unstained cells. ×150.

(Fig. 7). Like homotypic pairs, they do not undergo the nuclear changes of conjugation. However, if a singlet cell of the complementary mating type unites at one end of such a chain, not only the doublet with which the singlet unites but also other doublets in the same chain undergo the nuclear changes (Figs. 15C, 16). Whenever cells in a chain show different stages of the nuclear changes, cells closer to the singlet are in a more advanced stage. These results suggest that an initiation factor for meiosis and other nuclear changes of conjugation is produced by the heterotypically united cells and is transferred through the chain.

This hypothetical factor was further investigated by Miyake *et al.* (1977). Using the same system, they studied the time of activation, i.e., the time at which a cell is irreversibly determined to undergo meiosis and other nuclear changes. In this way, the mode of propagation of nuclear activation, rather than the timing of nuclear changes, was obtained. The method of their experiment is diagrammatically shown in Fig. 17. Homotypic chains of red doublet cells of mating type II (R) were induced by gamone 1 and then mixed with albino singlet cells of mating type I (A) pretreated with gamone 2. When A united at one end of a chain, the chain was isolated. Heterotypic chains thus formed were named A + 3R, A + 4R, A + 5R as A united with homotypic chains consisting of 3, 4, and 5 R cells, respectively. R cells in these chains were numbered R_1, R_2, R_3—starting the one closest to A.

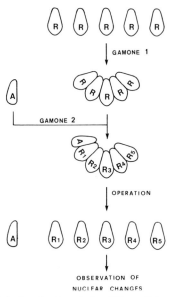

FIG. 17. Experimental design for the study of the cell-to-cell propagation of nuclear activation in *Blepharisma japonicum*. R, red doublet cell of mating type II; A, albino singlet cell of mating type I.

After a given incubation time, all cells in a chain were surgically separated with a fine flexible glass needle and isolated. If the occurrence of nuclear changes was later ascertained in an isolated cell, the cell was considered to be activated at the time of the operation. The number of chains operated on every 10 minutes were 9, 7, and 5 for A + 3R, A + 4R, and A + 5R, respectively.

As the time of incubation increased, activated R_1, R_2, R_3, R_4, and R_5 cells appeared in this order. Whenever any cell in a chain was activated, all cells between this and the A cell were also activated. Therefore, the activation of R cells begins in R_1 and propagates cell-to-cell without saltation. The percentages of activated R_1–R_5 cells calculated for 20-minute intervals are shown in Fig. 18. The times of 50% activation of R_1–R_4 cells obtained from these data are shown in Fig. 19. These figures, particularly Fig. 19, demonstrate how activation propagates through the chain. The longer the chain, the slower the propagation at the corresponding site in the chain. By and large, propagation slows down as it proceeds in the chain. It may also be pointed out that the activation of R_1 takes a slightly longer time in longer chains. These results strongly indicate that activation is induced by something that is "diluted" in the chain, thus providing cogent evi-

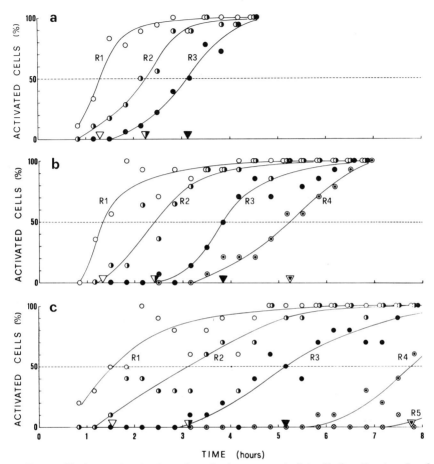

FIG. 18. Nuclear activation in conjugation between a singlet cell of mating type I and chains of homotypically united doublet cells of mating type II in *Blepharisma japonicum*. (a) A + 3R. (b) A + 4R. (c) A + 5R. Triangles: Time of 50% activation. Further explanation is given in the text. From Miyake *et al.* (1977).

dence that the activation-inducing factor is a substance that is transferable from cell to cell.

This factor may be regarded as the meiosis-initiating factor, since the first two micronuclear divisions in conjugation are meiotic in many ciliates including *B. japonicum*. The mechanism of the cell-to-cell transfer of this factor is left for future study, but it might be a simple diffusion through cytoplasmic bridges that are formed both in heterotypic and homotypic unions several hours after the uniting of cells (Bedini *et al.*, 1974, 1978).

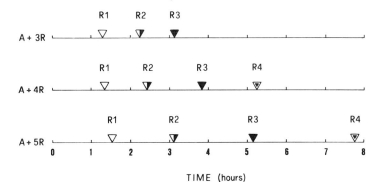

FIG. 19. Cell-to-cell propagation of nuclear activation in chains of homotypically united doublet cells of mating type II conjugated with a singlet cell of mating type I in *Blepharisma japonicum*. Triangles: Time of 50% activation for doublet cells (R) indicated. Data from Fig. 18.

If the meiosis-initiating factor is such a transferable substance, it may be assayed by placing it in homotypically united or even in single vegetative cells. If successfully carried out, this will open the way to the isolation of the factor and also to the testing of cross reactions with similar factors of other ciliates as well as more remotely related organisms.

Earlier work on the initiation mechanism of ciliate meiosis was mainly carried out in *Paramecium*. In this ciliate, homotypic pairs undergo meiosis and other nuclear changes of conjugation just like heterotypic pairs, contrasting sharply with "resting" homotypic pairs in *Blepharisma*. A possible explanation for this discrepancy has been given (Miyake, 1974a). A more likely explanation would be that meiosis is triggered by a contact between a specific area of cell membranes, e.g., the posterior part of the oral groove, which may occur in homotypic pairs of *Paramecium*, but not in that of *Blepharisma* (see Section III, A).

In *P. aurelia*, Metz (1947) demonstrated that formalin-killed cells induce meiosis in single live cells of the complementary mating type. This result indicates that meiosis can be induced without holdfast and paroral unions. Thus Metz concluded that the mating reaction is sufficient to initiate meiosis. On the other hand, in *P. caudatum* (Hiwatashi, 1955a) and *P. multimicronucleatum*, syngen 2 (A. Miyake, unpublished), mating reaction and holdfast union are not sufficient to initiate nuclear changes. A more intimate union between cells appears to be needed for the initiation of meiosis. These problems have been discussed in more detail by Hiwatashi (1969) and Miyake (1974a). Such a difference among species of *Paramecium* might be related to the fact that *P. aurelia,* but not the other two species mentioned above, practices natural autogamy. The reaction between conjugation signal and receptor which may occur during the mating reaction might touch the initiation mechanism of autogamy, thus triggering the nuclear changes.

C. INITIATION MECHANISM OF AUTOGAMY

For the occurrence of autogamy, neither cell communication nor cell union is needed. This provides yet another approach to the initiation mechanism of meiosis. As in conjugation, deprivation of food is a prerequisite for autogamy. This is the only environmental factor so far known to induce natural autogamy, suggesting that changes in the nutritive condition turn on a cellular switch for meiosis and other nuclear changes of autogamy.

Beisson and Capdeville (1966) reported that cells of *P. aurelia* taken from a log-phase culture and washed (1.5–2 hours) free of food were prevented from undergoing autogamy by treatment with 100 μg of puromycin per milliliter, which reversibly inhibits vegetative multiplication of this ciliate. The same treatment did not prevent cells from gaining the competence for conjugation and completing it. A similar but less striking inhibition was observed by using 2.5 μg of actinomycin D per milliliter. Both inhibitors failed to prevent autogamy if added 2 hours after completion of the washing. They concluded that synthesis of specific proteins is needed for the occurrence of autogamy and suggested that they are produced by genes activated by the deprivation of food. These proteins have not been further analyzed.

In conjugation, not only the deprivation of food, but also the mixing of two types of cells, exposure to conjugation signals or conjugation-inducing chemicals, and the formation of cell union, serve as milestones on the way to meiosis. But in autogamy no such markers are available except for the deprivation of food. If a clearly visible signboard were additionally introduced, it would greatly help in analyzing the initiation mechanism of meiosis. The chemical induction of autogamy described below might meet this requirement.

In *P. multimicronucleatum,* syngen 2, natural autogamy is not known to occur, but autogamy can be chemically induced by combinations of KCl (10–20 mM) + acriflavine (0.2–0.8 mg/100 ml) + ficin (20–60 mg/100 ml) + Ca-poor conditions (Miyake, 1968c, 1969b; for methods, see Sonneborn, 1970). Both crude ficin preparation and crystallized ficin are effective, but heated ficin (5 minutes at 100°C in water) is not effective. Although genetic confirmation is still lacking, these chemical agents induce nuclear changes that appear cytologically to be autogamy. Remarkably, these chemical agents, except ficin, are identical to those for chemical induction of conjugation (Section III, B). Indeed, they can induce conjugation if ficin is omitted. However, if ficin at the above concentration is added, no conjugant pairs are formed, whereas single cells undergo the nuclear changes of autogamy. At lower concentrations of ficin, conjugant pairs are induced, but in fewer and fewer cells as ficin concentration is increased, until they are completely inhibited at 22 mg/100 ml. Activated cells (cells in which the nuclear changes occur either by conjugation or autogamy) also decrease accordingly (Fig. 20). As ficin concentration is increased further, conjugant pairs are no longer formed, but now activated cells increase, reaching a maximum (59% activated cells) at 40 mg/100 ml. Thus the effective range of ficin concentration for chemical induction of autogamy appears to begin at the concentration that completely inhibits the formation of conjugant pairs. This strongly indicates that the role of ficin consists not only of the inhibition of cell union, but also of specifically modifying cells, in collaboration with other chemical agents, so that meiosis and other nuclear changes are initiated. The same conclusion is indicated also by the fact that bromelin (10–20 mg/100 ml, crude preparation), papain (100 mg/100 ml, crude preparation), and lipase (1–10 mg/100 ml), all of which prevent cells from

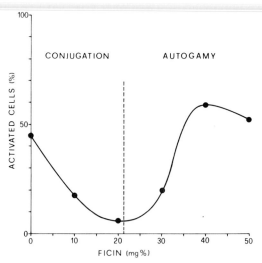

Fig. 20. Effect of ficin concentration on chemical induction of conjugation and chemical induction of autogamy in *Paramecium multimicronucleatum,* syngen 2. Chemical agents: KCl (20 mM) + acriflavine (0.8 mg/100 ml). No conjugant pairs were induced on the right side of the dashed line. Modified from Miyake (1968c).

uniting in conjugation, cannot replace ficin in the chemical induction of autogamy, whereas the induction is still possible under the presence of lipase at 5 mg/100 ml.

To the similarity between chemical inductions of conjugation and autogamy described above, it may be added that methylurea, which enhances the chemical induction of conjugation, also enhances the chemical induction of autogamy. These results suggest that mechanisms of the two chemical inductions, and hence initiation mechanisms of conjugation and autogamy, are closely related. Prior discussions about these relationships will be found elsewhere (Metz, 1954; Hiwatashi, 1969; Miyake, 1974a). It is tempting to speculate that conjugation-inducing chemicals change the surface of cells so that they can form cell unions, and then ficin further modifies it in a way similar to cell union, resulting in the production of the initiation factor of meiosis.

V. General Discussion

If ciliates in ponds or streams are compared with cells in multicellular organisms with respect to cell interaction, differences might loom large at first glance. But a closer examination will reveal similarities. Recognition of cell types, cell communication, formation and termination of cell union, and the control of meiosis through interaction of cells, will all be found in both. Ciliates exploit them for conjugation as described in the preceding sections, whereas cells in multicellular organisms do so not only for fertilization and development, but also for the maintenance of daily life in more diverse ways. This is but another example of the ubiquitous occurrence of cell communication, cell union, and meiosis in the living world. Since these phenomena are so universal, it may be expected that their basic mechanisms might be similar in many or all organisms. However, the validity of such expectations largely depends on whether the observed phenomenal similarities are due to evolutionary homology or convergence. The firm answer to this problem will be obtained only after the mechanisms of these phenomena are elucidated in diverse groups. Nevertheless the problem deserves consideration, because the possibility of homology and convergence will strongly influence the strategy in approaching this goal.

It may be assumed that the uniting of cells to undergo recombination is so established a character that unicellular organisms had already obtained it before multicellular organisms evolved from them. It may also be assumed that nature tends to meet a new evolutionary necessity by modifying already existing mechanisms rather than by creating brand new ones. If these assumptions are valid, ciliates and multicellular organisms would have exploited the common ancestral molecular devices for specific cell union and recombination to meet their need for cell communication, cell union, and meiosis, and therefore, the basic mechanism of cell interaction and meiosis would be found in conjugation of ciliates.

In this connection it may be interesting to point out similarities between a conjugation signal of *Blepharisma,* blepharismone, and a neurotransmitter, serotonin. They are chemically alike and are both derived from tryptophan (Fig. 21). Functionally they are both intercellular molecular messengers of specific information. Since conjugation signals must transmit particular information to cells of the same species, one would expect that proteins would have been exploited for these signals. Indeed, many conjugation signals appear to be proteins. However, one of the two gamones so far isolated is a derivative of an amino acid, suggesting that such a small molecule may also be used by some other ciliates. Even if only a small fraction of about 7500 known species of ciliates (Corliss, 1974) use such simple molecules for conjugation signals, the number could be considerable. If the array of molecular species of conjugation signals and that of neurotransmitters and hormones overlap, it would provide supporting evidence for homology between cell communication systems in ciliates and in multicellular organisms. It would also indicate the possibility that a search for new conjugation signals and a search for new neurotransmitters and hormones might help each other in the future. It is suggestive that *T. pyriformis* has serotonin (Janakidevi *et al.,* 1966a; Brizzi and Blum,

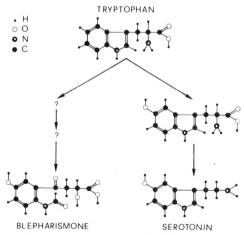

FIG. 21. Serotonin, blepharismone (gamone 2 of *Blepnarisma japonicum*) and pathways of their formation from tryptophan.

1970), epinephrine, and norepinephrine (Janakidevi *et al.,* 1966b; Blum *et al.,* 1966) and that *P. aurelia* has cholinesterase activity (Andrivon, 1975), although functions of these molecules in ciliates are still to be demonstrated.

Shortly after mating types were discovered (Sonneborn, 1937), Metz began an analytical study on cell interaction in conjugation. This study led him to a hypothetical scheme for activation of *Paramecium,* which is a series of chain reactions beginning with the surface interaction between two types of cells and eventually branching into various processes in conjugation (Metz, 1948, 1954). He pointed out that interaction between cell surfaces in the mating reaction of *Paramecium* is essentially the same as that in cell interactions in Metazoa, particularly in fertilization, and suggested that further analysis of the former will help in discovering the basic mechanism of the latter. Current discussions along these lines have been presented by Hiwatashi (1969), who neatly synthesized new experimental results on *Paramecium,* and Miyake (1974a). Miyake attempted to establish a unifying view on cell interaction in conjugation of various ciliates and to identify and "isolate" additional component steps in conjugation, continuing this approach in the present article. Reissig (1974) surveyed microorganisms for the "perisemic" process, the process by which the cell envelope transduces a regulatory signal, and suggested that the complications of the perisemic process may be tackled best by the use of microbial systems. Crandall (1977) also made a similar suggestion in her recent comprehensive review on mating-type interactions in microorganisms.

Such expectations are mainly based on the simplicity of microbial systems. However, cell interaction in unicellular organisms is still a compound of component steps. These components must be identified and isolated so that analysis can be performed on individual steps. A potentially powerful tool for this operation is the genetic method, but in ciliates the application is still preliminary (Metz, 1954; Cronkite, 1974, 1975, 1976). It appears, however, that the operation has already been carried out reasonably well in *Blepharisma* by other means.

A hypothetical diagram (Fig. 22) of the molecular mechanism of cell interaction in *Blepharisma* was constructed (Miyake, 1974b) and is further supported by the experimental results described in this article. In this diagram, a type I cell excretes gamone 1, a glycoprotein, which reacts with a hypothetical receptor on a type II cell. This reaction induces protein synthesis in the type II cell. Most of the synthesized proteins participate in cell union, changing the surface of the cell (blackened area) so that it can form a cell union. The other proteins are enzymes which transform tryptophan to gamone 2. This molecule is

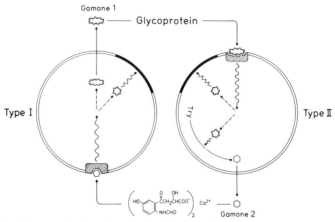

FIG. 22. Diagram of the molecular mechanism of cell interaction in conjugation of *Blepharisma japonicum*. Circles rimmed with a waved line represent proteins. From Miyake (1974b).

excreted, reacts with a hypothetical receptor on a type I cell, and induces protein synthesis. One of the induced proteins is gamone 1. The others change the surface of the cell (blackened area) so that it can form a cell union. Since both gamones are available in pure form and since conjugation is apparently arrested at the stage of cell union in homotypic pairs, some of the steps in this diagram or a small groups of them can be separated from other processes of conjugation, making them amenable to chemical analysis.

The search for the universal mechanism of cell interaction in ciliate conjugation would have been less profitable a few decades ago. Only genetic interaction in conjugation was successfully demonstrated to conform to universal principles (Sonneborn, 1947, 1974a,b). Other aspects of cell interaction, e.g., cell recognition, cell communication, cell union, control of meiosis, fertilization and other nuclear changes, were largely left untouched. The neglect was probably due to the lack of a powerful experimental method, comparable to genetic analysis, to uncover universal principles, rather than to the lack of appreciation of the potentiality of ciliate conjugation. Now, however, the progress and expansion of biology at the molecular and subcellular levels are rapidly changing the situation. The search will be more fruitful in the future as studies of life at these levels advance.

ACKNOWLEDGMENT

Most sincere thanks are due to Dr. R. Nobili for his warm hospitality and for stimulating discussions throughout the preparation of the manuscript and to Dr. L. K.

Bleyman, Baruch College, The City University of New York, for critically reading the manuscript.

This work was supported by Consiglio Nazionale delle Ricerche and by EMBO.

REFERENCES

Allewell, N. M., Oles, J., and Wolfe, J. (1976). *Exp. Cell Res.* **97,** 394.

Andrivon, C. (1975). *J. Protozool.* **22,** 87A.

Barnett, A. (1966). *J. Cell Physiol.* **67,** 239.

Bedini, C., Lanfranchi, A., Nobili, R., and Miyake, A. (1974). *Boll. Zool.* **41,** 457.

Bedini, C., Lanfranchi, A., Nobili, R., and Miyake, A. (1978). In preparation.

Beisson, J., and Capdeville, Y. (1966). *C. R. Hebd. Seances Acad. Sci.* **263,** 1258.

Beyer, J., and Miyake, A. (1973). *Prog. Protozool., Int. Conf. Protozool., 4th, 1973* Abstract, p. 42.

Bhandary, A. V. (1962). *J. Protozool.* **9,** 435.

Bleyman, L. K. (1964). *Genetics* **50,** 236.

Bleyman, L. K. (1971). *In* "Developmental Aspects of the Cell Cycle" (I. L. Cameron, G. H. Padilla, and A. M. Zimmerman, eds.), p. 67. Academic Press, New York.

Blum, J. J., Kirshner, N., and Ultey, J. (1966). *Mol. Pharmacol.* **2,** 606.

Braun, V., and Miyake, A. (1975). *FEBS Lett.* **53,** 131.

Brizzi, G., and Blum, J. J. (1970). *J. Protozool.* **17,** 553.

Bruns, P., and Brussard, T. B. (1974). *J. Exp. Zool.* **188,** 337.

Bruns, P., and Palestine, R. F. (1975). *Dev. Biol.* **42,** 75.

Byrne, B. C. (1972). Ph.D. Dissertation, Indiana University, Bloomington.

Carlile, M. J., and Machlis, L. (1965). *Am. J. Bot.* **52,** 478.

Cohen, L. W. (1964). *Exp. Cell Res.* **36,** 398.

Cohen, L. W. (1965). *Exp. Cell Res.* **37,** 360.

Corliss, J. O. (1974). *Syst. Zool.* **23,** 91.

Crandall, M. (1977). *In* "Receptors and Recognition III A" (P. Cuatrecasas and M. F. Greaves, eds.). Chapman & Hall, London (in press).

Cronkite, D. L. (1972). Ph.D. Dissertation, Indiana University, Bloomington.

Cronkite, D. L. (1974). *Genetics* **76,** 703.

Cronkite, D. L. (1975). *Genetics* **80,** 13.

Cronkite, D. L. (1976). *J. Protozool.* **23,** 431.

Dini, F., and Miyake, A. (1976). *J. Protozool.* **24,** 32A.

Dini, F., and Miyake, A. (1978). In preparation.

Ehret, C. F. (1953). *Physiol. Zool.* **26,** 274.

Elliott, A. M. (1973). *In* "Biology of *Tetrahymena*" (A. M. Elliott, ed.), pp. 259–286. Dowden, Hutchinson & Ross, Stroudsburg, Pennsylvania.

Elliott, A. M., and Tremor, J. W. (1958). *J. Biophys. Biochem. Cytol.* **4,** 839.

Elliott, A. M., and Zieg, R. G. (1968). *J. Cell Biol.* **36,** 391.

Esposito, F., and Ricci, N. (1975). *Boll. Zool.* **42,** 237.

Esposito, F., Ricci, N., and Nobili, R. (1976). *J. Exp. Zool.* **197,** 275.

Flickinger, C. J., and Murray, R. L. (1974). *Cell Tissue Res.* **153,** 357.

Förster, H., Wiese, L., and Braunitzer, G. (1956). *Z. Naturforsch., Teil B* **11,** 315.

Friedman, L. A., Colwin, A. L., and Colwin, L. W. (1968). *J. Cell Sci.* **3,** 115.

Frisch, A., Levkowitz, H., and Loyter, A. (1976). *Biochem. Biophys. Res. Commun.* **72,** 138.

Frisch, A., Levkowitz, H., and Loyter, A. (1977). *Exp. Cell Res.* **106,** 293.

Fukushi, T., and Hiwatashi, K. (1970). *J. Protozool.* **17,** Suppl., 21.

Goodenough, U. W., and Weiss, R. L. (1975). *J. Cell Biol.* **67**, 623.
Heckmann, K. (1964). *Z. Vererbungsl.* **95**, 114.
Heckmann, K., and Siegel, R. W. (1964). *Exp. Cell Res.* **36**, 688.
Hirshfield, H. I., Isquith, I. R., and DiLorenzo, A. M. (1973). *In "Blepharisma"* (A. C. Giese, ed.), p. 304. Stanford Univ. Press, Stanford, California.
Hiwatashi, K. (1949). *Sci. Rep. Tohoku Univ., Ser. 4* **18**, 141.
Hiwatashi, K. (1955a). *Sci. Rep. Tohoku Univ., Ser. 4* **21**, 199.
Hiwatashi, K. (1955b). *Sci. Rep. Tohoku Univ., Ser. 4* **21**, 207.
Hiwatashi, K. (1959). *Sci. Rep. Tohoku Univ., Ser. 4* **25**, 81.
Hiwatashi, K. (1961). *Sci. Rep. Tohoku Univ., Ser. 4* **27**, 93.
Hiwatashi, K. (1969). *In "Fertilization"* (C. B. Metz and A. Monroy, eds.), Vol. 2, p. 255. Academic Press, New York.
Honda, H., and Miyake, A. (1975). *Nature (London)* **257**, 678.
Honda, H., and Miyake, A. (1976). *Dev. Biol.* **52**, 221.
Inaba, F., Imamoto, K., and Suganuma, Y. (1966). *Proc. Jpn. Acad.* **42**, 394.
Janakidevi, K., Dewey, V. C., and Kidder, G. W. (1966a). *J. Biol. Chem.* **241**, 2576.
Janakidevi, K., Dewey, V. C., and Kidder, G. W. (1966b). *Arch. Biochem. Biophys.* **113**, 758.
Jurand, A., and Selman, G. G. (1969). *"The Anatomy of Paramecium aurelia."* Macmillan, New York.
Kanatani, H. (1973). *Int. Rev. Cytol.* **35**, 253.
Karakashian, M. W. (1968). *J. Cell. Physiol.* **71**, 197.
Katashima, R. (1959). *J. Protozool.* **6**, 75.
Katashima, R. (1961). *Jpn. J. Zool.* **13**, 39.
Kimball, R. F. (1939). *Am. Nat.* **73**, 57.
Kimball, R. F. (1942). *Genetics* **27**, 269.
Kitamura, A., and Hiwatashi, K. (1976). *J. Cell Biol.* **69**, 736.
Klein, M. S., Hirshfield, H. I., and Bleyman, L. K. (1975). *J. Protozool.* **22**, 40A.
Kroll, R. J., and Barnett, A. (1968). *J. Protozool.* **15**, Suppl., 10.
Kubota, T., Tokoroyama, T., Tsukuda, Y., Koyama, H., and Miyake, A. (1973). *Science* **179**, 400.
Kuo, S. C., and Lampén, J. O. (1974). *Biochem. Biophys. Res. Commun.* **58**, 287.
Kurita, M. (1968). *Biol. J. Nara Women's Univ.* **18**, 50.
Luporini, P., and Dini, F. (1975). *J. Protozool.* **22**, 541.
McCoy, J. W. (1972). *J. Exp. Zool.* **180**, 271.
Maupas, E. (1889). *Arch. Zool. Exp. Gen.* **7**, 149.
Metz, C. B. (1947). *J. Exp. Zool.* **105**, 115.
Metz, C. B. (1948). *Am. Nat.* **82**, 85.
Metz, C. B. (1954). *In "Sex in Microorganisms"* (D. H. Wenrich, ed.), p. 284. Am. Assoc. Adv. Sci., Washington, D.C.
Miwa, I. (1973). *Sci. Rep. Tohoku Univ., Ser. 4* **36**, 217.
Miwa, I., and Hiwatashi, K. (1970). *Jpn. J. Genet.* **45**, 269.
Miwa, I., Haga, N., and Hiwatashi, K. (1975). *J. Cell Sci.* **19**, 369.
Miyake, A. (1958). *J. Inst. Polytech., Osaka City Univ., Ser. D* **9**, 251.
Miyake, A. (1964). *Science* **146**, 1583.
Miyake, A. (1966). *J. Protozool.* **13**, Suppl., 28.
Miyake, A. (1968a). *Proc. Jpn. Acad.* **44**, 837.
Miyake, A. (1968b). *J. Exp. Zool.* **167**, 359.
Miyake, A. (1968c). *Jpn. J. Dev. Biol.* **22**, 62.
Miyake, A. (1969a). *Jpn. J. Genet.* **44**, Suppl., 388.

Miyake, A. (1969b). *Proc. Int. Congr. Genet., 12th, 1968* Vol. I, p. 72.

Miyake, A. (1974a). *Curr. Top. Microbiol. Immunol.* **64,** 49.

Miyake, A. (1974b). *In* "Biochemistry of Sensory Functions" (L. Jaenicke, ed.), p. 299. Springer-Verlag, Berlin and New York.

Miyake, A. (1975). *Science* **189,** 53.

Miyake, A., and Beyer, J. (1973). *Exp. Cell Res.* **76,** 15.

Miyake, A., and Beyer, J. (1974). *Science* **185,** 621.

Miyake, A., and Bleyman, L. K. (1976). *Genet. Res.* **27,** 267.

Miyake, A., and Honda, H. (1976). *Exp. Cell Res.* **100,** 31.

Miyake, A., and Nobili, R. (1974). *J. Protozool.* **21,** 584.

Miyake, A., Maffei, M., and Nobili, R. (1977). *Exp. Cell Res.* **108,** 245.

Miyake, A., Nobili, R., Lanfranchi, A., and Bedini, C. (1978). In preparation.

Miyake, K. (1970). *Biol. J. Nara Women's Univ.* **20,** 19.

Nanney, D. L. (1974). *Mech. Ageing Dev.* **3,** 81.

Nanney, D. L. (1977). *In* "Microbial Interactions" (J. Reissig, ed.). Chapman & Hall, London (in press).

Nobili, R. (1963). *J. Protozool.* **10,** Suppl., 24.

Nobili, R. (1967). *Monit. Zool. Ital.* **1,** 73.

Nobili, R., and Kotopolus De Angelis, F. (1963). *Atti Assoc. Genet. Ital.* **8,** 45.

Ofer, L., Mercazi, M., and Loyter, A. (1976). *J. Cell Biol.* **70,** 287.

Ototake, Y. (1969). *Biol. J. Nara Women's Univ.* **19,** 45.

Phillips, R. B. (1971). *J. Protozool.* **18,** 163.

Pieri, J. (1965). *C. R. Hebd. Seances Acad. Sci.* **261,** 2742.

Pieri, J., Vaufhien, C., and Trouiller, M. (1968). *J. Cell Biol.* **36,** 664.

Raikov, I. B. (1972). *Res. Protozool.* **4,** 147.

Ray, C. (1956). *J. Protozool.* **3,** 88.

Reissig, J. L. (1974). *Curr. Top. Microbiol. Immunol.* **67,** 43.

Revoltella, R., Ricci, R., Esposito, F., and Nobili, R. (1976). *Monit. Zool. Ital.* **10,** 279.

Ricci, N., Esposito, F., and Nobili, R. (1975). *J. Exp. Zool.* **192,** 343.

Ricci, N., Esposito, F., Nobili, R., and Revoltella, R. (1976). *J. Cell. Physiol.* **88,** 363.

Schneider, L. (1963). *Protoplasma* **56,** 109.

Smith, L. D., and Ecker, R. E. (1970). *Curr. Top. Dev. Biol.* **5,** 1.

Sonneborn, T. M. (1937). *Proc. Natl. Acad. Sci. U. S. A.* **23,** 378.

Sonneborn, T. M. (1947). *Adv. Genet.* **1,** 263.

Sonneborn, T. M. (1950). *J. Exp. Zool.* **113,** 87.

Sonneborn, T. M. (1970). *Methods Cell Physiol.* **4,** 241.

Sonneborn, T. M. (1974a). *In* "Handbook of Genetics—1974" (Robert C. King, ed.), Vol. 2, p. 433. Plenum, New York.

Sonneborn, T. M. (1974b). *In* "Handbook of Genetics—1974" (Robert C. King, ed.), Vol. 2, p. 469. Plenum, New York.

Sugai, T., and Hiwatashi, K. (1974). *J. Protozool.* **21,** 542.

Takagi, Y. (1970). *Jpn. J. Genet.* **45,** 11.

Takagi, Y. (1971). *Jpn. J. Genet.* **46,** 83.

Takahashi, M. (1973). *Sci. Rep. Tohoku Univ., Ser. 4* **36,** 223.

Takahashi, M., Takeuchi, N., and Hiwatashi, K. (1974). *Exp. Cell Res.* **87,** 415.

Tavrovskaya, M. V. (1974). *In* "Functional Morphology, Genetics and Biochemistry of the Cell" (A. S. Troshin, ed.), p. 83. Inst. Cytol. Leningrad (in Russian).

Tkacz, J. S., and Lampén, J. O. (1975). *Biochem. Biophys. Res. Commun.* **65,** 248.

Tokoroyama, T., Hori, S., and Kubota, T. (1973). *Proc. Jpn. Acad.* **49,** 461.

Tyler, L., and Wolfe, J. (1972). *J. Protozool.* **19,** Suppl., 42.

Vinnikova, N. N.. and Tavrovskaya, M. V. (1973). *In* "Structure Function and Reactivity of the Cell," p. 43. Acad. Sci. URSS, Leningrad (in Russian).

Vivier, E., and André, J. (1961). *J. Protozool.* **8,** 416.

Wasserman, W., and Masui, Y. (1976). *Science* **191,** 1266.

Wiese, L. (1961). *Fortschr. Zool.* **13,** 119.

Wolfe, J. (1973). *Dev. Biol.* **35,** 221.

CHAPTER 4

SPERM–EGG ASSOCIATION IN MAMMALS

R. Yanagimachi

DEPARTMENT OF ANATOMY AND REPRODUCTIVE BIOLOGY
UNIVERSITY OF HAWAII SCHOOL OF MEDICINE
HONOLULU, HAWAII

I. Introduction

The question of when fertilization begins and ends is a matter of semantics, but perhaps it is relevant to consider from the cytological point of view that fertilization begins at the moment of sperm–egg fusion and ends when the sperm and egg chromosomes arrange themselves on the metaphase plate of the first mitotic (cleavage) division. In many invertebrates (e.g., the sea urchin) and lower forms of vertebrates (e.g., the fish and frog), the entire process of fertilization is completed in a few hours or less, whereas in mammals it usually takes 12 hours or more despite the high temperature (30°–40°C) of the female's body in which fertilization takes place. Although the reason for this is not clear, it could be partly differences in the timing and rate of DNA synthesis in the pronuclei (Simmel and Karnofsky, 1961; Szollosi, 1966; Luthardt and Donahue, 1973; Siracusa *et al.*, 1975). Figure 1 illustrates the sequence of major events in fertilization in mammals (rat). Since many books and review articles dealing with the general aspects of mammalian fertilization are already available (Austin and Bishop, 1957; Austin, 1961, 1968; Blandau, 1961; Pikó, 1969; Thibault, 1969; Bedford, 1970a,b; Moghissi and Hafez, 1972; Longo, 1973), this chapter is primarily concerned with the results of some recent studies conducted in the author's laboratory and some of the problems to be solved by further investigations.

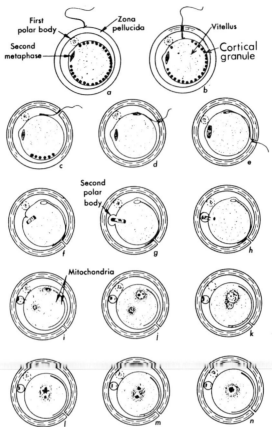

FIG. 1. Fertilization of the rat egg. *(a–d)* Entry of the spermatozoon. The shading of the zona pellucida denotes the occurrence of the cortical granule-mediated zona reaction. *(d–h)* Completion of the second meiotic division. *(i–l)* Pronuclear development. *(m)* Reappearance of chromosome groups. *(n)* First cleavage metaphase. From Austin (1965), with slight modification, reprinted by permission of Prentice-Hall.

II. Membrane Fusion between Sperm and Egg

Eggs fusing with spermatozoa can be obtained by flushing oviducts of mated females shortly after ovulation, but the chance of obtaining eggs in the initial stage of the fusion is very poor because of asynchronous sperm penetration and the rapidity of the fusion process. The chance can be improved to some extent by inseminating eggs *in vitro* with capacitated spermatozoa, since these spermatozoa, unlike freshly ejaculated spermatozoa, are capable of penetrating the egg zona pellucida and fusing with the egg within 1 hour after insemination. The problem of asynchronous sperm penetration, however, remains. We solved this problem by freeing the eggs from their surrounding investments (the cumulus oophorus and zona pellucida), then inseminating the "naked" eggs *in vitro* with capacitated and acrosome-reacted spermatozoa. Under such conditions, "synchronous" and multiple sperm penetration occurred within a few minutes, and we could readily examine the entire process of sperm–egg fusion (in the hamster, Yanagimachi and Noda, 1970a; in the guinea pig, Noda and Yanagimachi, 1976). The advantage of using *in vitro* fertilized, polyspermic eggs over *in vivo* fertilized, monospermic eggs is obvious, particularly in ultrastructural studies of fertilization. As far as the manner of sperm–egg fusion is concerned, there appears to be no substantial difference between the polyspermic fertilization of naked (zona-free) eggs *in vitro* (Yanagimachi and Noda, 1970a; Noda and Yanagimachi, 1976) and the monospermic fertilization of intact eggs *in vivo* (Szollosi, and Ris, 1961; Pikó and Tyler, 1964; Pikó, 1969; Bedford, 1968, 1972; Stefanini *et al.,* 1969; Presley and Marston, 1971; Thompson *et al.,* 1974; Oura, 1975a,b).

The procedure we are routinely using for the examination of sperm–egg fusion in the golden (Syrian) hamster is as follows. Oviducts of superovulated females (Yanagimachi, 1969) are flushed with Tyrode's solution (Table I) and the eggs obtained are treated

TABLE I

COMPOSITION OF MEDIA USED FOR STUDIES OF SPERM–EGG FUSION IN THE HAMSTER

Component	Tyrode (mg/100 ml)	Modified Tyrode (mg/100 ml)	BWW[a] (mg/100 ml)
NaCl	800.0	665.0	554.0
KCl	20.0	20.0	35.6
$CaCl_2$	20.0	20.0	—
Ca lactate	—	—	52.7
$MgCl_2 \cdot 6H_2O$	10.0	10.0	—
$MgSO_4 \cdot 7H_2O$	—	—	29.4
$NaH_2PO_4 \cdot H_2O$	5.0	5.0	—
KH_2PO_4	—	—	16.2
$NaHCO_3$	100.0	100.0	210.6
Glucose	100.0	100.0	100.0
Na lactate	—	241.6	241.6
Na puruvate	—	3.7	2.8
Bovine serum albumin	100.0	100.0	100.0

[a] From Biggers *et al.* (1971).

10–15 minutes at room temperature with 0.1% bovine testicular hyaluronidase in Tyrode's solution to disperse cumulus cells. The eggs are rinsed with enzyme-free Tyrode's solution, then exposed to 0.1% pancreatic trypsin for 1–2 minutes to dissolve the zona pelluida. Other proteolytic enzymes (e.g., chymotrypsin, and Pronase) and disulfide-reducing reagents (e.g., 2-mercaptoethanol and dithiothreitol) can also be used for dissolving the zona. The zona-free eggs are thoroughly rinsed with fresh Tyrode's solution and placed in 0.1–0.2 ml of BWW medium (Table I) under liquid paraffin in a watchglass (or plastic petri dish) and kept at 37°–38°C. Spermatozoa to be used for insemination are collected from the distal portion of the cauda epididymis and suspended in a sperm-capacitating medium at a concentration of approximately 10^7 spermatozoa per milliliter. The medium consists of two parts of BWW medium (or modified Tyrode's solution) and one part of heat-pretreated (56°C for 30–60 minutes) human serum. An aliquot (0.15–0.3 ml) of the sperm suspension thus prepared is placed under paraffin oil in a watchglass (or plastic petridish) and incubated at 37°–38°C for 4–6 hours. As the incubation atmosphere we use pure air for the medium containing Tyrode's solution and 5% CO_2 in air for the medium containing BWW medium. By the end of this incubation period, many spermatozoa are capacitated and show both the acrosome reaction and "activation" (Yanagimachi, 1970a,b). Insemination is performed by transferring a small drop (0.01–0.04 ml) of the sperm suspension into the BWW medium containing zona-free eggs (Fig. 2A). For examination of the fusion process, an atmosphere of pure air can be used, but for long-term culture of eggs (beyond 2–3 hours), 5% CO_2 in air is preferable. Alternatively, the zona-free eggs in a drop of BWW medium can be mounted between a slide and cover slip supported by

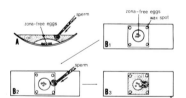

FIG. 2. Two methods used for examination of sperm–egg fusion. (A) Spermatozoa are mixed with zona-free eggs in a medium that has been previously placed under paraffin oil in a watchglass or petri dish; this is suitable for general experiments, including the preparation of samples for electron microscopy. ($B_{1–3}$) Eggs in a drop of medium are first mounted between a slide and cover slip (supported by wax dots) then exposed to spermatozoa from one side; this method is suitable for both low and high magnification observations of live eggs and their reactions to spermatozoa.

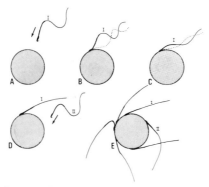

Fɪɢ. 3. Diagram showing that acrosome-reacted hamster spermatozoa lose their motility rather abruptly soon after contact with the egg plasma membrane (for chronology, see text.)

wax dots (paraffin–petroleum jelly mixture) and exposed to spermatozoa from one side (Fig. 2B).

When the spermatozoa were examined from the moment of insemination, it was observed that the sperm flagella, which were vigorously beating while the spermatozoa were freely swimming (Fig. 3A) and for a while after the sperm contact with egg surfaces (Fig. 3B), suddenly beat more slowly 5–15 seconds after contact (Fig. 3C) and became motionless by 15–25 seconds after contact (Fig. 3D). By 5 minutes after insemination, each egg had many motionless spermatozoa stuck on its surface (Fig. 3E). This rather sudden loss of flagellar motion of the spermatozoa may be due to a swift change in the properties of the sperm plasma membrane upon its physical contact or fusion with the egg plasma membrane. It was difficult to obtain thin sections of spermatozoa in the very earliest stage of fusion with eggs, since the spermatozoa were readily removed from the egg surfaces during routine preparations for electron microscopy. Once the fusion had advanced, however, the spermatozoa remained on the egg surfaces during the manipulation, and we could examine almost the entire process of sperm incorporation into the egg (Fig. 4). The earliest stage of sperm–egg fusion we observed (Fig. 4B) was seen in eggs fixed 3 minutes after insemination (Yanagimachi and Noda, 1970a). Fusion was observed between the egg plasma membrane of microvilli and the sperm plasma membrane in the postacrosomal region. By 15 minutes after insemination, the entire sperm head was incorporated into the egg cytoplasm (Fig. 4E). It is interesting to note that the inner acrosomal membrane, which covers the anterior half of the sperm head, does not fuse with the egg plasma membrane and is incorporated into the egg in a phagocytic

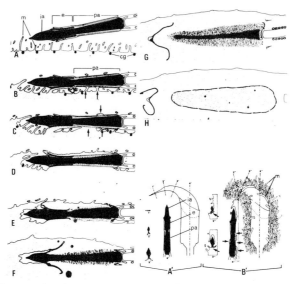

FIG. 4. Diagram showing successive stages of sperm incorporation into a zona-free hamster egg. (A and A') Acrosome-reacted spermatozoa prior to fusing with the egg. (B, B', C, and D) Membrane fusion advancing; arrows indicate areas where fusion is in progress. (E–H) Transformation of the sperm nucleus into a pronucleus. cg, Cortical granules; e, equatorial segment of the acrosome; ia, inner acrosomal membrane; m, egg microvilli; pa, postacrosomal region. A–H, from Yanagimachi (1973). Courtesy of Charles C Thomas, Publisher, Springfield, Illinois; A', B', from Yanagimachi and Noda (1972) with permission of Birkhaüser Verlag, Basel.

fashion (Fig. 4C–F). This is in marked contrast with fertilization in many invertebrates, where membrane fusion begins between the sperm inner acrosomal membrane and the egg plasma membrane (Colwin and Colwin, 1967). Decondensation of the sperm nucleus (chromatin) was detectable as early as 15 minutes after insemination (Fig. 4E) and became distinct in the next 30 minutes (Fig. 4F and G). Early sperm pronuclei surrounded by newly formed nuclear envelopes were seen in eggs examined 1 hour after insemination (Fig. 4H).

It is not known why the inner acrosomal membrane of mammalian spermatozoa cannot fuse with the egg plasma membrane, but it could be due in part to a lack of "fluidity" of the inner acrosomal membrane. In invertebrates the inner acrosomal membrane, at the time of the acrosome reaction, stretches enormously, forming the acrosomal process (Colwin and Colwin, 1967; Dan, 1967) (Fig. 5A). Apart from the question of whether the membrane of the acrosomal process results from the stretching of the intrinsic inner acrosomal membrane or from *de novo* synthesis from precursor substance (Dan, 1970), the membrane

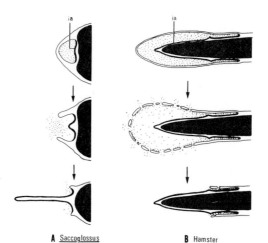

A Saccoglossus   **B** Hamster

FIG. 5. Differences in the behavior of the inner acrosomal membrane of invertebrate and mammalian spermatozoa during the acrosome reaction. The inner acrosomal membrane (ia) is shown as a bold line. In invertebrates (A, *Saccoglossus*), the inner acrosomal membrane stretches to form an acrosomal process; redrawn from Colwin and Colwin (1967). In mammals (B, the golden hamster), the membrane does not visibly change.

of the acrosomal process of invertebrate spermatozoa must be rather "fluid" in nature. In mammals, the inner acrosomal membrane remains "unchanged" during and after the acrosomal reaction (Fig. 5B). Using ferritin conjugates of *Ricinus communis* lectin and wheat germ lectin, we studied the "fluidity" (or "mobility" of membrane components) of the inner acrosomal membrane of hamster spermatozoa (R. Yanagimachi and G. L. Nicolson, unpublished data). In this study, we labeled live, acrosome-reacted spermatozoa at 4°C with ferritin–lectin conjugates. Part of the sample was kept at 4°C and part was incubated at 37°C. After 15–20 minutes, both samples were rinsed and fixed for electron microscopic observations. If the membrane is fluid and the mobility of the membrane components is high, we expect to see clustering of the lectin-binding sites in the 37°C-incubated sample in contrast to a more or less even distribution of the sites in the 4°C-incubated sample (Nicolson and Yanagimachi, 1974). As anticipated, the inner acrosomal membrane was evenly labeled by the conjugates in spermatozoa incubated at both temperatures, suggesting that the components of this membrane almost totally lack mobility. The inner acrosomal membrane of mammalian spermatozoa is difficult to cleave by the freeze-fracture technique (J. K. Koehler, personal communication), and, when fractured, it has a paracrystalline appearance (Koehler, 1975) (Fig. 6). The inner acrosomal membrane of mammalian sper-

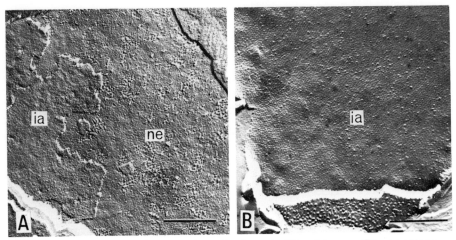

FIG. 6. Freeze-fractured preparations of guinea pig (A) and human (B) spermatozoa showing the highly particulate, almost crystalline nature of the inner acrosomal membrane (ia). ne, Nuclear envelop. Bar equals 0.5 μm. Courtesy of J. K. Koehler, University of Washington.

matozoa must have characteristics very different from ordinary biological membranes. The primary function of the inner acrosomal membrane of mammalian spermatozoa appears to be the recognition and penetration of the zona pellucida (Yanagimachi, 1977), not the fusion of spermatozoa with the egg. Although possibilities exist that (1) the inner acrosomal membrane assists spermatozoa in firmly attaching to the egg surfaces and (2) enzymes localized on the inner acrosomal membrane (Morton, 1975) render the egg plasma membrane capable of fusing with spermatozoa (Wolf, 1976), they are purely speculative at the present time.

The fusion of a spermatozoon with an egg seems to be facilitated by the presence of numerous microvilli on the egg surface. The area where the second polar body is to be extruded after fertilization is devoid of microvilli. This area is rather small in the hamster (Yanagimachi and Noda, 1970a), but occupies almost one-fifth of the total surface area of the mouse egg. Sperm–egg fusion is seldom seen in this microvilli-free area. A close approximation of two membranes (less than 15 Å apart), which is an essential prerequisite to successful membrane fusion (Poste and Allison, 1973), appears to be difficult to achieve when the spermatozoon with a "flat" membrane comes into contact with the "flat" area of the egg. As in the case of virus-induced cell fusion (Poste and Allison, 1973), microvilli (of the egg) with a low radius of curvature (<0.1 μm) must readily overcome electrostatic repulsion opposing a close approximation of the sperm and egg membranes.

At the time of normal fertilization, a spermatozoon which has passed through the zona pellucida and is about to fuse or is fusing with the egg has already completed the acrosome reaction (Austin and Bishop, 1958; Yanagimachi, 1966; Austin, 1968; Bedford, 1968, 1972; Yanagimachi and Noda, 1970b). A question that naturally comes to mind is whether acrosome-intact spermatozoa are capable of fusing with eggs if they are brought directly onto the egg surfaces. Yanagimachi and Noda (1970c) prepared zona-free hamster eggs and inseminated them *in vitro* with either acrosome-intact or acrosome-reacted spermatozoa. The results showed clearly that although both types of spermatozoa are able to stick to egg surfaces, only the acrosome-reacted spermatozoa fuse with the eggs. Acrosome-intact spermatozoa may be trapped by the egg microvilli (Fig. 7), but they never fuse with the eggs. This has also been found to be true of the guinea pig (Yanagimachi, 1972a; Noda and Yanagimachi, 1976). It

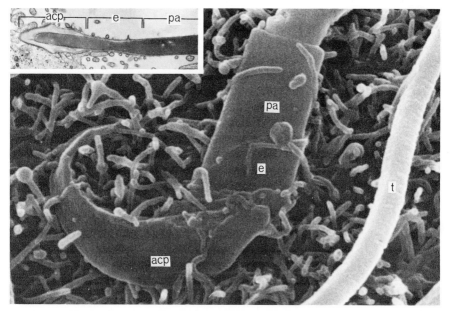

Fig. 7. Heads of acrosome-intact hamster spermatozoa trapped by egg microvilli. Such spermatozoa do not fuse with the egg as long as they do not undergo the acrosome reaction. acp, Anterior segment of the acrosome or the acrosomal cap; e, the posterior (or equatorial) segment of the acrosome; pa, postacrosomal region of the sperm head; t, tail of another spermatozoon. Courtesy of Y. D. Noda, Ehime University.

appears that the sperm plasma membrane covering the postacrosomal region of the sperm head undergoes some physiological changes concomitant with or as a result of the acrosome reaction, and these changes in the membrane make the spermatozoon capable of fusing with the egg plasma membrane. The nature of these changes is unknown at the present time, but may involve an alteration or removal of sperm surface components that hinder a close approximation of the sperm membrane with the egg plasma membrane.

In some mammals (e.g., the Chinese hamster and field vole), the tails of the spermatozoa often detach from the heads during fusion with eggs and are not incorporated into the egg cytoplasm (Austin, 1961). In most mammals, however, the entire length of the sperm tail is incorporated into the egg by fusion between the plasma membranes of the sperm tail and egg. This fusion proceeds from the proximal to the distal end of the tail in a zipperlike fashion (Fig. 8A). In some cases, straightforward fusion occurs between the egg plasma membrane and the sperm tail membrane (Fig. 8B). In some other cases, however, the sperm tail is encapsulated by egg microvilli before fusion takes place (Fig. 8C). After incorporation into the egg cytoplasm, the middle-piece mitochondria and the axial filament of the sperm tail are destined to eventually disintegrate (Szollosi, 1965; Szollosi and Hunter, 1973; Zamboni, 1972), and it is unlikely that these sperm elements make any significant contribution in embryonic development.

It would be interesting to learn the behavior and fate of the sperm plasma membrane after it has been integrated into the plasma membrane of a fertilized egg. The use of sperm surface-specific antibodies as

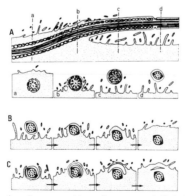

FIG. 8. Diagram showing incorporation of a sperm tail into hamster egg. (A) Longitudinal and cross sections through the middle and principal pieces of the tail. (B, C) Cross sections through the principal piece of the tail, showing two different ways in which the sperm tail is incorporated.

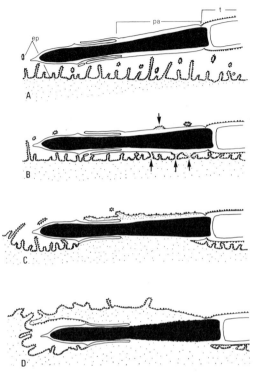

FIG. 9. Diagram showing the binding of positively charged iron hydroxide particles
(●) to egg and sperm surfaces before (A) and during (B–D) sperm–egg fusion in the
hamster. ep, Egg plasma membrane; pa, postacrosomal region; t, tail. Arrows indicate
areas where membrane fusion has begun. See text for explanation.

membrane probes would be the ideal approach to this problem, although some technical difficulties may be encountered (Schechtman
and Metz, 1967). Yanagimachi *et al.* (1973) used a less specific technique involving labeling of the sperm and egg surfaces with positively
charged collodial iron hydroxide particles (CIH). Prior to fusion with
the egg, the surface of the sperm head did not bind CIH whereas the egg
plasma membrane bound CIH heavily (Fig. 9A). Once fusion began,
however, the membrane over the sperm head quickly gained the ability
to bind CIH (Fig. 9B–D), suggesting the possibility that the sperm
membrane components quickly intermingled with the components of
the egg plasma membrane. It is most probable that the sperm tail
membrane also intermingles with the egg plasma membrane, although
we could not demonstrate this because CIH bound equally to both the
sperm tail and egg plasma membranes.

Among many questions to be solved by future studies are

1. Why are only the acrosome-reacted spermatozoa capable of fusing with an egg? How is the plasma membrane of the acrosome-reacted spermatozoon different from that of the acrosome-intact spermatozoon? Is the difference purely physical (e.g., electrostatic charge of the sperm surface components), or does it include complicated chemical changes in the membrane components?

2. Will it be possible to make acrosome-intact spermatozoa capable of fusing with an egg by artificially altering the properties of the sperm surfaces?

3. Will it be possible to make the acrosome-reacted spermatozoa incapable of fusing with the egg plasma membrane? How important is the composition of extracellular environment (e.g., Na^+, K^+, and Ca^{2+}) in sperm–egg fusion? Will membrane-active reagents block or promote fusion?

4. Must the spermatozoa be motile or "alive" to fuse with the egg plasma membrane?

5. Will it be possible to make the egg plasma membrane incapable of fusing with spermatozoa by treating the egg surface with enzymes, lectins, or other membrane-active reagents?

6. Spermatozoa and eggs do not usually fuse with somatic cells. Do spermatozoa and eggs carry some specific fusiogenic agents?

III. Vitelline Block to Multiple Sperm–Egg Fusion

Under normal conditions *in vivo,* only one spermatozoon unites (fuses) with the egg and participates in embryonic development. The entry of more than one spermatozoon into the egg (polyspermy) inevitably results in abnormal development or death of the embryo (Bomsel-Helmreich, 1965; Pikó, 1961). In mammals, the incidence of polyspermy is minimized by the relatively small number of spermatoza reaching the site of fertilization (Austin and Braden, 1952; Braden and Austin, 1954) as well as by the cortical granule-mediated reactions of the egg zona pellucida and vitelline surface. In the hamster, the zone pellucida of an egg which has been penetrated by a fertilizing spermatozoon quickly becomes impenetrable to excess spermatozoa as a result of the action of material released from the cortical granules (Austin and Braden, 1956; Austin, 1961; Barros and Yanagimachi, 1971; Gwatkin *et al.,* 1973). The egg plasma membrane appears to remain capable of fusing with spermatozoa even long after fertilization (up to the 4-cell stage) (Usui and Yanagimachi, 1976). Thus in the hamster, the change in the zona pellucida, the zona reaction (Braden *et al.*, 1954; Austin and Braden, 1956), is of critical importance for preventing multiple penetration by spermatozoa. In some other species (e.g., the rabbit), on the other hand, the zona reaction is not obvious and the block to multiple penetration by spermatozoa appears to be almost entirely dependent on changes on/in the egg plasma membrane (Austin and Bishop, 1957; Austin, 1961). According to Cooper and Bedford (1971), the net negative surface charge on the rabbit egg (possibly due to *N*-acetyl-*O*-diacetylneuraminic acid residues) increases markedly after penetration by a fertilizing spermatozoon. Concanavalin A-binding sites on the rabbit egg plasma membrane also increase considerably after fertilization (Gordon *et al.*, 1975). It is not clear at the present time whether such changes occur immediately upon contact of the fertilizing spermatozoon with the egg surface or only as a consequence of the release of the cortical granule material (Cooper and Bedford, 1971). Gordon *et al.* (1975) postulated that a protease released from the cortical granules alters the characteristics of a glycoprotein coat over the egg plasma membrane so that the sperm-binding sites on the egg plasma membrane become inaccessible to additional spermatozoa.

Other possibilities that come to the author's mind are: (1) cortical granule contents (glycoproteins?) mask the surface of the egg plasma membrane; (2) membrane components of the cortical granule intermingle with the egg plasma membrane, forming a new mosaic membrane that is markedly different in its characteristics from the intrinsic egg plasma membrane; (3) the cortical granule material binds to or masks the surfaces of excess spermatozoa approaching the egg surfaces; and (4) the molecular organization of the egg plasma membrane itself changes as the result of egg activation by the fertilizing spermatozoon, which occurs independently from the breakdown of the cortical granules. As stated already, a close approximation of the sperm and egg plasma membrane (less than 15 Å apart) appears to be an essential requirement for their successful fusion. Changes in the egg and/or sperm membranes, as mentioned above, must hinder such close membrane approximation.

IV. Interaction between Sperm Nucleus and Egg Cytoplasm

The nucleus of mammalian spermatozoa is highly condensed and elastic. It can be stretched with microneedles (Moench and Holt, 1929) like a rubber ball (Fig. 10). Even if isolated and exposed to distilled water for 2 days at 38°C, the sperm nucleus retains its original size and shape (Fig. 11). This elasticity and stability of the nucleus appear to be due to extensive cross-linking of the nuclear proteins by —SS— bonds

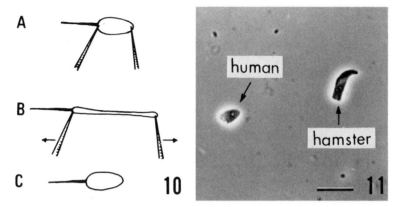

FIG. 10. Human sperm head (A) is stretched with microneedles (B). Its original shape is restored upon release from the needles (C). Redrawn from Moench and Holt (1929).

FIG. 11. Human and hamster sperm nuclei isolated by sonication and exposed to distilled water for 2 days at 38°C. Most human and all hamster sperm nuclei retain their original shapes and sizes. Bar equals 10 μm.

(Calvin and Bedford, 1971; Bedford and Calvin, 1974). In spite of its great stability, the nucleus of a fertilizing spermatozoon that has penetrated into an egg quickly decondenses (Figs. 1 and 4), indicating that the egg cytoplasm possesses extremely efficient mechanisms (enzyme systems?) for decondensing sperm nucleus. These mechanisms could well involve cleavage of —SS— bonds in the sperm chromatin complex (Calvin and Bedford, 1971; Mahi and Yanagimachi, 1975).

Yanagimachi and Usui (1972) and Usui and Yanagimachi (1976) questioned whether the egg cytoplasm has the ability to decondense sperm nuclei at all times. We collected hamster eggs at various stages of maturation (from the ovary) and development (from the ovuduct or uterus), freed them from the zona pellucida, and inseminated them *in vitro* with acrosome-reacted spermatozoa. We found that the spermatozoa were able to fuse with eggs throughout all stages from the germinal vesicle stage through the 4-cell stage, but the ability of the egg cytoplasm to decondense sperm nuclei varied depending on the stage of the egg. When spermatozoa entered the eggs at the germinal vesicle stage, the intrinsic nuclear envelop surrounding the sperm nuclei quickly disappeared, but the sperm nuclei remained condensed even 3 hours after their entry (Fig. 12A). When spermatozoa penetrated eggs at prometaphase I, partial decondensation of the sperm chromatin was evident 1 hour after sperm entry (Fig. 12B). When spermatozoa penetrated eggs at metaphase-anaphase I, most of the sperm chromatin decondensed by 1 hour after sperm entry. The fastest

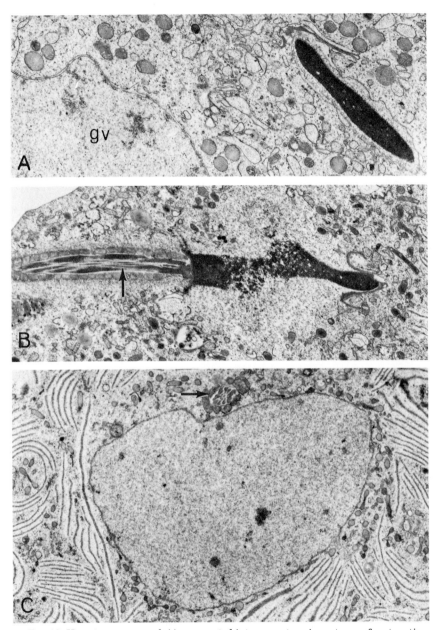

Fig. 12. Hamster sperm nuclei incorporated into eggs at various stages of maturation. (A) Three hours after entry into an egg at the germinal vesicle (gv) stage. (B) One hour after entry into an egg shortly after breakdown of the germinal vesicle. (C) One hour after entry into a fully mature oviductal egg. Arrows indicate sperm tails.

decondensation of the sperm chromatin was observed when spermatozoa penetrated mature oviductal eggs at metaphase II (Fig. 12C).
A comparison of the speed and degree of sperm chromatin decondensation in eggs at various stages of maturation has indicated that the
capacity of ovarian eggs to decondense sperm chromatin begins to appear about the time of germinal vesicle breakdown and increases with
the progression of nuclear maturation. Fertilized eggs at the pronuclear stage failed to decondense the chromatin of secondarily incorporated spermatozoa even 3 hours after their entry. Curiously enough,
sperm nuclei incorporated into eggs shortly before the first cleavage of
the eggs decondensed during the cleavage. Spermatozoa could penetrate (fuse with) some 2-cell and 4-cell eggs, but chromatin failed to
decondense at least during the 3 hours the eggs were studied. These
observations indicate that egg cytoplasmic conditions or factors that
cause the decondensation of sperm chromatin appear (or become active) only during a certain period of the cell cycle. The origin of the
sperm chromatin-decondensing factor (SCDF) in the egg cytoplasm is
not known. Usui and Yanagimachi (1976) suggested the possibility
that SCDF is synthesized in the egg cytoplasm, quickly transported
and accumulated in the egg nucleus during interphase of the cell cycle,
and released in concentrated form into the egg cytoplasm during
breakdown of the nuclear envelop. The site where SCDF is stored in the
nucleus could be the nucleoli (Fig. 13). In the dog, SCDF produced in
the egg cytoplasm may reach a significantly high concentration before
breakdown of the nuclear envelop, since sperm nuclei incorporated into

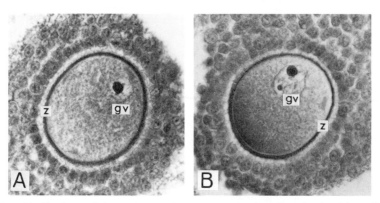

Fig. 13. Sections of hamster ovarian oocytes fixed and stained with a ferric
ferricyanide reduction technique (Lillie, 1965). The positive reaction of the zona pellucida (z) is probably due to protein-bound disulfide; the thinness of the zona is obviously
an artifact of fixation. The strong reaction of the nucleoli in the germinal vesicle (gv)
could be due to sulfhydryl groups.

immature eggs with intact germinal vesicles decondense (Mahi and Yanagimachi, 1976).

According to Hiramoto (1962), live sea urchin spermatozoa injected into the cytoplasm of unfertilized eggs remain unchanged, whereas those injected into eggs that were subsequently activated by spermatozoa from outside participated in the mitotic (cleavage) process. Uehara and Yanagimachi (1976) at first thought that activation of the egg cytoplasm is necessary for decondensation of the sperm nucleus (chromatin), but later found that the sperm nuclei (of the hamster) can decondense in apparently "unactivated" eggs (Uehara and Yanagimachi, 1977b). The fully activated state of the egg cytoplasm appears to be necessary not for the decondensation of the sperm nucleus, but for the transformation of the decondensed nucleus into a functional sperm pronucleus (Uehara and Yanagimachi, 1977b).

The microsurgical injection of sperm nuclei into eggs is a powerful tool for learning the characteristics of the sperm nucleus as well as for studying the interaction between the sperm nucleus and egg cytoplasm. Using this technique, we have learned that the nuclei of testicular spermatozoa of the hamster can develop into apparently "normal" pronuclei when injected into the cytoplasm of mature oviductal eggs (Uehara and Yanagimachi, 1977b). We have also found that the nuclei of hamster and human spermatozoa retain their ability to decondense and develop into apparently "normal" pronuclei even after the spermatozoa are freeze-dried (Uehara and Yanagimachi, 1977a) (Fig. 14), but not after they are autoclaved (unpublished data). It would be interesting to learn whether the eggs injected with testicular sperm nuclei or freeze-dried sperm nuclei are capable of developing into live fetuses or young, which is highly probable. Transplantation of somatic cell nuclei into mammalian eggs and of sperm nuclei into somatic cells

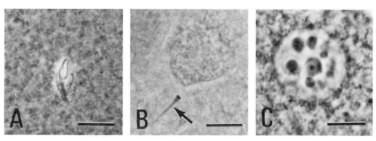

FIG. 14. Human spermatozoa freeze-dried and stored in a desiccator at 4°C for 6 months. (A) Immediately after injection into a hamster egg. (B) One hour after injection, showing decondensed sperm nucleus and tail (an arrow). (C) Three hours after injection, showing a well developed sperm pronucleus. Bar equals 10 μm.

has been achieved successfully by microsurgical operation (Bromhall, 1975) and by the use of fusiogenic agents, such as Sendai virus and lysolecithin (Baranska and Koprowski, 1970; Senin and Shapiro, 1971; Koprowski and Croce, 1973; Gavara *et al.*, 1973; Bromhall, 1975). Studies on this nature will assist us in understanding the mechanisms and the specificity of interactions between the sperm nucleus and the egg cytoplasm.

V. Species Specificity

The primary mechanisms by which hybridization in mammals is prevented are the "physiological" and "behavioral" separation of males and females of different species. The physiological incompatibility of spermatozoa in the female genital tract of another species as well as the inability of hybrid embryos to develop may also play a part in preventing hybridization. Nevertheless, the eggs and spermatozoa of each species have distinct species-specific properties and are capable of fusing with the opposite gametes only of the homologous species. There are, of course, some exceptions to this rule as evidenced by the presence of many mammalian hybrids (Gray, 1954; Chang and Hancock, 1967), but the rule holds in the vast majority of cases. The most prominent site for the species specificity in mammalian fertilization is the egg zona pellucida (Yanagimachi, 1977). Spermatozoa of foreign species are generally unable to attach (bind) to the zona, and, even if they attach, they cannot penetrate it. The lack of a strong species specificity at the level of the egg plasma membrane is evident from experiments in which zona-free eggs were inseminated with spermatozoa of heterologous species. Zona-free hamster eggs, for instance, are penetrable by spermatozoa of the rat, mouse (Hanada and Chang, 1972, 1976), guinea pig (Yanagimachi, 1972b; Barros *et al.*, 1973), and even human (Yanagimachi *et al.*, 1976) (Fig. 15). At least in the combinations of *hamster eggs × guinea pig or human spermatozoa,* the sperm penetration is due to a true membrane fusion between the gametes, not to a phagocytic engulfment of spermatozoa by the egg. It is interesting to note that the successful fusion of spermatozoa with heterologous eggs requires the sperm acrosome reaction (Yanagimachi, 1972b; Barros *et al.*, 1973; Yanagimachi *et al.*, 1976), just as in the case of normal fertilization.

Visible indications of egg activation (the breakdown of cortical granules and the resumption of meiotic division) following the fusion of heterologous spermatozoa are quite "normal" (Yanagimachi, 1972b; Yanagimachi *et al.*, 1976), indicating that the mechanisms by which the spermatozoon triggers egg activation are not strictly species specific. The development of egg and sperm pronuclei and their union

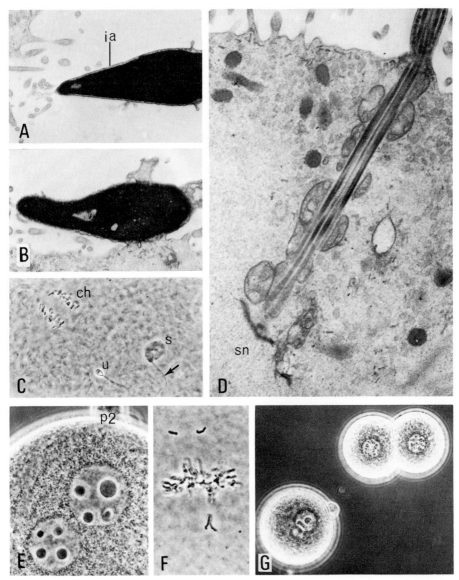

Fɪɢ. 15. Zona-free hamster eggs penetrated by human spermatozoa. (A) Head of an acrosome-reacted spermatozoon approaching the surface of a zona-free egg; ia, the inner acrosomal membrane. (B) A sperm head just starting to fuse with an egg. (C) A swollen sperm head (s) with tail (arrow); compare its size with that of an unswollen sperm head (u); ch, anaphase II chromosomes of the egg. (D) Sperm tail being incorporated into the egg; the sperm nucleus (sn) has already decondensed. (E) Two pronuclei, one of which is believed to be a human sperm pronucleus, about 7 hours after sperm entry; p2, the second polar body. (F) Side view of chromosomes on the metaphase plate of the first cleavage division, about 15 hours after sperm entry. (G) Two eggs shortly before and after the first cleavage, about 17 hours after sperm entry; more than 60% of the eggs penetrated by human spermatozoa reached the 2-cell stage, but none developed further.

also appear to proceed "normally" (Fig. 15), indicating that the mechanisms controlling pronuclear development and union are again not strictly species specific. The incompatibility of the sperm nucleus (chromosomes) with the egg cytoplasm of the unrelated species must be exhibited in later stages of development.

VI. Summary

1. The process of sperm–egg fusion in mammals can be readily studied by inseminating zona pellucida-free eggs with acrosome-reacted spermatozoa. The sperm membrane that initially fuses with the egg plasma membrane is the plasma membrane in the posterior region of the sperm head, not the inner acrosomal membrane. The inability of the acrosomal membrane to fuse with the egg membrane could be due to its lack of the "fluidity."

2. The acrosome reaction appears to be essential for successful fusion of the spermatozoon with the egg. It is very likely that the plasma membrane over the posterior region of the sperm head undergoes some physiological changes concomitant with or as a result of the acrosome reaction, and these changes make the spermatozoon capable of fusing with the egg plasma membrane. The changes may involve an alteration or removal of sperm surface components that hinder a close approximation of the sperm and egg membranes.

3. In some mammals (e.g., the hamster), the egg plasma membrane remains capable of fusing with spermatozoa even long after penetration of the fertilizing spermatozoon into the egg. The principal site of the block to polyspermy in these species resides in the zona pellucida. In some other mammals (e.g., the rabbit), the egg plasma membrane quickly becomes incapable of fusing with excess spermatozoa. The molecular bases of these blocks to polyspermy are not fully understood, but the blocks appear to be mediated by the action of cortical granule material released from the egg upon its activation by the fertilizing spermatozoon.

4. In the hamster, the egg cytoplasmic factor responsible for the decondensation of a sperm nucleus begins to appear about the time of germinal vesicle breakdown, increases with the progression of nuclear maturation, diminishes (or becomes inactive) following fertilization and reappears (or becomes active again) during the first cleavage. The origin and chemical nature of this sperm chromatin-decondensing factor are a matter of speculation at the present time.

5. Experiments involving the microsurgical injection of spermatozoa into the egg have demonstrated that sperm nuclei retain their ability to decondense and develop into pronuclei even after the sper-

matozoa have been freeze-dried. Egg activation (activation of the egg cytoplasm) appears to be necessary for the transformation of the sperm nucleus into a pronucleus, not for the decondensation of the sperm chromatin.

6. The most prominent site for the species specificity of fertilization in mammals is the zona pellucida. The mechanisms involved in sperm–egg fusion, egg activation, and the development and union of pronuclei do not appear to be highly species specific.

ACKNOWLEDGMENT

This work was supported by grants from the Ford Foundation, the Population Council, and the National Institute of Child Health and Human Development (HD-03402) and by the University of Hawaii Research and Training Revolving Fund. The assistance of Cherrie Mahi, Jacqueline Hayashida, and Pauline Abe in the preparation of the manuscript is gratefully acknowledged.

REFERENCES

Austin, C. R. (1961). "The Mammalian Egg." Thomas, Springfield, Illinois.
Austin, C. R. (1965). "Fertilization." Prentice-Hall, Englewood Cliffs, New Jersey.
Austin, C. R. (1968). "Ultrastructure of Fertilization." Holt, New York.
Austin, C. R., and Bishop, M. W. H. (1957). Biol. Rev. Cambridge Philos. Soc. 32, 296.
Austin, C. R., and Bishop, M. W. H. (1958). Proc. R. Soc. London, Ser. B 149, 241.
Austin, C. R., and Braden, A. W. H. (1952). Nature (London) 170, 919.
Austin, C. R., and Braden, A. W. H. (1956). J. Exp. Biol. 33, 358.
Baranska, W., and Koprowski, H. (1970). J. Exp. Zool. 174, 1.
Barros, C., and Yanagimachi, R. (1971). Nature (London) 233, 268.
Barros, C., Berrios, M., and Herrera, E. (1973). J. Reprod. Fertil. 34, 547.
Bedford, J. M. (1968). Am. J. Anat. 123, 329.
Bedford, J. M. (1970a). In "Mammalian Reproduction" (H. Gibian and E. J. Poltz, eds.), p. 124. Springer-Verlag, Berlin and New York.
Bedford, J. M. (1970b). Biol. Reprod., Suppl. 2, 128.
Bedford, J. M. (1972). Am. J. Anat. 133, 213.
Bedford, J. M., and Calvin, H. I. (1974). J. Exp. Zool. 188, 137.
Biggers, J. D., Whitten, W. K., and Whittingham, D. G. (1971). In "Methods in Mammalian Embryology" (J. C. Daniel, Jr., ed.), p. 86, Table 6-5. Freeman, San Francisco, California.
Blandau, R. J. (1961). In "Sex and Internal Secretion" (W. C. Young, ed.), 3rd ed., Vol. 2, p. 797. Williams & Wilkins, Baltimore, Maryland.
Bomsel-Helmreich, O. (1965). Preimplantation Stages Pregnancy, Ciba Found. Symp., 1965 p. 246.
Braden, A. W. H., and Austin, C. R. (1954). Aust. J. Biol. Sci. 7, 543.
Braden, A. W. H., Austin, C. R., and David, H. A. (1954). Aust. J. Biol. Sci. 6, 391.
Bromhall, J. D. (1975). Nature (London) 258, 719.
Calvin, H. I., and Bedford, J. M. (1971). J. Reprod. Fertil., Suppl. 13, 65.
Chang, M. C., and Hancock, J. L. (1967). In "Comparative Aspects of Reproductive Failure" (K. Benirschke, ed.), p. 206. Springer-Verlag, Berlin and New York.
Colwin, L. H., and Colwin, A. L. (1967). In "Fertilization" (C. B. Metz and A. Monroy, eds.), Vol. 1, p. 295. Academic Press, New York.

Cooper, G. W., and Bedford, J. M. (1971). *J. Reprod. Fertil.* **25**, 431.

Dan, J. C. (1967). *In* "Fertilization" (C. B. Metz and A. Monroy, eds.), Vol. 1, p. 237. Academic Press, New York.

Dan, J. C. (1970). *In* "Comparative Spermatology" (B. Baccetti, ed.), p. 487. Academic Press, New York.

Gavara, B., Gledhill, B. L., Croce, C. M., Cesarini, J. P., and Koprowski, H. (1973). *Proc. Soc. Exp. Biol. Med.* **143**, 1120.

Gordon, M., Fraser, L. R., and Dandekar, P. V. (1975). *Anat. Rec.* **181**, 95.

Gray, A. P. (1954). "Mammalian Hybrids." Commonw. Agric. Bur., Farnham Royal, Bucks, England.

Gwatkin, R. B. L., Williams, D. T., Hartmann, J. F., and Kniazuk, M. (1973). *J. Reprod. Fertil.* **32**, 259.

Hanada, A., and Chang, M. C. (1972). *Biol. Reprod.* **6**, 300.

Hanada, A., and Chang, M. C. (1976). *J. Reprod. Fertil.* **46**, 239.

Hiramoto, Y. (1962). *Exp. Cell Res.* **27**, 416.

Koehler, J. K. (1975). *In* "The Biology of the Male Gamete" (J. G. Duckett and P. A. Racey, eds.), p. 337. Academic Press, New York.

Koprowski, H., and Croce, C. M. (1973). *Methods Cell Biol.* **7**, 251.

Lillie, R. D. (1965). "Histopathologic Technique and Practical Histochemistry." 3rd ed., p. 211. McGraw-Hill, New York.

Longo, F. J. (1973). *Biol. Reprod.* **9**, 149.

Luthardt, F. W., and Donahue, R. P. (1973). *Exp. Cell Res.* **82**, 143.

Mahi, C. A., and Yanagimachi, R. (1975). *J. Reprod. Fertil.* **44**, 293.

Mahi, C. A., and Yanagimachi, R. (1976). *J. Exp. Zool.* **196**, 189.

Moench, G. L., and Holt, H. (1929). *Zentrabl. Gynaekol.* **21**, 1300.

Moghissi, K. S., and Hafez, E. S. E., eds. (1972). "Biology of Mammalian Fertilization and Implantation." Thomas, Springfield, Illinois.

Morton, D. B. (1975). *J. Reprod. Fertil.* **45**, 375.

Nicolson, G. L., and Yanagimachi, R. (1974). *Science* **184**, 1294.

Noda, Y. D., and Yanagimachi, R. (1976). *Dev., Growth & Differ.* **18**, 15.

Oura, C. (1975a). *Seitai No Kagaku* **26**, 279.

Oura, C. (1975b). *Proc. Int. Congr. Anat., 10th* p. 5.

Pikó, L. (1961). *Ann. Biol. Anim., Biochim., Biophys.* **1**, 323.

Pikó, L. (1969). *In* "Fertilization" (C. B. Metz and A. Monroy, eds.), Vol. 2, p. 325. Academic Press, New York.

Pikó, L., and Tyler, A. (1964). *Proc. Congr. Anim. Reprod. Artif. Insem., 5th, 1963* Vol. 2, p. 372.

Poste, G., and Allison, A. C. (1973). *Biochim. Biophys. Acta* **300**, 421.

Presley, R., and Marston, J. H. (1971). *J. Anat.* **108**, 587.

Schechtman, L. M., and Metz, C. B. (1967). *Biol. Bull. (Woods Hole, Mass.)* **133**, 482.

Senin, B. M., and Shapiro, I. M. (1971). *Dokl. Biol. Sci. (Engl. Transl.)* **197**, 201.

Simmel, E., and Karnofsky, D. A. (1961). *J. Biophys. Biochem. Cytol.* **10**, 59.

Siracusa, G., Coletta, M., and Monesi, V. (1975). *J. Reprod. Fertil.* **42**, 395.

Stefanini, M., Oura, C., and Zamboni, L. (1969). *J. Submicrosc. Cytol.* **1**, 1.

Szollosi, D. (1965). *J. Exp. Zool.* **159**, 367.

Szollosi, D. (1966). *Anat. Rec.* **154**, 209.

Szollosi, D., and Hunter, R. H. F. (1973). *J. Anat.* **116**, 181.

Szollosi, D., and Ris, H. (1961). *J. Biophys. Biochem. Cytol.* **10**, 275.

Thibault, C. (1969). *In* "Traité de Zoologie" (P.-P. Grassé, ed.), Vol. 16, p. 911. Masson, Paris.

Thompson, R. S., Smith, D. M., and Zamboni, L. (1974). *Fertil. Steril.* **25**, 222.

Uehara, T., and Yanagimachi, R. (1976). *Biol. Reprod.* **15**, 467.

Uehara, T., and Yanagimachi, R. (1977a). *J. Exp. Zool.* **199**, 269.

Uehara, T., and Yanagimachi, R. (1977b). *Biol. Reprod.* **16**, 315.

Usui, N., and Yanagimachi, R. (1976). *J. Ultrastruct. Res.* **57**, 276.

Wolf, D. F. (1976). *Fed. Proc., Fed. Am. Soc. Exp. Biol.* **35**, 1464 (Abstr. No. 563).

Yanagimachi, R. (1966). *J. Reprod. Fertil.* **11**, 359.

Yanagimachi, R. (1969). *J. Reprod. Fertil.* **18**, 275.

Yanagimachi, R. (1970a). *Biol. Reprod.* **3**, 147.

Yanagimachi, R. (1970b). *J. Reprod. Fertil.* **23**, 193.

Yanagimachi, R. (1972a). *Anat. Rec.* **174**, 9.

Yanagimachi, R. (1972b). *J. Reprod. Fertil.* **28**, 477.

Yanagimachi, R. (1973). *In* "The Regulation of Mammalian Reproduction" (S. J. Segal *et al.*, eds.), p. 215. Thomas, Springfield, Illinois.

Yanagimachi, R. (1977). *In* "Immunobiology of Gametes" (M. Edidin and M. H. Johnson, eds.), p. 255. Cambridge Univ. Press, London and New York.

Yanagimachi, R., and Noda, Y. D. (1970a). *Am. J. Anat.* **128**, 429.

Yanagimachi, R., and Noda, Y. D. (1970b). *J. Ultrastruct. Res.* **31**, 465.

Yanagimachi, R., and Noda, Y. D. (1970c). *J. Ultrastruct. Res.* **31**, 486.

Yanagimachi, R., and Noda, Y. D. (1972). *Experientia* **28**, 69.

Yanagimachi, R., and Usui, N. (1972). *J. Cell Biol.* **55**, 293a.

Yanagimachi, R., Noda, Y. D., Fujimoto, M., and Nicolson, G. L. (1973). *J. Ultrastruct. Res.* **43**, 344.

Yanagimachi, R., Yanagimachi, H., and Rogers, B. J. (1976). *Biol. Reprod.* **15**, 471.

Zamboni, L. (1972). *In* "Biology of Mammalian Fertilization and Implantation" (K. S. Moghissi and E. S. E. Hafez, eds.), p. 213. Thomas, Springfield, Illinois.

CHAPTER 5

SPERM AND EGG RECEPTORS INVOLVED IN FERTILIZATION

Charles B. Metz

INSTITUTE FOR MOLECULAR AND CELLULAR EVOLUTION
UNIVERSITY OF MIAMI
CORAL GABLES, FLORIDA

I. Introduction—Model Systems

Sperm–egg interaction can begin at a distance (sperm activation, chemotaxis, agglutination, acrosome reaction). Subsequent fertilization involves specific sperm–egg attachment, activation or derepression of the egg resulting in initiation of preprogrammed metabolic events, and finally membrane fusion (see Metz and Monroy, 1967, 1969; Epel, 1975). These phenomena are not unique to fertilization. One or more of them applies to cell–cell interactions in general.

Specific cell–cell binding and specific cell-surface interaction with substances in solution (e.g., toxins, drugs, hormones, agglutinins) imply interaction of specific receptors on the apposed or exposed surfaces (cell membranes, surface coats) of the cells involved. By analogy with specific immunological reactions (e.g., hemagglutination), specific cell attachment and adhesion are commonly explained by assuming attachment and/or binding by receptor substances that interact in "lock-and-key" fashion. Examples include components of Lillie's fertilizin theory of fertilization (1919) and its modern equivalent (Tyler and Tyler, 1966b), mating in protozoa (Metz, 1954a; Miyake, 1974; Snell, 1975a,b), yeast, and other microorganisms (Crandall and Brock, 1968a,b; Crandall *et al.*, 1974; Crandall, 1977), and some specific somatic tissue cell adhesions (Henkart *et al.*, 1973; Cauldwell *et al.*, 1973; Reed *et al.*, 1976; Muller *et al.*, 1976; Zahn *et al.*, 1976) in Metazoa. Agglutinins obtained from mammalian cell surfaces may also act, at least in part, in this fashion (e.g., Yamada *et al.*, 1975; Hausman and Moscona, 1975). Enzyme and substrate interaction has also been proposed as a cell recognition and attachment mechanism (e.g., cell surface glycosyltransferase system; Roth *et al.*, 1971). Specific interaction of cholera toxin with cells involves an initial attachment of the toxin molecule with a specific cell surface glycolipid (Cuatrecasas, 1974). Finally, antibodies actually attached to or built into the cell membranes of lymphocytes can mediate specific cell attachment ("rosette formation," see Dresser and Greaves, 1973).

Specific complementary antibody or antibodylike receptors at the cell surface not only can function in cell attachment, but, at least in some systems, can mediate cellular transformation following interaction with complementary agents. Perhaps the best examples are lymphocyte transformations by specific antigen to surface immunoglobulin [at least with T ("helper") lymphocyte or macrophage cooperation (Schreiner and Unanue, 1976)] and by lectins, such as concanavalin A (Con A) (for review, see Cunningham *et al.* and other authors, in Edelman, 1974). Initiation of hormone action by binding of hormone to a specific surface receptor of the target cell is another example (Ryan and Lee, 1976) of wide current interest.

In these activation or transformation phenomena, surface interaction must result in message transmission or "transduction" across the cell membrane and coupling to metabolic events. Proteinaceous hormone action appears to involve adenylate cyclase activation and cyclic AMP (cAMP) mediation (Marsh, 1976; Catt and Hufau, 1976). The linkage events following antigen or lectin interaction with B lymphocyte surface receptors for antigen (monomeric IgM and/or IgD; Vitetta and Uhr, 1975; Parkhouse *et al.*, 1976) are unknown but could involve conformational changes in transmembrane macromolecules reflected in altered aggregation states among macromolecules in the cell cortex (e.g., Cunningham *et al.*, in Edelman, 1974; Melcher, 1975; Schreiner and Unanue, 1976). Specific interaction of cholera toxin with cells, including activation of adenylate cyclase, involves an initial attachment of the toxin molecule to the specific cell-surface glycolipid, apparently followed by fragmentation of the toxin molecule, and possible penetration of the cell membrane by an "active unit" (Cuatrecasas, 1974).

Several specific sperm–egg interactions can be attributed to cell surface receptors comparable to those involved in other specific cell–cell interactions. Unfortunately, specification of most such "fertilization receptors" in chemical terms and precise understanding of their mode of action has yet to be attained among metazoa. Present knowledge is reviewed here, much of which consists of biological information defining problems for further study. For convenience "action-at-a-distance" (action of agents in solution) is considered separately from direct cell–cell boundary interactions. Studies on marine invertebrates are emphasized. Miyake (1974; this volume, Chapter 3) has recently reviewed information about protozoa; Crandall (1977) and Goodenough (1977) have surveyed these and other microorganisms, and Dunbar and Shivers (1976) have reviewed mammalian material.

II. Action at a Distance

Upon approaching the egg or female tissue, spermatozoa can encounter gradients of soluble products emanating from the female cells. Specific physiological action on the sperm would imply a role of appropriate receptors in reproduction. Four such "action at a distance" effects occur in some species, at least under laboratory conditions, namely, increased sperm motility, chemotaxis of sperm, sperm agglutination, and the sperm acrosome reaction. The last three of these are considered below.

A. CHEMOTAXIS

Chemotaxis, the oriented movement of cells in a chemical gradient, has been accepted for certain plant spermatozoids in the vicinity of female tissue since the classical experiments of Pfeffer (1884; for review, see Machlis and Rawitscher-Kunkel, 1967). Chemotaxis of animal spermatozoa, although claimed by many (for discussion, see Lillie, 1919; Morgan, 1927; Tyler, 1956; Rothschild, 1956; Metz, 1957b), has until recently been largely discredited. However, the sperm chemotaxis in the hydroid *Campanularia,* reported by Miller and Nelson (1962), has been convincingly demonstrated by cinephotomicrography. Miller (1966) showed that the spermatozoa orient and swim toward female gonangia, or a gradient of female gonangium extract. The phenomenon has been reported in a total of eight species in five hydroid genera, most of which fertilize internally. However, in one species *(Hydractinia)* sperm have been seen to orient and move to naturally spawned unfertilized eggs, which are surrounded only by a jelly coat (Miller, 1974, 1977). The chemotactic effect is incompletely species specific (one intergeneric cross reaction; three intrageneric cross reactions). These tests of specificity indicate at least four, and possibly five, different active chemotactic agents among the eight hydroids tested.

Chemical characterization of the *Tubularia crocea* agent has been examined in most detail. Chemotactically active solutions are obtained by alcohol extraction of female polyps. Specificity of action of these extracts parallels that of living female gonophores. Gel filtration, ion-exchange chromatography, electrophoresis, and sensitivity to proteolysis (Pronase) suggest a basic peptide of low molecular weight (M_r 1000) (Miller and Tseng, 1974).

The cinemicrophotographic demonstration of oriented turning and swimming ("homing") in a gradient, the specificity of action, and chemical data clearly eliminate "trap action" and nonspecific gradients of ubiquitous metabolites (e.g., CO_2, pH) as explanations and confirm an actual physiological sperm chemotaxis of apparent importance in hydroid reproduction.

In addition to chemotactic response to the female gonangium, *Campanularia* sperm undergo a loss of vesicles (O'Rand and Miller, 1974) and a remarkable capacitation-like phenomenon after entering the gonangium. The latter is a prerequisite for fertilization and depends upon contact with a trypsin-sensitive surface component of gonangium epithelial cells (O'Rand, 1972, 1974). It is not known whether these events occur in other internally fertilizing hydroids. However, foreign sperm *(Clava, Gonothyrea)* fail to show vesicle loss following exposure to female *Campanularia* gonophores. Accordingly, the vesicle loss in *Campanularia* could contribute to exclusion of these foreign sperm from cross fertilization (O'Rand, 1972).

More recently, R. L. Miller (personal communication) has examined 16 hydromedusae and six hydroids from the Friday Harbor, Washington area, all of which spawn internally. Reciprocal cross tests for sperm chemotaxis among these showed positive intraspecific reactions in all but one species with almost absolute species specificity. Interestingly, gel exclusion studies on the chemotactic factors suggest molecular weights of 5000 or less for Leptomedusae and 10,000 or greater (approximately 15,000 for *Leuckartiara*) for Anthomedusae, the Limnomedusae, and Trachymedusae. This suggests that different classes of substances are operative within the several groups of hydroids and medusae investigated.

Species-specific sperm chemotaxis toward eggs has recently been described in species phylogenetically remote from the Cnidaria, namely, the tunicates (Chordata) *Ciona intestinalis* (Miller, 1975) and *Ascidia callosa* (R. L. Miller personal communication). Interestingly, sperm of the tunicates examined in the genus *Styela (S. clava, S. monteregensis,* and *S. plicata)* respond chemotactically to pH gradients by swimming in the direction of higher acidity (Miller, 1977). The chemotaxis toward eggs in these species is not specific, and any requirement for a chemotactic gradient may be met by metabolically mediated low pH in the vicinity of the egg.

It appears to be established then that sperm chemotaxis occurs in two widely separated metazoan groups (hydroids and tunicates). It seems reasonable to expect demonstration of the phenomenon in other groups when properly examined (Miller, 1977).

Much remains unknown about animal sperm chemotaxis, including the exact source of the agents, details of their chemical composition and mode of action. However, the specificity reported by Miller (1977) implies specific sperm receptors for the chemotactic agents. Since chemotaxis involves directed motion in a chemical gradient, the postulated receptors should be distributed in an ordered pattern presumably on the sperm surface, and "coupled" in some way to sperm flagellar geometry and/or the flagellar locomotor apparatus. Activation of receptor sites should be quantitative; for example, the number of activated sites per unit area should be proportional to concentration of the chemotactic agent. The result should be detection of the chemical gradient (Miller and Brokaw, 1970) and a response to it by some physicochemical change that produces alteration in flagellar wave pattern or related asymmetry. Perhaps the simplest arrangement would be a grid of receptor molecules on the flagellum itself such that interaction of receptor and chemotactic molecule results in a local permeability change. This could translate into an asymmetry of flagellar beat, "manipulate" an asymmetrical structure, such as the asymmetric centriolar satellite of *Hydractinia* (Kleve and Clark, 1976) or the pericentriolar complex characteristic of coelenterate sperm (Hinsch and Clark, 1973). It could be mediated by localized differential ion efflux or influx. It is already clear that Ca^{2+} is an absolute requirement for chemotaxis in *Tubularia* (Miller, 1975). Any such model would seem to require a mechanism to prevent irreversible saturation of the sperm surface receptor sites since these must continually monitor the chemotactic gradient. Enzymatic destruction of the chemotactic agent by the receptor might supply this requirement. Further knowledge about these fascinating problems will be awaited with interest.

B. NATURAL SPERM AGGLUTININS

Spermatozoa of a variety of animal species agglutinate dramatically when mixed with supernatant from egg suspensions. As first recognized by F. R. Lillie (1913, 1919), the reaction constitutes a prime example of a specific interacting cell-surface receptor system. Lillie (1913) termed the sperm agglutinin *fertilizin* because of its presumed essential role in fertilization. By definition, fertilizin combines with a complementary sperm surface receptor, antifertilizin. By analogy with antibody agglutination, fertilizin is multivalent with respect to receptors that bind to antifertilizin and agglutinates by cross-linking sperms (Tyler, 1941). Analogy with antibodies also includes convertibility of fertilizin to a nonagglutinating, univalent form functionally similar to Fab antibody fragments (Metz, 1942, 1957b, 1967).

The extensive studies of several generations of investigators since Lillie's classical investigations have been reviewed repeatedly (Metz, 1957a,b, 1967; Monroy 1965; Tyler, 1948, 1949, 1959; Tyler and Tyler, 1966a,b). The present status, with emphasis on studies during the last 10 years, is presented below. Sea urchins have been the material for most research. The discussion will imply this material unless otherwise specified.

The role of the fertilizin–antifertilizin system in fertilization has been debated since Lillie's original studies (for detailed discussion, see Metz, 1967; Tyler and Tyler, 1966a,b). The primary function of the system is now widely believed to be initiation of the sperm acrosome reaction. It should be noted that certain teleost fish sperm which lack acrosomes (Matlei and Matlei, 1975; Colwin and Colwin, 1967) nevertheless agglutinate with homologous egg water (Runnström *et al.*, 1944). It is also important to note that agglutination is not dependent upon the acrosome reaction, because Ca^{2+} is required only for the latter in most species. The fertilizin–antifertilizin interaction may also contribute to sperm–egg attachment. These roles will be considered in later sections (II, C and III, respectively).

The most striking feature apart from the reaction itself is the tissue and species specificity of the agglutination. When cross agglutination occurs, it is generally among related species where cross fertilization is frequent (Tyler, 1949) (Table I), and the strongest agglutination reactions are in the intraspecific combinations. "Divergence from exact parallelism represents, to some extent, experimental error but may also indicate that, while fertilizin–antifertilizin interaction is a major factor determining the specificity of fertilization, there may be some contribution to this from interactions involving other substances"

TABLE I

COMPARISON OF CROSS-FERTILIZATION WITH CROSS-AGGLUTINATION AMONG ECHINOIDS[a,b]

Eggs or fertilizin of	Spermatozoa of			
	Strongylocentrotus purpuratus	S. franciscanus	Lytechinus pictus	Dendraster excentricus
S. purpuratus	3000	3	1	5
	512	8	64	4
S. franciscanus	1	600	1	2.5
	0	512	4	0
L. pictus	2	4	850	2.5
	64	32	64	8
D. excentricus	1.5	40	2	4400
	4	2	1	128

[a] From Tyler (1949).

[b] The upper figures of each pair of rows represent the number of times the sperm suspension is diluted in giving the end-point value (2%) of fertilization under certain conditions. The lower figures are the agglutination titers in terms of the highest dilution of fertilizin solution that gives visible agglutination.

(Tyler and Tyler, 1966b). Sperm agglutination by egg water (supernatant from egg suspensions) from distantly related species, as in the case of *Nereis, ♂* × *Arbacia ♀* (Lillie, 1913), until demonstrated otherwise, can be attributed to action of natural nonspecific heteroagglutinins frequently present in contaminating blood, body fluid, or genital tract fluid (Tyler and Metz, 1945; Tyler, 1946).

Occurrence of egg-water agglutination of animal sperm is widespread (e.g., molluscs, annelids, echinoderms, chordates; see Rothschild, 1956), and comparable agglutination of microorganisms (Crandall, 1977) and plant spermatozoids is common (Wiese, 1969). Nevertheless, the total number of species is small, and many fail to give the reaction, suggesting limited occurrence of a fertilizin–antifertilizin system. However, among certain species that ordinarily fail, special methods have produced striking agglutination reactions. The classic case is the starfish (Metz, 1945, 1957b, 1967). Starfish sperm obtained by dissection fail to agglutinate when mixed with egg water. However, in the presence of a chelating agent, strong, species-specific, and permanent agglutination results. Evidently, chelating agents expose sperm surface receptors (antifertilizin) for interaction with the multivalent agglutinin (fertilizin) in the egg-water solutions (Metz, 1957b). In other species fertilizin may exist naturally in a nonagglutinating, univalent form (Tyler, 1941). Failure to demonstrate universal occurrence of fertilizin agglutination has been used to argue against the significance of the system in fertilization. However, logic and demonstrated fertilization inhibitory action on fertilizing capacity of sperm (Tyler and Metz, 1955) suggest that readily soluble fertilizin is an unusual aberration or a specialized adaptation and that in a normal system the receptors should be firmly bound to or inserted into the cell coats and surfaces of the complementary gametes (Metz, 1957b), for example, the mating substances of *Paramecium* (Metz, 1954a; Hiwatashi, 1969; Miyake, 1974).

The chemistry of fertilizin has been studied most thoroughly in sea urchins. The agglutinin is a main, but not the only, macromolecular component of the egg jelly (Gregg, 1969). Concentrated solutions are obtained by dissolving the jelly from eggs in weakly acid seawater. "Fertilization product," the supernatant from previously dejellied and demembranated fertilized eggs, contains a sperm agglutinin, "cytofertilizin," with biological and immunological properties identical to egg jelly fertilizin (Gregg, 1969). Cytofertilizin is probably a component of the cortical granules released when these granules discharge at fertilization.

Egg jelly fertilizins are acid polysaccharide–amino acid complexes. Acidity is attributed to the sulfate content (20–25%) of most fertilizins. The 20% of amino acids includes the commonly occurring forms (Tyler and Tyler, 1966a). One or at most a few monosaccharides are found in hydrolyzates. Fucose is the main sugar in two-thirds of the species (see, Monroy, 1965; Tyler and Tyler, 1966a). Amino sugars including sialic acid are also found (Ishihara and Dan, 1970; Warren *et al.*, 1960). *Arbacia* fertilizin, purified to a single moving-boundary electrophoretic peak, has a molecular weight of 300,000 and an axial ratio of 20:1 (Tyler, 1956). Organization of the fertilizin molecule is not thoroughly understood but probably consists of small peptides interlinked with sugars (Tyler, 1949). Vesseur (1952) suggested that monosaccharides form a branching chain because only half are readily oxidized by periodate. Fertilizin has not been separated into distinct protein and carbohydrate components.

Since fertilizin surrounding the egg is a gel, it is not surprising that it can exist in several states of aggregation. The 300,000 dalton form of *Arbacia* fertilizin examined by Tyler (1956) is clearly a reasonably stable, multivalent, sperm-agglutinating form. However, such multivalent material can be converted to univalent fertilizin by several physical and chemical agents. Sperm treated with the univalent fertilizin do not agglutinate on subsequent addition of the normal multivalent agglutinin. Evidently, the univalent fragments combine with the sperm-surface antifertilizin preventing interaction with the multivalent agglutinating fertilizin. Such univalent fertilizin can be prepared by heating (Tyler, 1941), proteolytic enzyme digestion (Tyler, 1941), although *Hemicentrotus* fertilizin may be an exception (Ishihara and Dan, 1970), ultraviolet light, X- and γ-irradiation (Metz, 1942; Piatigorsky and Austin, 1962), and H_2O_2 treatment (see Table III for references). Starfish fertilizin, which agglutinates sperm irreversibly, is also rendered univalent by ultraviolet light (Metz, 1945).

H_2O_2 conversion to the univalent form has been examined in most detail in the sea urchin *Lytechinus variegatus* (Stern, 1967; Stern and Metz, 1967). The conversion results in marked reduction in sedimentation rate and viscosity without release of dialyzable SO_4^{2-} or fucose. Additional evidence for a major cleavage of the fertilizin into fragments or subunits was obtained by cellulose acetate strip electrophoresis. *Lytechinus* fertilizin loses sperm agglutinating activity on standing (Stern, 1967). Such "aged" fertilizin becomes univalent. It migrates in cellulose acetate electrophoresis, producing a broad, diffuse band beyond the origin, indicating progressive dissociation or depolymerization. After conversion to "authentic" univalent fertilizin by H_2O_2, both the freshly prepared and aged preparations give four sharp and identical electrophoretic bands. The four bands with different electrophoretic mobilities indicate degradation of the material into at least four relatively stable components. Prior absorption with sperm should remove the univalent fertilizin fragments with combining sites for sperm surface antifertilizin, leaving any "inert" components lacking combining sites for sperm. Such sperm-absorbed material gives only two electrophoretic bands. The two missing band components evidently have combining sites for sperm. Further interpretation is complicated by the fact that sperm supernatant controls produce a strong metachromatic band in the position of two of the univalent egg jelly bands. Thus, the latter may also combine with sperm, or, alternatively, they may include inert material lacking combining sites for sperm.

Chemistry of the fertilizin "reactive sites" that combine with antifertilizin has received limited study. It should be emphasized that inactivation of sperm agglutinating action is insufficient to demonstrate active-site inactivation. Tests for active univalent fertilizin, namely inhibition of sperm agglutination by active, multivalent fertilizin, are required to distinguish between conversion to active univalent fertilizin and blocking or destruction of active sites. With these precautions, it is found that classic blocking reagents for SH, S—S, phenolic, and amino groups do not impair reaction of fertilizin with sperm. However, fertilizin rendered nonagglutinating by periodate oxidation fails to combine with sperm (Metz, 1957b). This suggests that carbohydrate rather than the indicated amino acid residues are involved in the active-site structure. The high sulfate content and nonspecific interaction of fertilizin with many basic materials suggests that sulfate groups may contribute to the active sites. Calcium is not ordinarily required for fertilizin agglutination (Dan, 1954). In species where such a requirement exists, calcium may serve as an essential component at the active site necessary for interaction with sperm. It is also possible that calcium ions link univalent fragments and thereby stabilizes the multivalent condition at least sufficiently for transient agglutination. According to this view, the complex would decompose into univalent fragments in the absence of the cation.

The antifertilizin of the sperm surface with which fertilizin reacts has not been studied extensively in recent years, and its chemical nature remains uncertain. Extracts of sperm can be prepared with properties expected of antifertilizin, namely neutralization of the sperm-agglutinating action of fertilizin, agglutination of eggs, and precipitation of egg jellies. Extraction methods include aging, mild (pH 3) acid treatment (Tyler and O'Melveny, 1941), boiling (Frank, 1939), and freeze-thawing (Tyler, 1939). Earlier studies (see Metz, 1957b) indicate a heat-stable acidic protein of molecular weight less than 10,000. However, activity of some preparations obtained by freeze-thawing is associated with particulates since the antifertilizin activity sediments readily at 30,000 g (Koehler and Metz, 1959; Piatigorsky and Austin, 1962). Heating to 100°C does not destroy the activity of frozen-thawed sperm extracts, but does reduce the molecular weight, since activity is not sedimented by ultracentrifugation (100,000 g). An additional problem is specificity of antifertilizin action, which can be broader than that of fertilizin agglutination of sperm. Although formal arguments have been offered to resolve some of these problems, a clear-cut identification of this receptor in sperm extracts, chemical characterization, and localization on the sperm surface has yet to be achieved. If a fertilizin–antifertilizin interaction initiates the acrosome reaction, a concentration of antifertilizin might be expected in the cell membrane over the acrosome (see Section II, C).

Additional points about fertilizin agglutination of sperm that continue to command interest are the characteristic spontaneous reversal of agglutination in sea urchins and the relation of sperm agglutination to sperm motility. Immediately upon addition of egg water, sea urchin sperm agglutinate strikingly, and just as strikingly the agglutinates break up a few minutes later, freeing most if not all clumped sperm.

Two fundamental related facts first recognized by Lillie (1914) are the following: (1) if sperm are in excess of fertilizin in agglutinating mixtures, all agglutinating activity disappears from the solution; (2) if fertilizin is in excess, sperm will not reagglutinate following reversal of agglutination, even on further addition of fertilizin. In conventional immunological terms (1) above means that sperm interact with and absorb the agglutinin from solution, and (2) means that the anti-fertilizin reactive sites of the sperm are complexed with the agglutinin following reversal and cannot react with additional fertilizin. To explain spontaneous reversal of agglutination in the light of these facts, Tyler (1941) proposed decomposition of the fertilizin to univalent fragments during the reaction. Following reversal, the fragments should remain bound to the sperm surface. Removal of fucose (Monroy et al., 1954) and ^{35}S from labeled fertilizin solutions (Hathaway and Metz, 1961) by sperm is consistent with the univalent explanation. In addition, Hathaway and Metz (1961) found a release of over half of the sperm-bound ^{35}S label following reversal of agglutination. This "released" ^{35}S material was nondialyzable and did not bind to fresh sperm. It could be an "inert" component of fertilizin lacking reactive sites and released during conversion of fertilizin to the univalent form, perhaps by action of a sperm-bound sulfatase. This same "inert" component may also be formed during H_2O_2 conversion of fertilizin to the univalent form (Stern and Metz, 1967). Reversal of agglutination by rapid fragmentation of the agglutinin should result in the observed loose, fluid type of association or "cluster formation" (Loeb, 1914; Collins, 1976), individual sperm changing position with respect to each other and the group as a whole. Upon saturation of all sperm-surface receptors (antifertilizin) with univalent fertilizin, the sperm should no longer clump (reversal of agglutination).

Collins (1976) raises the additional interesting point that fertilizin agglutination of sea urchin sperm is associated with motility. Cell motility or the living state is not ordinarily required for agglutination by conventional agents (e.g., antibodies, lectins), yet immobilized or killed sea urchin sperm do not agglutinate well when treated with fertilizin. However, sea urchin sperm killed by heat (Metz, 1945) or alcoholic picric acid solution (Metz and Donovan, 1951) are reported to agglutinate with fertilizin. Appropriateness of the latter system as a model is questionable, since *Arbacia* egg water agglutinates a variety of similarly fixed unrelated sperm (Metz, 1957b). Apparent association between motility and agglutinability is not confined to sea urchins but is characteristic of starfish (Metz, 1945, 1954b, 1957b; Metz and Birky, 1955) and *Nereis* (C. B. Metz, unpublished) as well. Conditions in starfish are explained to the extent that motility and agglutinability are both induced by metal-chelating agents. The metal chelating requirement for agglutination is further complicated by the fact that motility (and respiration) is stimulated by certain metal cations (including Co^{2+} and Ni^{2+}) that inhibit sperm agglutinability. Hypothetical explanations for an apparent correlation between sea urchin sperm motility and agglutination could be generated by analogy with the starfish system or other concepts, such as metabolically coupled sperm surface receptor movement (e.g., from a cryptic to an exposed surface position), or the dynamics of the system where the agglutinin is destroyed or "self destructs" (rendered univalent) after interaction with the cells.

C. The Acrosome Reaction

The acrosome consists of a membrane-bound apical granule of Golgi origin beneath the plasma membrane in association with subacrosomal cytoplasm containing actin (Tilney *et al.*, 1973). Since this acrosomal granule contains hydrolytic enzymes (Dan, 1967; Tyler, 1949; Colwin and Colwin, 1967; Brown, 1966; Brookbank, 1958; Conway and Metz, 1976; especially well documented in mammals, McRorie and Williams, 1974), it is regarded as a modified lysosome (Allison and Hartree, 1970). The acrosomal enzymes digest a path for the sperm through the egg envelopes (Dan, 1967; Franklin, 1970). Release of the vesicle contents results from the acrosome reaction, first clearly described by Dan (1952). This consists of one or more membrane fusion events and, in many invertebrates, concomitant extrusion of the acrosomal process. The acrosomal process contains longitudinal fibers that evidently provide a cytoskeleton of the process. The fibers arise by polymerization of the G actin of the subacrosomal cytoplasm (Tilney *et al.*, 1973). The acrosome reaction occurs in the vicinity of the egg in most species, probably at the external boundary of the egg envelopes (e.g., starfish, R. Chambers, 1930; *Saccoglossus,* Colwin and Colwin, 1967; *Thyone,* Colwin *et al.*, 1975; see also Austin, 1968, for comparative review). The question of concern here is the nature of the triggering mechanism that initiates the reaction (Metz, 1957a).

The acrosome reaction in sea urchins can be initiated by various physical and chemical agents (Dan, 1952). These include elevated pH (Dan, 1952; Gregg and Metz, 1976; Decker *et al.*, 1976), Ca^{2+} (Dan, 1954; Gregg and Metz, 1976; Decker *et al.*, 1976), Ca^{2+} ionophore A23187, acridine orange (Shivers and Evans, 1962), and contact with indifferent objects including glass surfaces (Dan, 1952). Some moribund sperm also extrude an acrosomal process. Finally, contact with eggs of the species and exposure to egg water (egg jelly solutions) are effective (Dan, 1967; Conway and Metz, 1976; Decker *et al.*, 1976; Gregg and Metz, 1976) in many species.

This last is presumably the physiologically active agent(s) operative under natural conditions during sperm–egg interaction. The other means of initiating the acrosome reaction are probably artifactual, with the possible exception of calcium, which is required (with one exception) for the acrosome reaction (Dan, 1954) and must be controlled in experiments on acrosome reaction initiation (Decker *et al.*, 1976; Gregg and Metz, 1976). Initiation of the acrosome reaction by egg water suggests reaction of a specific egg jelly component with a complementary receptor on the sperm surface. The fertilizin–antifertilizin system immediately comes to mind. Since the acrosome reaction is readily induced "nonspecifically" by physical and chemical agents and response of the sperm apparently can be a function of time in the breeding season and of aging (Haino and Dan, 1961), experiments to identify the "natural" acrosome reaction inducing agent must be designed with unusual care and interpreted with caution. Ideally, a criterion such as specificity should be used to identify the natural agent.

Unfortunately, substantial quantitative specificity data about the acrosome-inducing action of eggs and egg water have not been published. Attempts to correlate sperm-agglutinating and acrosome-inducing action of egg water in interspecific combinations have given "confusing" results in one study (Dan, 1956). Comparison of sperm-agglutinating and acrosome-inducing action of egg jelly solutions from five species of sea urchins are given in Table II. The Ca^{2+} concentration was optimized (Gregg and Metz, 1976) for acrosome reactions in these experiments (Gregg, 1971). Reasonably good correlation between agglutination and acrosome reactions are evident for *Arbacia* and *Echinometra* sperm. *Tripneustes* sperm show less correlation; for example, some heterologous jelly solutions agglutinated, but did not elicit acrosome reactions. Nevertheless, no significant acrosome reactions occurred in the absence of cross-agglutination—with the possible exception of *Echinometra* sperm.

Using intact eggs, Summers and Hylander (1975) obtained no cross-fertilization among four sea urchin species. However, acrosome-reacted sperm of three of the four species were found in egg jellies or attached to the vitelline envelopes of the four species tested. Others have obtained cross-fertilizations in some of the combinations (e.g., *Lytechinus variegatus* × *Tripneustes esculentus;* Badman and Brookbank, 1970) used by Summers and Hylander (1975). Hybridization in sea urchins requires high sperm concentrations (see Branham, 1969,

TABLE II

SPECIFICITY OF ACROSOME-INDUCING ACTION OF SEA URCHIN EGG-JELLY SOLUTIONS[a]

Sperm	EJ solution	Percent AR in EJ trial			Percent AR in SW trial			Average percent AR	Aggl., ++++ to −	Aggl. (Stern, 1967), + or −
		1	2	3	1	2	3			
Arbacia	Arbacia	69	91	88	7	3	2	85	++++	+
	Echinometra	10	3	4	−	−	−	6	−	−
	Tripneustes	1	3	2	−	−	−	2	−	−
	Lytechinus	3	2	6	−	−	−	4	−	ND
	Eucidaris	6	−	−	9	3	5	6	ND	ND
Echinometra	Echinometra	80	89	88	9	3	5	86	++++	+
	Arbacia	21	17	34	−	−	−	24	−	−
	Tripneustes	34	13	22	−	−	−	23	−	−
	Lytechinus	97	96	95	−	−	−	96	++++	ND
	Eucidaris	81	79	83	−	−	−	81	ND	ND
Tripneustes	Tripneustes	85	80	93	8	7	6	86	++	+
	Arbacia	13	75	30	−	−	−	39	+	−
	Echinometra	5	2	14	−	−	−	7	++	−
	Lytechinus	0	4	94	−	−	−	33	+++	+
	Eucidaris	0	9	−	−	−	−	4	++	ND

[a] For acrosome reaction (AR) assays, mixtures of 10% egg jelly (EJ) and 90% artificial seawater containing calcium were used. Calcium concentrations were approximately: *Arbacia*, 37 μM; *Echinometra*, 13 μM; *Tripneustes*, 7 μM. Sperm agglutination action (aggl.) of the egg water preparations is also shown (Gregg, 1967). ND = not determined.

for detailed study), and with sufficient sperm most, if not all, of the combinations of Summers and Hylander produce hybrids. Sperm agglutination tests were not performed. Therefore, it is uncertain whether the reacted acrosomes in the heterologous combinations could have resulted from fertilizin–antifertilizin interactions.

Apart from specificity, acrosome reaction-inducing and sperm-agglutinating actions of sea urchin egg waters do show certain striking correlations. Both activities are retained in dialysis (Ishihara and Dan, 1970; Gregg and Metz, 1976), titers of both activities can be related (Collier, 1959; Haino and Dan, 1961; Piatigorsky and Austin, 1962) and are proportional to fucose content (*Arbacia,* Piatigorsky and Austin, 1962; Gregg and Metz, 1976) or sialic acid (*Hemicentrotus,* Ishihara and Dan, 1970), are retained through considerable purification, including alcohol precipitation (method of Tyler, 1949; Tyler and Tyler, 1966a; Piatigorsky and Austin, 1962), and appear in the same Sephadex G-200 gel filtration fraction (Ishihara and Dan, 1970), which however, is probably the void volume of the column. Both the sperm-agglutinating and acrosome reaction-inducing actions of egg jelly solutions show parallel stabilities to a variety of physical and chemical agents. Thus, heating (100°C, pH 4, 30 minutes) essentially destroyed both activities in *Arbacia* (Piatigorsky and Austin, 1962); intermediate heating (100°C, 15 minutes) sufficient to destroy the agglutinating activity reduced acrosome-initiating activity in *Strongylocentrotus purpuratus* (Collier, 1959), and brief heating (100°C, 3 minutes) had little effect on either activity in *Hemicentrotus pulcherimus* (Ishihara and Dan, 1970). Proteolytic enzymes, long known to destroy sperm-agglutinating activity of egg jelly (Tyler and Fox, 1940), reduced but did not destroy both agglutinating and acrosome-initiating activities of *Hemicentrotus* egg jelly solutions (Ishihara and Dan, 1970). Various irradiation treatments (ultraviolet light, X- or γ-irradiation) and H_2O_2 treatment rapidly destroy sperm-agglutinating activity of egg-jelly solutions (Metz, 1942, 1957b; Piatigorsky and Austin, 1962) by conversion of fertilizin to the nonagglutinating, univalent form. In the experiments of Piatigorsky and Austin (1962) γ-irradiation also destroyed the acrosome-initiating activity of egg water. These data are summarized in Table III.

These comparisons indicate a relationship between sperm-agglutinating and acrosome-initiating action and support the view that interaction with sperm agglutining fertilizin initiates the acrosome reaction. If this is indeed the case, only multivalent, not univalent, fertilizin appears to be effective. This in turn bears on the question of the mechanism of action. The requirement for multivalent fertilizin

TABLE III

EFFECT OF VARIOUS AGENTS ON THE SPERM AGGLUTINATING AND ACROSOME-INITIATING
ACTION OF HOMOLOGOUS EGG-JELLY SOLUTIONS

Treatment and species	Conditions	Agglutination	Acrosome reactions
Heating			
Arbacia[a]	pH 4; 30 min; 100°C	−	−
Hemicentrotus[b]	3 min; 100°C	+	+
Strongylocentrotus purpuratus[c]	15 min; 100°C	−	+ (reduced)
Proteolytic enzymes			
Hemicentrotus[b]		+	+
Gamma irradiation			
Arbacia[a]	6–9 min; 5000 r/min	−[d]	−
H₂O₂			
Hemicentrotus[b]	30 min; room temperature	−	+
	60 min; 37°C	−	−
Periodate			
Hemicentrotus[b]	pH 4; 60 min; 50°C	−	−

[a] Piatigorsky and Austin (1962).
[b] Ishihara and Dan (1970).
[c] Collier (1959).
[d] The nonagglutinating egg jelly solution was demonstrated to have univalent fertilizin activity.

implies an essential cross-linking of sperm surface antifertilizin for the acrosome reaction. This might result in concentration of antifertilizin in the fluid membrane (e.g., "capping") thereby producing a local permeability increase. Alternatively, the effective component of the multivalent fertilizin immediately involved in the acrosome reaction might be independent of the antifertilizin binding sites of the fertilizin. It could be lost during conversion to the univalent form and correspond to the inert fragment(s) of Hathaway and Metz (1961) and Stern and Metz (1967).

Finally, the role of Ca^{2+} requires discussion. Calcium is not required for fertilizin agglutination of sperm in most sea urchin species (Dan, 1954; Metz, 1967), but it is an absolute requirement for the acrosome reaction in all species examined with the notable exception of *Clypeaster japonica*. In fact, lack of Ca^{2+} induces the acrosome reaction in this species (Dan, 1954, 1956). This exceptional behavior of *Clypeaster* has not been reconciled with conditions in other species. Acrosome reaction initiation by elevated Ca^{2+} alone could be a manifestation of the Ca^{2+} requirement for egg water-initiated reactions. Dan and associates (1964, 1975) have proposed that the initial event in acrosome reaction initiation is interaction of an egg jelly component with a sperm plasma-membrane receptor at the acrosomal "trigger," a region of the sperm apex where plasma and acrosomal membranes are closely apposed. This results in increased plasma membrane permeability permitting influx of Ca^{2+}. Dan's hypothesis is supported to the extent that the Ca^{2+} ionophore A23187 initiates the reaction only if Ca^{2+} is present in the medium (Decker et al., 1976; Talbot et al., 1976) and that the acrosome reaction is inhibited by the Ca^{2+} inhibitor La^{3+} (Decker et al., 1976). As Decker et al. pointed out, this means an essential influx of Ca^{2+}, not a mobilization of internal Ca^{2+} as in egg activation (E. Chambers et al., 1974; Steinhardt and Epel, 1974; Azarnia and Chambers, 1976). Dan et al. (1964, 1975) suggested that the role of Ca^{2+} may be activation of acrosomal enzymes.

Decker et al. (1976) made interesting comparisons between the role of Ca^{2+} in various membrane fusion events in other systems and the acrosome reaction. The phospholipases released at the time of the acrosome reaction probably function in sperm–egg membrane fusion rather than the acrosome reaction (Conway and Metz, 1976).

In summary, an expanded version of Dan's hypothesis for initiation of the acrosome reaction is the most consistant with available data. This involves a key, initial reaction between multivalent fertilizin and a sperm membrane receptor, namely antifertilizin, with a specificity approximating that of the fertilizin–sperm agglutination reaction. This reaction initiates cell membrane permeability increase, perhaps by concentrating antifertilizin molecules to form "pores" in this plasma membrane. This permits influx of Ca^{2+} and other seawater ions. Either or both of these events may initiate or contribute to fusion of plasma and acrosomal membranes. Finally, the subacrosomal actin polymerizes, in the presence of ATP and the influx of cations (particularly Mg^{2+}, K^+), to the fibrous form (F actin), which extends the acrosomal filament and provides its "cytoskeleton."

III. Sperm–Egg Attachment and Binding

Sperm and egg make contact initially at the periphery of the outermost egg envelope. The number, composition, and origin of egg envelopes vary among diverse species (for discussion, see Metz, 1967; Monroy, 1965; Austin, 1968; Franklin, 1966), so detailed comparisons and homologies are probably valid only between related species. Nevertheless, some generalization can be made. First, several sperm attach firmly or "bind" to an egg coat specific for the group of species. Second, concomitantly with or prior to such attachment, the acrosomes of the attached sperms react. Third, the acrosomal process of at least one sperm penetrates intervening investments, generally by action of lysins (Dan, 1967; Austin, 1968; Franklin, 1970), until one contacts the egg plasma membrane and activates the egg. The plasma membranes of this acrosome and the egg then fuse. After egg activation, acrosomal processes of other sperm ordinarily detach, probably through dissolution of the attachment site, and are eventually lost (R. Chambers, 1930; Vacquier *et al.*, 1973). The classical example is the starfish. Most components of this pattern are seen in *Saccoglossus* and *Thyone* (Colwin *et al.*, 1975), *Hydroides* (Colwin and Colwin, 1967), *Callinectes* (Brown, 1966), and many others (for reviews, see Dan, 1967; Colwin and Colwin, 1967; Austin, 1968; Franklin, 1970).

These events imply attachment or binding systems at the egg jelly periphery (outer border layer in *Hydroides*), an additional acrosome process–vitelline membrane-specific binding system, and finally an acrosome process–egg plasma membrane binding system. On the uncertain premise that morphologically separable steps in sperm–egg interaction depend upon separate sperm–egg binding complexes, additional binding systems could be postulated for special cases.

Apart from some interesting studies on the annelid *Tylorrhynchus heterochaetus* (Osanai, 1976), amphibians (Wolf *et al.*, 1976), and mammals (Metz, 1973; Dunbar and Shivers, 1976), efforts to chemically identify and define metazoan fertilization receptor systems and their components have involved echinoderm gametes using extraction, destruction (e.g., enzymes), and specific inhibition (especially antibodies and lectins) methods. The results of these approaches are considered separately.

A. EGG JELLY ATTACHMENT

In starfish attachment to the jelly and initiation of the acrosome reaction can be attributed to a fertilizin–antifertilizin interaction. This view is consistent with the high order of species specificity, irreversibility, and head-to-head character of agglutination and the acrosome-initiating action of starfish egg water (Metz, 1945, 1957b). Additional attachment systems may operate at the vitelline envelope and plasma membrane levels but have not been investigated in this material.

The sea urchin acrosome process is unusually short, requiring penetration of the egg jelly by the sperm head. Penetration is probably largely mechanical, since it is nonspecific [*Asterias* sperm are trapped in *Arbacia* egg jellies (Hathaway *et al.*, 1960)]. Penetration is not dependent upon a fertilizin–antifertilizin interaction because it is not inhibited by Fab antisperm antibodies that inhibit the fertilizin agglutination capacity of sperm (Eckberg and Metz, 1974; P. M. Saling, W. R. Eckberg and C. B. Metz, unpublished). Any fertilizin–antifertilizin binding of sperm in the egg jelly is necessarily transient, because of rapid conversion of fertilizin to the univalent form (as in reversal of agglutination) (Monroy, 1965). Figures of Summers and Hylander (1975) show that the acrosome reaction occurs prior to sperm–vitelline envelope contact as in other species. Sperm–egg jelly interaction, then, may contribute to fertilization by a transitory sperm binding and acrosome reaction initiating action. This interpretation is consistent with repeated observations that pretreatment of sperm with egg water or egg jelly removal reduces the fertilizability of the treated gametes (see Tyler and Metz, 1955; Metz, 1967).

B. VITELLINE ENVELOPE BINDING

The vitelline envelope has long been recognized as a significant structure in sperm–egg interaction (Hultin, 1948a,b). Sperm attachment to the vitelline envelope is clearly a normal step in fertilization. Recent SEM studies (Tegner and Epel, 1973; Schatten and Mazia, 1976) show multiple binding involving the reacted acrosomes of the attached sperm. After egg activation, the supernumerary sperm detach from the vitelline envelope [reminiscent of the starfish (R. Chambers, 1930)]. The detachment is attributed to a trypsinlike protease from the newly discharged cortical granules (Vacquier *et al.*, 1973; Schuel *et al.*, 1973) and is evidently a major component of the block to polyspermy.

Sperm binding to the vitelline envelope clearly requires interaction between sperm acrosome and vitelline envelope level substances. In sea urchins, the sperm acrosome substance(s) appears to be a component of the acrosomal granule material that surrounds the acrosomal process of the reacted sperm, not the plasma membrane of the process. Transmission electron micrographs uniformly suggest that this material may be a gellike capsule (e.g., Franklin, 1965; Summers and Hylander, 1975; Summers *et al.*, 1975). Its adhesive properties are probably responsible for nonspecific acrosomal adhesion to glass (Dan, 1954) and interaction between reacted acrosomes to form sperm "rosettes" (Collins, 1976). Active preparations of the acrosome granule material should inhibit fertilizability of dejellied eggs by combining with and blocking the complementary receptors on the vitelline envelope. Preparations of demembrated, isolated acrosome granules, called "bindin," do agglutinate dejellied eggs. In SDS acrylamide gel electrophoresis the material gave a single protein staining hand of approximately 30,500 daltons (Vacquier and Moy, 1977). In reciprocal tests between *S. purpuratus* and *S. franciscanus* the egg agglutinating action was species specific. Agglutination of dejellied eggs by bindin was not in-hibited by egg jelly solutions (Glabe and Vacquier, 1977).

Sperm extracts prepared by freeze-thawing do agglutinate dejellied and trypsin-treated (demembranated) eggs and markedly reduce their fertilizability. Species specificity of extract action was not examined in these studies of Tyler and Metz (1955). The results indicate a receptor from the sperm surface present in the extracts that blocks an essential egg surface receptor. Rigorous analysis of such sperm extracts, includ-ing specificity tests, purification, and localization of the source of the active material, relation to bindin and site of action on the egg, should be of interest.

Examination for receptors on sperm by the use of inhibitors shows considerable promise. The actions of a number of fertilization in-hibitors of fortuitous origin have been analyzed, but lack of knowledge about their nature and specificity of action has resulted in limited usefulness (for review, see Metz, 1961, 1967). "Made to order" in-hibitors, namely antibodies, are proving to be more informative, espe-cially since the advent of Fab (univalent) antibody preparations. Fab antisperm antibodies markedly inhibit the fertilizing capacity of sea urchin sperm. Analysis of this inhibition has led to isolation of a single glycoprotein fertilization antigen (Cordle and Metz, 1973; Maitra and Metz, 1974) from sperm extracts. This antigen evidently functions in sperm-egg attachment to the vitelline envelope and plasma membrane of the egg. Details are given in Section IV, A.

C. SPERM BINDING RECEPTOR OF THE VITELLINE ENVELOPE

Increasingly successful efforts have been made to examine the vitel-line envelope surface (scanning electron microscopy), isolate the en-velope, and analyze its components. Scanning electron microscopy of the dejellied egg shows a patterned vitelline envelope surface. Quan-titative sperm-binding studies (Vacquier and Payne, 1973) give appar-ent maximum numbers of sperm that bind to individual dejellied sea urchin eggs. Mean values are 1744 sperm/egg for *Strongylocentrotus purpuratus* and 1372 sperm/egg for *Lytechinus pictus*. These values when converted to sperm per square micrometer of egg surface area give one sperm/28.2 μm^2 for *L. pictus,* or a "territory" of approximately 6 μm diameter. Since the sperm head is only 1.3 μm wide, the total egg surface is not covered with attached sperm. With the reservations that the mean number of attached sperm in the experiments may be mini-mal owing to physical interactions between sperm (Vacquier and Payne, 1973) and that the sperm do not "cap" receptors from the local binding area, the results imply that the entire egg surface is not covered with receptors and that the number could be as low as the number of attached sperm (e.g., 1372 for *L. pictus*). The question of a uniform grid *vs* restricted mosaic of receptors was examined by Schuel *et al.* (1976), using protease inhibitors that retard vitelline envelope elevation (Longo and Schuel, 1973). Retardation is limited to 2–3 minutes over the cortical granules but extends 15–20 minutes between the cortical granules ("cortical projections"). During the first 2–3 minutes after an initial insemination, the susceptibility of eggs to polyspermy remains constant, e.g., when vitelline envelope elevation occurs preferentially over the cortical granules. Subsequently, this susceptibility to polyspermy declines in proportion to the decrease in undetached vitelline envelope over the "cortical projections." These observations imply sperm binding receptors at the "cortical projection" regions and suggests that the sperm binding sites are not uniformly distributed but may be largely restricted to the "cortical projections" region of the vitelline envelope surface (Schuel *et al.,* 1976).

Serious attempts to isolate sea urchin vitelline envelopes, solubilize them, and isolate the receptor for binding sperm were begun by Aketa and co-workers. In initial experiments Aketa (1967) stripped *Hemicentrotus pulcherimus* vitelline envelopes from eggs as they elevated following insemination. They were subsequently solubilized in alkali. Extracts were also prepared by 1 *M* urea treatment of unfertilized eggs. Sperm attached to air bubbles in these solutions, but not to bubbles in solutions of unrelated substances. Sperm attachment to bubbles was Ca^{2+} dependent, as is attachment to the vitelline envelope of dejellied eggs (Aketa, 1967; Vacquier and Payne, 1973). The first method of preparation used by Aketa, namely stripping following insemination, is questionable, since sperm–vitelline envelope binding is normally reversed, apparently by action of cortical granule trypsinlike enzyme, at the time of egg activation in Aketa's experiment. The enzyme could have destroyed the vitelline envelope receptors (Schuel *et al.,* 1973; Vacquier *et al.,* 1973). Aketa *et al.* (1968) reported that the purified sperm binding receptor from vitelline envelopes in a conjugated protein (protein–carbohydrate–lipid complex) giving a single peak ($s_{20,w} = 2.3$ at 2.0 mg/ml) in the ultracentrifuge. Sperm binding is largely eliminated by reducing agents (Aketa and Tsuzuki, 1968). It seems likely that Aketa's preparations are rather complex mixtures in spite of the single schlieren peak in the ultracentrifuge, because 1 *M* urea extracts after some manipulation produced up to six precipitin bands in immunodiffusion tests (Onitake *et al.,* 1972). It is not surprising that the antisera to the preparations inhibited the fertilizing capacity of jellyless eggs. Native, multivalent egg antisera inhibit the fertilizing capacity of dejellied sea urchin eggs by secondary action (surface precipitation; Metz *et al.*, 1968b) not by direct combination with and blocking of fixed surface receptors. Critical examination requires use of Fab antibody fragments, and which do not inhibit egg-fertilizing capacity (see Metz, 1972; and Section IV).

A more direct test showed that the solubilized receptor inhibited fertilizing capacity of pretreated sperm (Aketa, 1973). This action was species specific. It was not associated with sperm agglutination or premature acrosome reactions.

Isolation of material with properties expected of the receptor of the vitelline envelope also has been achieved by Schmell *et al.* (1977). Envelope preparations were obtained by hypotonic swelling and lysis of unfertilized eggs, followed by differential centrifugation. Isolated envelopes bound sperm. Envelopes from trypsin-treated eggs lacked sperm-binding action, implying protein involvement. The binding was species specific between two species (*Arbacia punctulata* vs *Strongylocentrotus purpuratus*). Seawater extracts (100,000 *g* supernatants) of isolated envelopes also reduced the fertilizing capacity of sperm. Evidently, some of the receptor dissolves from the vitelline envelopes on standing in seawater. Sodium dodecyl sulfate (SDS)-acrylamide gel electrophoresis of such soluble preparations produced 7 bands that stained for both protein and carbohydrate. Finally, solutions of the receptor extract failed to inhibit the fertilizing capacity of sperm after absorption with Con A-coated Sepharose beads (Schmell *et al.*, 1977). The fertilization-inhibiting receptor solutions had no apparent sperm-agglutinating action, implying absence of multivalent fertilizin.

In summary, Aketa and colleagues and Schmell *et al.* have obtained a species-specific component(s) of the sea urchin egg vitelline envelope that combines with sperm and inhibits sperm fertilizing capacity. The component(s) is probably a glycoprotein(s). This information is consistent with requirements for an essential, species-specific egg-surface sperm-binding receptor. However, there are certain details to be worked out to provide complete understanding. The first concerns relationship to the acrosome reaction. As discussed in Section II, C, the sea urchin sperm apparently binds to the vitelline envelope by the acrosomal process. However, the receptor in solution evidently binds to the unreacted sperm. In fact, Aketa (1973) found no acrosome reaction inducing action by receptor preparations. This is difficult to reconcile with a reacted acrosome–vitelline envelope interaction as an ultimate basis for fertilization specificity (Summers and Hylander, 1975).

Finally, relationship of the sperm-binding receptor of the vitelline envelope to the egg jelly component, fertilizin, requires comment. Tyler and Tyler (1966b) argued that sperm attachment to the vitelline envelope involves fertilizin firmly bound to or inserted into the vitelline envelope. Con A does not inhibit the sperm-agglutinating activity of fertilizin (Howe and Metz, 1972) or interact with egg jelly (Schmell *et al.*, 1977), but when immobilized to Sepharose beads, it does absorb fertilization-inhibiting activity of vitelline envelope extracts. As these authors pointed out, this makes it unlikely that their receptor of the vitelline envelope is egg jelly coat material. Nevertheless, it is possible that a univalent, sperm-binding fertilizin fragment is linked to a glyco- or mannosyl-containing glycoprotein of the vitelline envelope, which can be detached from the isolated membrane as a unit to constitute the isolated receptor.

D. Plasma Membrane Attachment, Egg Activation, and Membrane Fusion

Sperm attachment to the egg plasma membrane is evidently an additional, but poorly understood, step in fertilization (Tyler and Metz, 1955; Epel, 1975). After damage or removal of the vitelline envelope by tryptic digestion or dithiothreitol exposure, fertilizability of the sea urchin egg is reduced (Tyler and Metz, 1955; Aketa *et al.*, 1972), but such eggs still fertilize upon heavy insemination. In addition, cross-fertilization occurs more readily, at least in crosses that will also occur in controls (Tyler and Metz, 1955). Polyspermy results more readily in such eggs, perhaps reflecting the role of the vitelline envelope in blocking polyspermy. Finally, the fertilized egg can be refertilized even during cleavage stages following removal of the fertilization envelope (Tyler *et al.*, 1956). Again, on the principle that cellular interactions are mediated by complementary surface receptors, such receptors should be present on or inserted into the plasma membranes of the interacting gametes.

Demembranated (protease treated) eggs clearly possess surface antigens. However, the antigenic sites are apparently not essential receptors for sperm, but neither are the antigenic sites of the vitelline envelope (Metz and Thompson, 1967; Graziano and Metz, 1967) (see Section IV, B). In the case of refertilization of demembranated fertilized eggs, the cortical vesicle (granule) membrane could contribute significantly. Upon egg activation the cortical granules discharge by a membrane fusion process that results in at least transitory incorporation of the cortical granule membrane into the egg plasma membrane. The cortical vesicle components include a sperm agglutinin identical to egg jelly fertilizin. This and other "fertilization products," if incorporated into the plasma membrane at cortical granule fusion, could function as receptors for sperm attachment. To the extent that the "inside" of the vesicle membrane has asymmetry comparable to the outside of the plasma membrane (Rothman and Lenard, 1977), the two membranes should be compatible after membrane fusion.

A question of major interest is the sequence and possible interdependence of the three final sperm–egg interaction events, namely, sperm attachment to the egg plasma membrane, initiation of egg activation, and sperm–egg membrane fusion. More specifically, does egg activation result from "transduction" (message transmission) through the egg membrane after interaction of sperm and egg surface receptors or does activation require membrane fusion of the two cells? The former situation would be comparable to other transduction phenomena, such as lymphocyte activation by lectins, by specific antigens, or by surface interactions leading to adenylate cyclase activation in some other systems (see Introduction). In the latter case, ion influx associated with membrane fusion or introduction of some sperm substance with ionophorelike action (Azarnia and Chambers, 1976; E. Chambers *et al.*, 1974; Steinhardt and Epel, 1974) to mobilize internally bound Ca^{2+} might be the critical activating event. Some indirect evidence supports the transduction hypothesis. In *Paramecium,* killed and fixed (e.g., formalin, picric acid) animals or isolated cilia of opposite sex clump with and specifically activate living animals of the opposite sex (Metz, 1954; Miyake, 1974). This activation is ascribed to interaction of complementary cilium surface mating-type substances. Membrane fusion would seem not to be involved. Among Metazoa certain natural and artificial hybrid crosses result in sperm attachment to the egg, activation of the egg, and subsequent detachment of the sperm from the egg (for review, see Wiese, 1966). In the absence of a detailed electron microscope study, it is assumed that such egg activation results from transduction, without membrane fusion.

In a recent study of this problem, Gwatkin *et al.* (1976) reported that zona-free hamster eggs give a cortical response (cortical granule discharge) after exposure to frozen-thawed capacitated hamster sperm, living capacitated mouse sperm, positively charged microbeads, Con A, and phytohemagglutinin P. Only living capacitated hamster sperm "penetrated" the eggs. Uncapacitated hamster sperm had no effect on eggs. The authors concluded that membrane fusion is involved in the initiation of these cortical reactions; but transduction seems to be an equally acceptable explanation until ultrastructural evidence is available. It should be noted also that lectins (Con A) are internalized by pinocytosis (Wise, 1976) after capping.

Cell membrane fusion theory as applied to fertilization events has been reviewed recently (Austin, 1975; Johnson, 1975; Woodring, 1975; Lucy, 1975). In accord with Lucy's (1971, 1975) hypothesis that lysophospholipids are involved, Conway and Metz (1976) have shown a transient appearance of lysophosphatidyl choline (L-PC) from added phosphotidyl choline coincident with the egg water-induced acrosome reaction. As seen in Fig. 1, L-PC increases rapidly and equally rapidly decreases over a 30-second interval after addition of semen to egg water containing substrate (hen's egg yolk). Appearance of the L-PC is attributed to hydrolytic action of phospholipase A released from sperm by the acrosome reaction. The initial 15-second lag is attributed to time required for the acrosome reaction. Phospholipase A activity decreased after 2 minutes. Disappearance of L-PC during the first minute results from a L-PCase. This cycle of L-PC appearance and disappearance over a 30-second interval fits the requirement for a role in sperm–egg membrane fusion. The L-PC is produced at the appropriate time to "destabilize" the plasma membranes by destruction of stabilizing phospholipids permitting sperm–egg membrane fusion. Subsequent destruction of

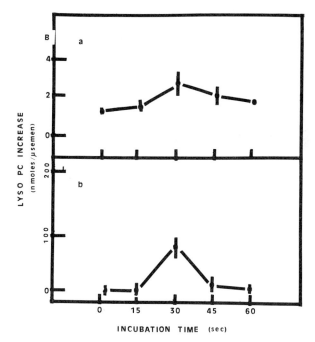

Fig. 1. Lysophosphatidyl choline in sperm suspensions after addition of egg water to initiate the sperm acrosome reaction. (a) *Lytechinus variegatus*. (b) *Arbacia punctulata*. From Conway and Metz (1976).

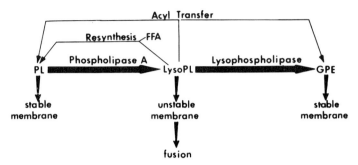

FIG. 2. Possible role of sea urchin sperm enzymes in membrane fusion. Heavy arrows indicate reactions that have been demonstrated. Tapered arrows show possible effects on cell membranes. FFA, free fatty acid; PL, phospholipid; Lyso PL, lysophospholipid; GPE, Glycerophosphoryl esters. From Conway and Metz (1976).

the L-PC by L-PCase provides a mechanism for removal of L-PC, thus preventing lytic action on the newly formed zygote membrane. These enzyme–phospholipid interactions are schematized in Fig. 2.

Apart from a role in membrane fusion, lysophospholipids released by sperm could contribute to egg activation by temporarily increasing egg membrane permeability. This would permit increased ion flux with triggering action on the preprogrammed biochemical events of fertilization and development as hypothesized by Monroy (1956, 1965).

IV. Antibodies and Lectins as Fertilization Inhibitors

Reference to antibody and lectin action on gametes and fertilization is included in previous sections. A coherent summary of the subject is appropriate here.

In the present context, antibodies are "made-to-order" reactants that can be used to identify, localize and isolate specific antigens and, through their inhibiting action, have potential for identifying antigenic functional macromolecules. Serious use of antibodies in the last context was begun by Tyler (1949) with sea urchins and has since been extended to other organisms (for review, see Metz, 1967, 1972, 1973). Use of Fab (univalent) antibody fragments (Porter, 1959) eliminates secondary effects of native antibody (e.g., agglutination, precipitation, Fc-complement dependent membrane alterations) and is required for meaningful study in the context of probes for functional macromolecules (for antibody structure and action, see Metz, 1972; Metz et al., 1976).

A. EFFECTS OF FAB ANTIBODIES ON SPERM

Fab anti-whole *Arbacia* sperm antibodies markedly inhibit the fertilizing capacity of *Arbacia* sperm (Metz *et al.*, 1964). The inhibiting action does not result from secondary effects including agglutination, alteration of sperm mobility, or longevity (Metz *et al.*, 1964; Eckberg and Metz, 1974; P. M. Saling, W. R. Eckberg and C. B. Metz, unpublished). It apparently involves a single antigen—antibody system because the fertilization-inhibiting action of the antibody is neutralized by a single glycoprotein purified from *Arbacia* sperm extracts (Cordle and Metz, 1973; Maitra and Metz, 1974). Thus, with respect to fertilization, the antisera may be regarded as monospecific for the "fertilization antigen." This *Arbacia* sperm fertilization antigen is shared with *Lytechinus variegatus*, but not *Echinarachnius parma* sperm (Metz *et al.*, 1964).

The fertilization-inhibiting action of the Fab antisperm antibody and its neutralization by the isolated "fertilization antigen" imply an essential role of this antigen in fertilization. This role is apparently not related to initiation of the acrosome reaction because antibodies to sperm do not affect that reaction (Fourtner and Metz, 1967). Preliminary tests with purified Fab antibody suggest sperm head localization of the antigen (Maitra and Metz, 1974). Fab antibody-treated sperm accumulate in the egg jelly but fail to fertilize or bind to dejellied or "demembranated" (trypsin, dithiothreitol treated) eggs. Data from typical experiments (Eckberg and Metz, 1974; P. M. Saling, W. R. Eckberg, and C. B. Metz, unpublished) are given in Fig. 3 and 4. Verification of inhibition by Fab antisperm antibodies of such sperm binding using scanning election microscopy is illustrated in Fig. 5. It is concluded from this that the Fab antisperm antibody preparations block the sperm surface receptor(s) that binds sperm to the vitelline envelope and plasma membrane. Since the single "fertilization antigen" neutralizes the fertilization-inhibiting action, it is concluded, subject to confirmation with antibody to the purified antigen, that only this sperm antigen is involved in the sperm binding and fertilization inhibition action of Fab antibody. This also implies that the same receptor binds sperm to the vitelline envelope and plasma membrane. In the last context it will be interesting to determine whether the Fab antibody-treated sperm are capable of binding to and refertilizing demembranated, fertilized eggs (Tyler *et al.*, 1956).

The purified "fertilization antigen" has no visible effect on eggs including the egg jelly and does not neutralize the sperm agglutinating action of jelly solutions. Thus the agent is not "antifertilizin" (Cordle

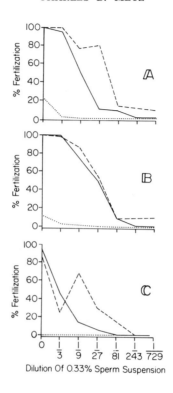

Fig. 3. Effect of Fab antisperm antibody on fertilizing capacity of *Arbacia punctulata* perm. (A) intact eggs; (B) acid-dejellied eggs; (C) trypsin "demembranated" eggs. . . . ., Antibody Fab-treated sperm; - - -, control Fab-treated sperm; ———, seawater-treated sperm.

and Metz, 1973). Preliminary tests indicate that the isolated ^{125}I labeled antigen binds to dejellied *Arbacia* eggs. The fertilization antigen is evidently the receptor of the sperm that binds sperm to the vitelline and probably the plasma membranes of the egg. Investigation of its relation to the acrosome and additional species-specificity tests may provide additional support for the role of this receptor in fertilization.

B. Action of Fab Antibodies on the Egg

Native antisera have several effects on sea urchin eggs. These include precipitation of the egg jelly, wrinkling of the egg surface, and inhibition of fertilization. In addition, Perlmann has reported parthenogenetic activation of eggs by antiserum treatment. Such parthenogenetic activating action has not been confirmed in attempts by

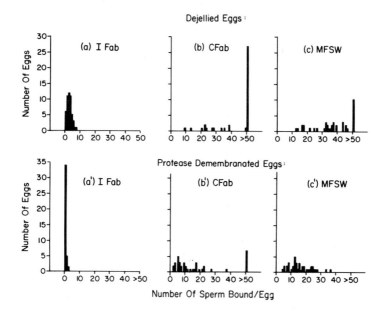

FIG. 4. Effect of Fab antisperm antibody on sperm binding to *Arbacia* eggs. (a) and (a') Antibody Fab-treated sperm. (b) and (b') Control Fab-treated sperm. (c) and (c') Seawater-treated sperm.

others. In addition to a "parthenogenesis antigen," Perlmann described other egg antigens (for review, see Metz, 1967).

Aketa and co-workers (1972) (see Section III) reported a "sperm-binding" glycoprotein obtained from vitelline envelope extracts of sea urchin eggs. Aketa also reported that antisera to this glycoprotein inhibit sperm binding to, and fertilization of, the egg. Aketa, like Perlmann, employed native, not Fab, antibody preparations (Aketa and Onitake, 1969).

Recently, Metz and colleagues have compared the action of Fab and the parent, native (multivalent) anti-egg antibody on eggs (Metz and Thompson, 1967; Graziano and Metz, 1967; Metz *et al.*, 1968a,b; reviewed in Metz, 1972). These studies show unequivocally that Fab antibodies have no morphological effect on sea urchin *(Arbacia punctulata; Lytechinus variegatus)* eggs other than a tendency to remove the egg jelly. Surprisingly, normal, dejellied, and vitelline envelope less eggs all fertilized as well as controls, after Fab antibody treatment. This implies that antibody affects on eggs, including blocking of Aketa's sperm-binding protein, result from secondary factors involving cross-linking of antigens by multivalent antibody (Acker-

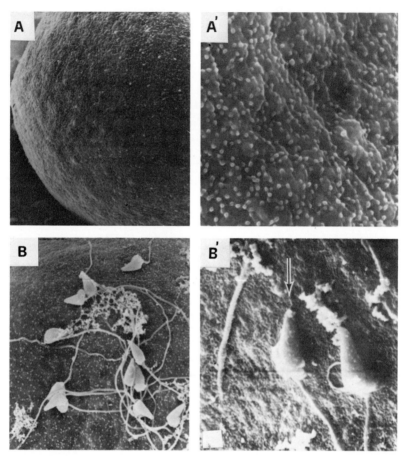

FIG. 5. Inhibition of sperm binding to acid-dejellied *Arbacia* eggs visualized by scanning electron microscopy. A (×3000) and A' (×10,000) egg inseminated with Fab antisperm antibody-treated sperm; B (×4000) and B' (×10,000) egg inseminated with control Fab treated sperm. Arrow in B' indicates sperm acrosome. From P. M. Saling, W. R. Eckberg, and C. B. Metz (unpublished).

man and Metz, 1972). This view is supported by several independent observations. These include demonstration that Fab anti-egg antibody-treated eggs fail to fertilize after secondary cross-linking of the Fab antibody with native (multivalent) antiglobulin antibody; demonstration of a 100-μm precipitation layer (Baxandall *et al.*, 1964) on the surface of native, but not of Fab antibody-treated, eggs (Metz *et al.,* 1968b); and finally reversal of fertilization inhibition by trypsin treatment of multivalent antibody-pretreated eggs.

These results were interpreted to mean that the egg possesses no fertilization antigens, e.g., no antigenic surface receptors, that are essential for fertilization and can be blocked by Fab antibody (Metz and Thompson, 1967; Metz *et al.,* 1968b). This interpretation is reasonable in the context of a static cell membrane. However, antigenic material is slowly released from dejellied, unfertilized eggs (Gregg, 1969), and extensive protrusions of microvilli can result from Fab anti-egg jelly antibody treatment (Metz, 1972). This implies an increase in egg surface area, possibly with new receptors. Finally, preliminary experiments (C. W. S. Howe and C. B. Metz, unpublished) show what appears to be "capping" following treatment of eggs with fluorescein labeled Con A. It is reasonable, then, and in keeping with current concepts of membrane structure, to consider a "dynamic" cell membrane for the unfertilized egg. Dynamic properties could include turnover of membrane surface antigens (Warren, 1969) by shedding [e.g., similar to Ig shedding by lymphocytes under some conditions (Uhr *et al.,* in Edelman, 1974]. Alternatively, surface antigens with bound Fab antibody could be internalized (Wise, 1976). Quite conceivably, such antigen turnover could result in loss of univalent antigen–antibody complexes followed by replacement with new antigen. The latter then could engage in sperm–egg interaction. This argument is appropriate for plasma membrane antigens but seems less probable for vitelline envelope antigens, including the glycoprotein receptor that binds sperm (Schmell *et al.,* 1977).

C. Action of Lectins on Sperm and Eggs

Action of lectins on gametes and fertilization is of special interest because several lectins react specifically with certain known carbohydrate-terminal residues (Sharon and Lis, 1972). These lectins, then, are specific probes for the carbohydrate residues. Con A, a natural agglutinin that combines specifically with glyco- and mannopyranosyl-terminal residues, has been examined most thoroughly on sea urchin gametes and fertilization (see Dunbar and Shivers, 1976; Nicholson *et al.,* 1975; Oikawa *et al.,* 1974, 1975; action of mammalian gametes). Sea urchin species examined are *Arbacia punctulata* (Howe and Metz, 1972; Schmell *et al.,* 1977), *Paracentrotus lividus* (Lallier, 1972), and *Hemicentrotus* and *Anthocidaris* (Aketa, 1975).

The reports agree that Con A does not agglutinate or otherwise visibly affect *Arbacia* sperm or eggs. However, Con A does bind to

Arbacia sperm, possibly by combination with cryptic receptors. The fertilizing capacity of Con A-treated sperm is unimpaired. Con A does not neutralize sperm-agglutinating action of *Arbacia* fertilizin, although the egg jelly does contain some mannose in addition to fucose (Tyler and Tyler, 1966a). However, native tetrameric Con A does inhibit fertilizability of *Arbacia* eggs. Inhibition is reversed by subsequent trypsin treatment, implying Con A receptors on the vitelline envelope (Howe and Metz, 1972). In addition, dimeric Con A (Schmell *et al.,* 1977) and papain-digested (probably dimeric or monomeric) Con A (Howe and Metz, 1972), like Fab antibody, does not inhibit fertilization. This implies that Con A does not combine directly with essential vitelline envelope receptors, but that native (tetrameric) Con A inhibits fertilization by steric factors possibly associated with crosslinking vitelline envelope components. Formal reconciliation of this with binding of the solubilized sperm attachment receptor of the vitelline envelope to Con A–Sepharose (Schmell *et al.,* 1977) can be made by assuming glyco- or mannopyranosyl residues on the receptor but located remote from the sperm-binding "active site" of the receptor.

Con A does agglutinate *Anthocidaris* sperm, reduces sperm binding to eggs, and inhibits the fertilizing capacity of the sperm (Aketa, 1975). Nonagglutinating, trypsin-digested Con A also inhibits the fertilizing capacity of *Anthocidaris* sperm, implying inhibition by direct blocking of a sperm surface receptor. Acrosomal fluorescence follows exposure of sperm to fluorescein-conjugated Con A, indicating localization of glyco- or mannopyranosyl residues, presumably the sperm surface receptor. Con A appears then to have localized an acrosomal surface fertilization receptor of *Anthocidaris* sperm. At least partial purification of this receptor from sperm extracts might result using a Con A affinity column. Con A failed to agglutinate or reduce fertilizing capacity of *Hemicentrotus* sperm, and no fluorescence followed treatment with conjugated Con A. Thus, *Hemicentrotus* sperm lacks surface Con A receptors. Aketa (1975) cited unpublished data showing that wheat germ agglutinin reduces the fertilizing capacity of *Hemicentrotus* but not of *Anthocidaris* sperm.

Con A treatment of *Anthocidaris* or *Hemicentrotus* eggs has no effect on egg jellies or on fertilization itself, although fertilization envelopes are abnormal in both. Fluorescent Con A binds to *Anthocidaris* egg surfaces (vitelline envelope?). Effects on vitelline envelope are attributed to interaction of Con A with cortical granule components (Aketa, 1975).

In examination for action of Con A on *Paracentrotus,* Lallier (1972) found no sperm or egg agglutination. Fertilization of Con A-treated eggs was reduced, and fertilization envelope abnormalities were observed. Abnormalities of embryonic development, including animalization, were reported following postfertilization Con A treatment. Bactophytohemagglutinin M and P had no effect on *Paracentrotus* fertilization.

In summary, Con A shows high species specificity for sperm and egg surface receptors. In those species where reaction occurs, no physiological damage may result (e.g., *Arbacia* sperm), inhibition of fertilizing capacity may occur (*Anthocidaris* sperm; *Arbacia* eggs), and inhibiting action may require multivalent Con A (*Arbacia* eggs) or result from di- or monomeric fragments as well (*Anthocidaris* sperm). The Con A receptor of *Anthocidaris* sperm appears to hold the most promise for isolation of a gamete surface fertilization receptor in sea urchins by use of lectins. From the reports reviewed above lectins could be powerful tools in isolating and characterizing additional fertilization receptors of eggs and sperm. A really thorough, systematic series of tests with a greater range of lectins followed by detailed exploitation of clear-cut inhibiting systems now seems to be in order.

V. Summary and Conclusions

Several sperm–interaction events leading to fertilization are recognized. Certain events are characterized by species specificity and, as originally proposed by F. R. Lillie, are evidently mediated by interaction of specific receptors of complementary gametes, comparable to cell-specific receptor systems of other cell types. Certain receptors are released into solution from gametes, notably eggs, which can act on sperm at a distance from the source. Others are evidently attached to or built into cell coats and the cell membrane. The former include chemotactic agents for sperm and acrosome initiating agents, which presumably interact with complementary sperm-bound receptors. At least two additional complementary sperm- and egg-bound receptor systems bind sperm to egg envelopes (egg jelly, vitelline envelope) and the egg plasma membrane.

Chemotactic action of products from eggs or female tissue has now been convincingly demonstrated by Miller (reviewed in 1977) in two widely separate metazoan groups (coelenterates and urochordates). The chemotactic reactions are rather specific. Chemical studies indicate agents in the molecular weight range 1000 to 15,000, depending on species. Some biochemical tests suggest peptides, at least for agents of the lower molecular weight. The nature of the interaction with sperm including postulated sperm surface "receptors" is unknown. Calcium is an absolute requirement for chemotaxis.

Egg jelly solutions of many species can produce one or both of two striking and specific effects on sperm: sperm agglutination and the sperm acrosome reaction. These effects result from interaction of two complementary receptor substances, namely fertilizin, an egg jelly mucopolysaccharide, and sperm surface antifertilizin, a material that is as yet imperfectly identified in sperm extracts. Sperm agglutination in sea urchins is characterized by rapid, spontaneous reversal resulting from fragmentation of the multivalent agglutinin to substructures including a univalent, nonagglutinating receptor. This remains bound to the sperm following reversal of agglutination. Univalent and inert components of fertilizin can be prepared by treatment of purified fertilizin solutions with a variety of physical and chemical agents. The fertilizin agglutination of sperm is here regarded primarily as an artifact of laboratory conditions, which, however, provides an assay procedure of unusual analytical value in terms of sperm–egg interacting receptor substances.

In sea urchins the acrosome reaction, unlike sperm agglutination, requires calcium in all but one species. Calcium levels can be quite critical for some species. The dual role of fertilizin in agglutination and acrosome-initiating action is evidenced by parallels in species specificity, in inactivation by physical and chemical agents, and in failure of separation of the two activities during purification of fertilizin.

An apparent requirement for the multivalent form of fertilizin for acrosome reaction initiation implies an essential cross-linking of sperm surface antifertilizin in acrosome reaction initiation, or alternatively an essential "inert" component of fertilizin that is lost or destroyed during conversion to the univalent form. The above is consistent with J. C. Dan's (1964) hypothesis for acrosome reaction initiation.

Fertilizin in the form of the intact egg jelly coat may function to bind sperm to the coat. This is especially likely for species such as the starfish, where many sperm may attach to the jelly surface followed by penetration of the long acrosome process through the egg jelly to the vitelline envelope. In sea urchins such jelly surface binding would be inimical to fertilization because the acrosome process is shorter than the jelly depth. Transitory jelly attachment and release (breakdown of fertilizin to the univalent form) could aid fertilization, even in sea urchins.

Sperm binding to the vitelline envelope surface involves the reacted sperm acrosome, quite possibly a gel coat of acrosome granule origin. This binding is highly specific, perhaps more so than fertilizin agglutination of sperm. The active material would be expected to have some of the properties of certain sperm extracts with "antifertilizin" activity, such as agglutination of eggs, including dejellied eggs.

The receptors of the vitelline envelope that bind sperm may be limited in number (Vacquier and Payne, 1973) and restricted to areas between the cortical granules, namely the "cortical projections" of Schuel et al. (1976).

Aketa (1973) and co-workers and Schmell et al. (1977) have isolated and examined vitelline envelopes for sperm binding receptors. The isolated envelopes bind sea urchin sperm. Treatment of sperm with solubilized envelopes inhibits sperm fertilizing capacity. In Arbacia this activity is removed by Con A–Sepharose, and envelopes from trypsin-treated eggs fail to bind sperm. These observations imply a glycoprotein receptor. The fertilization-inhibiting receptor extracts (solubilized isolated envelopes) have no apparent sperm agglutinating action, indicating absence of multivalent fertilizin. This and other data indicate that the vitelline envelope receptor for sperm binding is not fertilizin.

Little is known about possible egg plasma membrane receptors for sperm. Eggs denuded of jelly and vitelline envelope can be fertilized, but less readily than controls; polyspermy is increased and cross fertilization occurs more readily. Sperm do bind to such denuded eggs indicating a sperm–egg binding receptor system at the plasma membrane level.

The sequence of the three final sperm–egg interaction events, namely, sperm–egg plasma membrane binding, egg activation, and sperm–egg plasma membrane fusion, is a consideration of some importance. It is tentatively concluded on limited evidence that egg activation precedes sperm–egg plasma membrane fusion. This would imply egg activation by "transduction" of an activating "message" across the egg membrane comparable to lymphocyte activation by lectins or specific antigens. Sperm–egg plasma membrane fusion itself may be facilitated by lysophospholipids, which appear briefly following the sea urchin sperm acrosome reaction (Conway and Metz, 1976).

Specific inhibitors, notably antibodies and lectins, are becoming increasingly useful tools in studies of sperm–egg interaction. Univalent (Fab) antibodies and monomeric lectins have potential for direct inhibition of receptors without the secondary effects of the parent multivalent materials. Fab antisperm antibodies inhibit the fertilizing capacity of sea urchin sperm. This action is neutralized by a single glycoprotein purified from crude sperm extracts (Cordle and Metz, 1973; Maitra and Metz, 1974). This means that the sperm possesses only one single "fertilization antigen." The Fab antisperm antibody preparations do not affect sperm accumulation in the sea urchin egg jelly, but do dramatically inhibit sperm binding to the vitelline envelope and plasma membrane of eggs (Eckberg and Metz, 1974; W. R. Eckberg, P. M. Saling, and C. B. Metz, unpublished). The glycoprotein antigen, then, is the single antigen involved in both vitelline envelope and plasma membrane binding. Fab anti-egg antibodies do not affect the fertilizability of normal, dejellied, or demembranated sea urchin eggs. It was originally concluded from this that the egg lacked fertilization antigens (Metz and Thompson, 1967). However, such antigens may be shed or internalized when complexed with Fab, and new unblocked antigens may surface and engage in sperm–egg interaction.

Present knowledge suggests that we are finally approaching the understanding that seemed so imminent when Glaser (1921) wrote that "whatever transformations our views on the initiation of development may undergo within the next few years, the zone within which we seek for understanding is now marked off by the reaction capacities of perfectly definite physiological compounds."

ACKNOWLEDGMENTS

The author is grateful to Dr. E. L. Chambers and Dr. P. Luykx of the University of Miami, to Dr. M. G. O'Rand, University of Florida, and Mr. Andrew Eisen and Dr. Don P. Wolf, University of Pennsylvania, for helpful suggestions and exchange of ideas and for reading sections of the manuscript during its preparation. He is also grateful to Dr. R. L. Miller of Temple University for suggestions, for provision of unpublished data, and for reading the section on sperm chemotaxis and to Dr. W. J. Lennarz, Johns Hopkins University, Dr. Margorie A. Crandall, University of Kentucky, and Dr. M. J. Greenberg, Florida State University, for preprints of papers prior to publication.

During preparation of this review the author's laboratory was supported by grants from the National Institute for Child Health and Human Development (1-R01-HD0663-02), the National Science Foundation (PMC-76-19566), the Population Council (M-74-31), and the World Health Organization (H9-181-162A). This is Contribution #319 from the Institute for Molecular and Cellular Evolution.

REFERENCES

Ackerman, N. R., and Metz, C. B. (1972). *Exp. Cell Res.* **72,** 204–210.
Aketa, K. (1967). *Embryologia* **9,** 238–245.
Aketa, K. (1973). *Exp. Cell Res.* **80,** 439–441.
Aketa, K. (1975). *Exp. Cell Res.* **90,** 56–62.
Aketa, K., and Onitake, K. (1969). *Exp. Cell Res.* **56,** 84–86.
Aketa, K., and Tsuzuki, H. (1968). *Exp. Cell Res.* **50,** 675–676.
Aketa, K., Tsuzuki, H., and Onitake, K. (1968). *Exp. Cell Res.* **50,** 676–679.
Aketa, K., Onitake, K., and Tsuzuki, H. (1972). *Exp. Cell Res.* **71,** 27–32.
Allison, A. C., and Hartree, E. F. (1970). *J. Reprod. Fertil.* **21,** 501–515.
Austin, C. R. (1968). "Ultrastructure of Fertilization." Holt, New York.
Austin, C. R. (1975). *J. Reprod. Fertil.* **44,** 155–166.

Azarnia, R., and Chambers, E. L. (1976). *J. Exp. Zool.* **198**, 65–78.
Badman, W. S., and Brookbank, J. W. (1970). *Dev. Biol.* **21**, 243–256.
Baxandall, J., Perlmann, P., and Afzelius, B. A. (1964). *J. Cell Biol.* **23**, 609–629.
Branham, J. M. (1969). *Biol. Bull. (Woods Hole, Mass.)* **142**, 385–396.
Brookbank, J. W. (1958). *Biol. Bull. (Woods Hole, Mass.)* **115**, 74–80.
Brown, G. G. (1966). *J. Ultrastruct. Res.* **14**, 425–440.
Catt, K. J., and Hufau, M. L. (1976). *Biol. Reprod.* **14**, 1–15.
Cauldwell, C. B., Henkart, P., and Humphreys, T. (1973). *Biochemistry* **13**, 3051–3055.
Chambers, E. L., Pressman, B. C., and Rose, B. (1974). *Biochem. Biophys. Res Commun.* **60**, No. 1, 126–132.
Chambers, R. (1930). *Biol. Bull. (Woods Hole, Mass.)* **58**, 344–369.
Collier, J. R. (1959). *Acta Embryol. Morphol. Exp.* **2**, 163–170.
Collins, F. (1976). *Dev. Biol.* **49**, 381–394.
Colwin, A. L., Colwin, L. H., and Summers, R. G. (1975). *Wenner-Gren Cent. Int. Symp. Ser.* **23**, 27–38.
Colwin, L. H., and Colwin, A. L. (1967). *In* "Fertilization" (C. B. Metz and A. Monroy, eds.), Vol. 1, pp. 295–367. Academic Press, New York.
Conway, A. F., and Metz, C. B. (1976). *J. Exp. Zool.* **198**, 39–47.
Cordle, C. T., and Metz, C. B. (1973). *Biol. Bull.* **145**, 430.
Crandall, M. A. (1977). *In* "Mating-Type Interactions in Microorganisms, Receptors and Recognition" (P. Cuatrecasas and M. F. Greaves, eds.), Vol. 3, Sect. A. Chapman & Hall, London (in press).
Crandall, M. A., and Brock, T. C. (1968a). *Bacteriol. Rev.* **32**, 139–163.
Crandall, M. A., and Brock, T. D. (1968b). *Science* **161**, 473–475.
Crandall, M. A., Laurence, L. M., and Saunders, R. M. (1974). *Proc. Natl. Acad. Sci. U.S.A.* **71**, 26–29.
Cuatracasas, P. (1974). *Adv. Exp. Med. Biol.* **51**, 37–48.
Dan, J. C. (1952). *Biol. Bull. (Woods Hole, Mass.)* **103**, 54–66.
Dan, J. C. (1954). *Biol. Bull. (Woods Hole, Mass.)* **107**, 335–349.
Dan, J. C. (1956). *Int. Rev. Cytol.* **5**, 365–393.
Dan, J. C. (1967). *In* "Fertilization" (C. B. Metz and A. Monroy, eds.), Vol. 1, pp. 237–293. Academic Press, New York.
Dan, J. C., Ohori, Y., and Kushida, H. (1964). *J. Ultrastruct. Res.* **11**, 508–524.
Dan, J. C., Hashimoto, S., and Kubo, M. (1975). *Wenner-Gren Cent. Int. Symp. Ser.* **23**, 39–45.
Decker, G. L., Joseph, D. B., and Lennarz, D. B. (1976). *Dev. Biol.* **53**, 115–125.
Dresser, D. W., and Greaves, M. F. (1973). *In* "Handbook of Experimental Immunology" (D. M. Weir, ed.), Chap. 27, pp. 1–29. Blackwell, Oxford.
Dunbar, B. S., and Shivers, C. A. (1976). *Immunol. Commun.* **5**, 375–385.
Eckberg, W. R., and Metz, C. B. (1974). *Biol. Bull. (Woods Hole, Mass.)* **147**, 475.
Edelman, G. M., ed. (1974). "Cellular Selection and Regulation in the Immune Response." Raven, New York.
Epel, D. (1975). *Am. Zool.* **15**, 507–552.
Fourtner, C. R., and Metz, C. B. (1967). *Biol. Bull. (Woods Hole, Mass.)* **133**, 465.
Frank, J. A. (1939). *Biol. Bull. (Woods Hole, Mass.)* **76**, 190–216.
Franklin, L. E. (1965). *J. Cell Biol.* **25**, 28–100.
Franklin, L. E. (1966). *Exp. Cell Res.* **43**, 673–675.
Franklin, L. E. (1970). *Biol. Reprod.* **2**, 159–176.
Glabe, C. G., and Vacquier, V. D. (1977). *Nature (London)* **26**, 836–838.
Glaser, O. (1921). *Anat. Rec.* **20**, 227.

Goodenough, U. W. (1977). *In* "Microbial Interactions" (J. L. Reissig, ed.), Ser. B, Vol. 3, pp. 325–347. Chapman & Hall, London.

Graziano, K. D., and Metz, C. B. (1967). *Exp. Cell Res.* **46**, 220–222.

Gregg, K. W. (1969). *Biol. Bull. (Woods Hole, Mass.)* **137**, 146–154.

Gregg, K. W. (1971). Ph.D. Thesis, University of Miami, Coral Gables, Florida.

Gregg, K. W., and Metz, C. B. (1976). *Biol. Reprod.* **14**, 405–441.

Grey, R. D., Working, P. K., and Hedrick, J. L. (1976). *Dev. Biol.* **54**, 52–60.

Gwatkin, R. B. L., Rasmusson, G. H., and Williams, D. T. (1976). *J. Reprod. Fertil.* **47**, 299–303.

Haino, K., and Dan, J. C. (1961). *Embryologia* **5**, 376–383.

Hathaway, R. R., and Metz, C. B. (1961). *Biol. Bull. (Woods Hole, Mass.)* **120**, 360–369.

Hathaway, R. R., Warren, L., and Flaks, J. G. (1960). *Biol. Bull. (Woods Hole, Mass.)* **119**, 319.

Hausman, R. E., and Moscona, A. A. (1975). *Proc. Natl. Acad. Sci. U.S.A.* **72**, 916–920.

Henkart, P., Humphreys, S., and Humphreys, T. (1973). *Biochemistry* **12**, 3045–3050.

Hinsch, G. W., and Clark, W. H. (1973). *Biol. Reprod.* **8**, 62–73.

Hiwatashi, K. (1969). *In* "Fertilization" (C. B. Metz and A. Monroy, eds.), Vol. 2, pp. 255–293. Academic Press, New York.

Howe, C. W. S., and Metz, C. B. (1972). *Biol. Bull. (Woods Hole, Mass.)* **143**, 465.

Hultin, T. (1948a). *Ark. Zool.* **40A**, 1–9.

Hultin, T. (1948b). *Ark. Zool.* **40A**, 1–8.

Ishihara, K., and Dan, J. C. (1970). *Dev., Growth & Differ.* **12**, 179–188.

Johnson, M. H. (1975). *J. Reprod. Fertil.* **44**, 167–184.

Kleve, M. G., and Clark, W. H. (1976). *In* "Coelenterate Ecology and Behavior" (G. O. Mackie, ed.), pp. 309–317. Plenum, New York.

Koehler, K., and Metz, C. B. (1959). *Biol. Bull. (Woods Hole, Mass.)* **117**, 416.

Lallier, R. (1972). *Exp. Cell Res.* **72**, 157–163.

Lillie, F. R. (1913). *Science* **38**, 524–528.

Lillie, F. R. (1914). *J. Exp. Zool.* **16**, 523–590.

Lillie, R. (1919). "Problems of Fertilization." Univ. of Chicago Press, Chicago, Illinois.

Loeb, J. (1914). *J. Exp. Zool.* **17**, 123–140.

Longo, F. J., and Schuel, H. (1973). *Dev. Biol.* **34**, 187–199.

Lucy, J. A. (1971). *Nature (London)* **227**, 814–817.

Lucy, J. A. (1975). *J. Reprod. Fertil.* **44**, 193–205.

Machlis, L., and Rawitschcher-Kunkel, E. (1967). *In* "Fertilization" (C. B. Metz and A. Monroy, eds.), Vol. 1, pp. 117–161. Academic Press, New York.

McRorie, R. A., and Williams, W. L., (1974). *Annu. Rev. Biochem.* **43**, 77–803.

Maitra, U. S., and Metz, C. B. (1974). *Biol. Bull. (Woods Hole, Mass.)* **147**, 490.

Marsh, J. M. (1976). *Biol. Reprod.* **14**, 30–53.

Matlei, C., and Matlei, X. (1975). *Wenner-Gren Cent. Int. Symp. Ser.* **23**, 211–221.

Melcher, U. (1975). *Nature (London)* **258**, 434.

Metz, C. B. (1942). *Biol. Bull. (Woods Hole, Mass.)* **82**, 446–454.

Metz, C. B. (1945). *Biol. Bull. (Woods Hole, Mass.)* **89**, 84–94.

Metz, C. B. (1954a). *In* "Sex in Microorganisms (D. H. Wenrick, ed.), pp. 284–334. Am. Assoc. Adv. Sci., Washington, D.C.

Metz, C. B. (1954b). *Biol. Bull. (Woods Hole, Mass.)* **107**, 317.

Metz, C. B. (1957a). *In* "Physiological Triggers" (T. H. Bullock, ed.), pp. 17–45. Am. Phys. Soc., Washington, D.C.

Metz, C. B. (1957b). *In* "Beginnings of Embryonic Development" (A. Tyler, R. C. von Borstel, and C. B. Metz, eds.), Publ. No. 48, pp. 23–69. Am. Assoc. Adv. Sci., Washington, D.C.

Metz, C. B. (1961). *Int. Rev. Cytol.* **11**, 219–253.
Metz, C. B. (1967). *In* "Fertilization" (C. B. Metz and A. Monroy, eds.), Vol. 1, pp. 163–236. Academic Press, New York.
Metz, C. B. (1972). *Biol. Reprod.* **6**, 358–383.
Metz, C. B. (1973). *Fed. Proc., Fed. Am. Soc. Exp. Biol.* **32**, 2057–2064.
Metz, C. B., and Birky, C. W. (1955). *Biol. Bull. (Woods Hole, Mass.)* **109**, 365.
Metz, C. B., and Donovan, J. (1951). *Biol. Bull. (Woods Hole, Mass.)* **101**, 202.
Metz, C. B., and Monroy, A., eds. (1967). "Fertilization" Vol. 1. Academic Press, New York.
Metz, C. B., and Monroy, A., eds. (1969). "Fertilization," Vol. 2. Academic Press, New York.
Metz, C. B., and Thompson, P. H. (1967). *Exp. Cell Res.* **45**, 443–449.
Metz, C. B., Schuel, H., and Bischoff, E. R. (1964). *J. Exp. Zool.* **115**, 261–272.
Metz, C. B., Brown, G. G., and Thompson, P. H. (1968a). *J. Cell Biol.* **35**, PT2-93A.
Metz, C. B., Cone, M. V., and Bryant, J. (1968b). *J. Cell Biol.* **39**, 481–484.
Metz, C. B., O'Rand, M. G., and Cordle, C. T. (1976). *In* "Human Semen and Fertility Regulation in Men" (E. S. F. Hafez, ed.), pp. 276–286. Mosby, St. Louis, Missouri.
Miller, R. L. (1966). *J. Exp. Zool.* **162**, 23–44.
Miller, R. L. (1974). *Am. Zool.* **14**, 1250.
Miller, R. L. (1975). *Nature (London)* **254**, 244–245.
Miller, R. L. (1977). *In* "Advances in Invertebrate Reproduction" (K. G. Adiyodi and P. G. Adiyodi, eds.), Vol. 1, pp. 99–119. Peralam-Kenoth, Karivellur, India.
Miller, R. L., and Brokow, C. J. (1970). *J. Exp. Zool.* **52**, 609–704.
Miller, R. L., and Nelson, L. (1962). *Biol. Bull. (Woods Hole, Mass.)* **123**, 422.
Miller, R. L., and Tseng, C. Y. (1974). *Am. Zool.* **14**, 467–486.
Miyake, A. (1974). *Curr. Top. Microbiol. Immunol.* **64**, 49–77.
Monroy, A. (1956). *Exp. Cell Res.* **10**, 320–323.
Monroy, A. (1965). "Chemistry and Physiology of Fertilization." Holt, New York.
Monroy, A., Tosi, L., Giardina, G., and Maggio, R. (1954). *Biol. Bull. (Woods Hole, Mass.)* **106**, 169–177.
Morgan, T. H. (1927). "Experimental Embryology." Columbia Univ. Press, New York.
Muller, W. F. G., Muller, J., Zahn, R. K., and Kurelec, B. (1976). *J. Cell Sci.* **21**, 227–241.
Nicholson, G. L., Yanagimachi, R., and Yanagimachi, H. (1975). *J. Cell Biol.* **66**, 263–273.
Oikawa, T., Nicholson, G. L., and Yanagimachi, H. (1974). *Exp. Cell Res.* **83**, 283–246.
Oikawa, T., Yanagimachi, R., and Nicholson, G. L. (1975). *J. Reprod. Fertil.* **43**, 137–140.
Onitake, K., Tsuzuki, H., and Aketa, K. (1972). *Dev., Growth & Differ.* **14**, 207–215.
O'Rand, M. G. (1972). *J. Exp. Zool.* **182**, 299–305.
O'Rand, M. G. (1974). *Am. Zool.* **14**, 487–493.
O'Rand, M. G., and Miller, R. L. (1974). *J. Exp. Zool.* **188**, 179–194.
Osanai, K. (1976). *Bull. Mar. Biol. Stn. Asamushi, Tohoku Univ.* **15**, 147–155.
Parkhouse, R. M. E., Hunter, I. R., and Abney, E. R. (1976). *Immunology* **30**, 409–412.
Pfeffer, W. (1884). *Unters. Bot. Inst. Tubingen* **1**, 363–481.
Piatigorsky, J., and Austin, C. R. (1962). *Biol. Bull.* **123**, 473.
Porter, R. R. (1959). *Biochem. J.* **73**, 119–126.
Runnström, J., Lindnall, S., and Tiselius, A. (1944). *Nature (London)* **153**, 285–286.
Reed, C., Greenberg, M. J., and Pierce, S. K. (1976). *In* "Aspects of Sponge Biology" (F. W. Harrison, ed.), pp. 153–169. Academic Press, New York.
Roth, S., McGuire, E. J., and Roseman, S. (1971). *J. Cell Biol.* **51**, 536–547.
Rothman, J. E., and Lenard, J. (1977). *Science* **195**, 743–753.
Rothschild, Lord. (1956). "Fertilization." Wiley, New York.

Ryan, R. J., and Lee, C. Y. (1976). *Biol. Reprod.* **14**, 16–29.

Schatten, G., and Mazia, D. (1976). *J. Supramolec. Structure* **5**, 343–369.

Schmell, E., Earles, B. J., Breaux, C., and Lennarz, W. J. (1977). *J. Cell Biol.* **72**, 35–46.

Schreiner, G. F., and Unanue, E. R. (1976). *Adv. Immunol.* **24**, 37–165.

Schuel, H., Wilson, W. L., Chen, K., and Lorand, L. (1973). *Dev. Biol.* **34**, 175–186.

Schuel, H., Longo, F. J., Wilson, W. L., and Troll, W. (1976). *Dev. Biol.* **79**, 178–184.

Sharon, N., and Lis, H. (1972). *Science* **177**, 949–959.

Shivers, C. A., and Evans, T. E. (1962). *Biol. Bull. (Woods Hole, Mass.)* **123**, 473–474.

Snell, W. J. (1975a). *J. Cell Biol.* **68**, 48–69.

Snell, W. J. (1975b). *J. Cell Biol.* **68**, 70–79.

Steinhardt, R. A., and Epel, D. (1974). *Proc. Natl. Acad. Sci. U.S.A.* **71**, 1915–1919.

Stern, S. (1967). *Biol. Bull. (Woods Hole, Mass.)* **133**, 255–296.

Stern, S., and Metz, C. B. (1967). *Exp. Cell Res.* **48**, 224–226.

Summers, R. G., and Hylander, B. L. (1975). *Exp. Cell Res.* **96**, 63–68.

Summers, R. G., Hylander, B. L., Colwin, L. H., and Colwin, A. L. (1975). *Am. Zool.* **15**, 523–551.

Talbot, P., Summers, R. G., Hylander, B. L., Keough, E. M., and Franklin, L. E. (1976). *J. Exp. Zool.* **198**, 383–392.

Tegner, M. J., and Epel, D. (1973). *Science* **179**, 685–688.

Tilney, L. G., Hatano, S., Ishikawa, H., and Mooseker, M. S. (1973). *J. Cell Biol.* **59**, 109–126.

Tyler, A. (1939). *Proc. Natl. Acad. Sci. U.S.A.* **25**, 317–323.

Tyler, A. (1941). *Biol. Bull. (Woods Hole, Mass.)* **81**, 190–204.

Tyler, A. (1946). *Biol. Bull. (Woods Hole, Mass.)* **90**, 213–219.

Tyler, A. (1948). *Phys. Rev.* **28**, 180–219.

Tyler, A. (1949). *Am. Nat.* **83**, 195–219.

Tyler, A. (1956). *Exp. Cell Res.* **10**, 377–386.

Tyler, A. (1959). *Exp. Cell Res. Suppl.* **7**, 183–199.

Tyler, A., and Fox, S. W. (1940). *Biol. Bull. (Woods Hole, Mass.)* **79**, 153–165.

Tyler, A., and Metz, C. B. (1945). *J. Exp. Zool.* **100**, 387–406.

Tyler, A., and Metz, C. B. (1955). *Pubbl. Stan. Zool. Napoli* **27**, 128–145.

Tyler, A., and O'Melveny, K. (1941). *Biol. Bull. (Woods Hole, Mass.)* **81**, 364–374.

Tyler, A., and Tyler, B. S. (1966a). *In* "Physiology of *Echinodermata*" (R. A. Boolootian, ed.), pp. 639–682. Wiley, New York.

Tyler, A., and Tyler, B. S. (1966b). *In* "Physiology of Echinodermata" (R. A. Boolootian, ed.), pp. 683–741. Wiley, New York.

Tyler, A., Monroy, A., and Metz, C. B. (1956). *Biol. Bull. (Woods Hole, Mass.)* **110**, 184–195.

Vacquier, V. D., and Moy, G. W. (1977). *Proc. Natl. Acad. Sci. U.S.A.* **74**, 2456–2460.

Vacquier, V. D., and Payne, J. E. (1973). *Exp. Cell Res.* **82**, 227–235.

Vacquier, V. D., Tegner, M. J., and Epel, D. (1973). *Exp. Cell Res.* **80**, 111–119.

Vasseur, E. (1952). *Acta Chem. Scand.* **6**, 376–384.

Vitetta, E. S., and Uhr, J. W. (1975). *Science* **189**, 964–969.

Warren, L. (1969). *Curr. Top. Dev. Biol.* **4**, 197–222.

Warren, L., Hathaway, R., and Flaks, J. G. (1960). *Biol. Bull. (Woods Hole, Mass.)* **119**, 355.

Wiese, L. (1966). *Fortschr. Zool.* **18**, 139–206.

Wiese, L. (1969). *In* "Fertilization" (C. B. Metz and A. Monroy, eds.), Vol. 2, pp. 135–188. Academic Press, New York.

Wise, G. E. (1976). *J. Cell Sci.* **22,** 623–632.

Wolf, D. P., Nishihara, T., West, D. M., Wyrick, R. E., and Hedrick, J. L. (1976). *Biochemistry* **15,** 3671–3678.

Wooding, F. B. P. (1975). *J. Reprod. Fertil.* **44,** 185–192.

Yamada, K. M., Yamada, S. S., and Pastan, J. (1975). *Proc. Natl. Acad. Sci. U.S.A.* **72,** 3158–3162.

Zahn, R. K., Muller, W. E. G., Geisert, M., Reinmuller, L., Michaelis, M., Pondeluak, V., and Beyer, R. (1976). *Cell Differ.* **5,** 129–137.

CHAPTER 6

TRANSFORMATIONS OF SPERM NUCLEI UPON INSEMINATION

Frank J. Longo

DEPARTMENT OF ANATOMY
UNIVERSITY OF IOWA
IOWA CITY, IOWA

*and Mel Kunkle**

DEPARTMENT OF ANATOMY
UNIVERSITY OF TENNESSEE
MEMPHIS, TENNESSEE

I. Introduction

Numerous studies have demonstrated that a wide range of nuclear activities are controlled by cytoplasmic factors. Cytoplasmic components of unknown composition have been shown to induce or repress gene activity, exerting their effect on the nuclei of differentiated, as well as undifferentiated, cells (Gurdon and Woodland, 1968). Normal interactions between nucleus and cytoplasm are of fundamental importance at all stages of embryonic development. However, during fertilization a unique situation exists that demonstrates rather dramatically the presence of conditions within eggs that bring about major changes in nuclear morphology and function.

* Present address: Department of Pharmacology, Baylor College of Medicine, Houston, Texas 77025

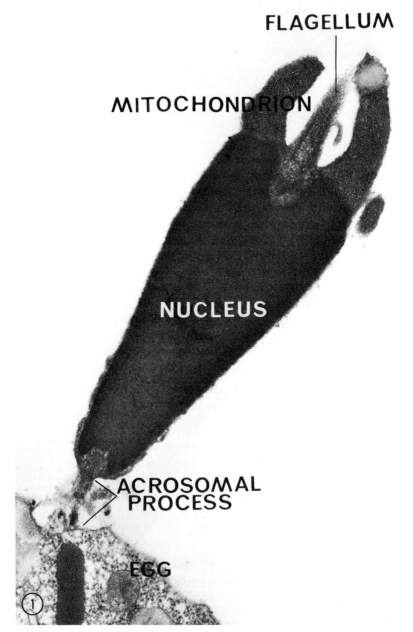

FIG. 1. *Arbacia* spermatozoon adjacent to the surface of an unfertilized egg. The spermatozoon has undergone an acrosomal reaction and is associated with the egg plasma membrane via its acrosomal process. ×42,000.

The relationship and possible functional equivalence of the transformations the maternally and paternally derived chromatin undergo at fertilization and the changes in size and behavior of transplanted nuclei has been elaborated upon (Gurdon, 1975; also Johnson and Rao, 1971). At fertilization the sperm nucleus is reorganized to form the male pronucleus, a structure that is morphologically and functionally different from its predecessor (Figs. 1 and 2). Transformation of the sperm nucleus into a male pronucleus involves morphological changes similar to those that have been described for transplanted nuclei; they include chromatin decondensation and nuclear enlargement (Gurdon, 1974, 1975; Harris, 1974).

The activity of genes has been shown to depend on the association of regulatory proteins with particular regions of chromosomes (Stein *et al.*, 1974). Gurdon (1975) suggested that proteins are dissociated from chromosomes as they become condensed for mitosis. They are released into the cytoplasm, where they become fixed with other regulatory polypeptides that had been synthesized during the preceding interphase. At the end of mitosis, when the chromosomes disperse, they are assumed to pick up a portion of these proteins, which then permits the genes to be active or inactive during the ensuing intermitotic period. In this way genes may be subjected to a cyclic reprogramming. Although direct evidence for this hypothetical system of regulation is lacking, Gurdon (1975) assumed that the enormous enlargement and chromosomal dispersal demonstrated by transplanted nuclei and male and female pronuclei of fertilized eggs may be a manifestation of the acquisition of regulatory proteins.

Nuclear transfer experiments have shown that preexisting and newly synthesized proteins move into, and become concentrated in, transplanted nuclei as they enlarge (Graham *et al.*, 1966; Arms, 1968; Merriam, 1969; Goto and Ringertz, 1974; Appels *et al.*, 1975; Appels and Ringertz, 1975; cf. Gurdon, 1974). Labeled proteins within transplanted nuclei do not appear in the cytoplasm immediately after transfer, but they may do so when the cell enters mitosis. Although, the results of nuclear transplantation studies have not substantiated the validity of the proposal suggesting that cycles of chromosomes condensation and nuclear swelling may be involved in changes of gene expression, they are, nevertheless, consistent with this possibility. Perhaps the changes demonstrated by the incorporated spermatozoon at fertilization are related.

The transformations of the sperm nucleus at fertilization into a male pronucleus may be grouped into three processes that have been described ultrastructurally in a number of animals and include (1)

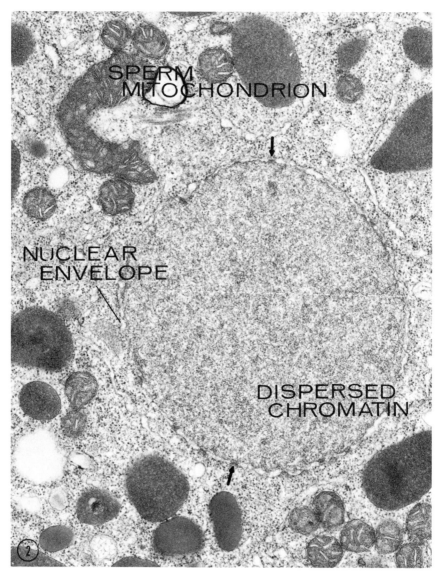

Fig. 2. *Arbacia* male pronucleus, 10 minutes after insemination. The dispersed chromatin is surrounded by a nuclear envelope possessing pores (arrows). ×28,000.

METAMORPHOSIS OF THE SPERM NUCLEUS INTO A
MALE PRONUCLEUS

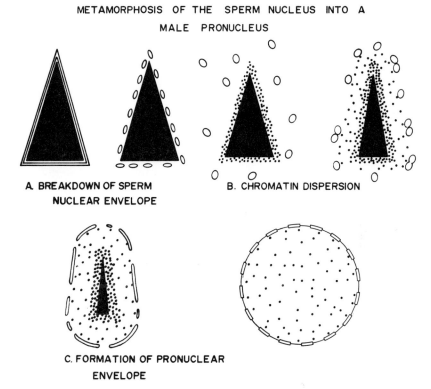

A. BREAKDOWN OF SPERM NUCLEAR ENVELOPE

B. CHROMATIN DISPERSION

C. FORMATION OF PRONUCLEAR ENVELOPE

FIG. 3. Diagrammatic representation (not to scale) of the events of pronuclear development in *Arbacia* zygotes. (A) The dark triangular structure represents the condensed chromatin of the sperm nucleus. It is surrounded by two lines representing the sperm nuclear envelope. The sperm nuclear envelope breaks down, forming numerous vesicles (ellipsoids) that are scattered within the cytoplasm (B) This is followed by dispersion of the condensed chromatin (B) Vesicles aggregate along the periphery of the dispersed chromatin (ellipsoids) and fuse together to form elongate cisternae which in turn coalesce to form a nuclear envelope (C) A spheroid male pronucleus containing dispersed chromatin and surrounded by a nuclear envelope possessing pores is shown on the lower right.

breakdown of the sperm nuclear envelope, (2) chromatin dispersion, and (3) formation of a "new" nuclear envelope (Fig. 3). Although the processes and final product, i.e., the male pronucleus, are similar, there are identifiable temporal, developmental, and structural differences that occur during the morphogenesis of the male pronuclei in the various organisms examined thus far (cf. Longo, 1973a). Moreover, differences exist in the manner in which the male and female pronuclei become associated (Wilson, 1925; Longo, 1973a).

II. Male Pronuclear Development: An Overview

Description of the events involving the development of male pronuclei has been the subject of a recent review (Longo, 1973a), nevertheless, a brief explanation of some of the major processes occurring in the
sea urchin *Arbacia punctulata* is outlined here as an aid in our consideration of the nuclear–cytoplasmic interactions at fertilization. Relatively few biochemical studies have been concerned with this area, and
much of the information we have concerning this process is derived
from ultrastructural investigations.

After its incorporation into the egg, the nuclear envelope limiting
the condensed chromatin of the *Arbacia* sperm nucleus breaks down
(Fig. 3). Disruption of the sperm nuclear envelope is a fairly rapid
event, which is initiated when the inner and outer laminae of the
sperm nuclear envelope fuse at multiple loci and form an array of
vesicles that loosely surround the condensed sperm chromatin. Although other possibilities have not been ruled out, these vesicles appear to migrate into the surrounding cytoplasm where they become
"lost" among other membranous elements of the zygote.

Breakdown of the sperm nuclear envelope exposes the condensed
sperm chromatin to the egg cytoplasm. This permits the interaction of
cytoplasmic components with this material and the alteration of its
genic capabilities. This is suggested by experiments of Hiramoto
(1962), who observed that disappearance of the plasma membrane de-
limiting the sperm nucleus was a necessary prerequisite in order for
pronuclei to form in eggs injected with whole sperm (cf. also Katagiri
and Moriya, 1976; Skoblina, 1974). Coincident with the breakdown of
the sperm nuclear envelope is the dispersion of the condensed chromatin (Fig. 3). Slight variations have been noted from one organism to
another concerning the pattern of sperm chromatin dispersal (Longo,
1973a) although the meaning of these differences has not been elucidated. During this process the condensed chromatin goes from a
coarsely aggregated mass of electron-dense material to a nucleoplasm
composed of dispersed fine threads. Concomitant with these changes is
an increase in the volume of paternally derived chromatin.

During the latter stages of chromatin dispersion a nuclear envelope
forms and encompasses the paternally derived chromosomes (Fig. 3).
This process has been studied in a number of organisms and has been
found to be basically the same in each (Longo, 1973a). Formation of the
pronuclear envelope is essentially the reverse of what occurs during
breakdown of the sperm nuclear envelope. Vesicles aggregate along the
periphery of the dispersed chromatin; these fuse and form a double
laminated porous structure characteristic of a nuclear envelope.

Subsequent to its development, the male pronucleus migrates centrad and becomes associated with the female pronucleus. When adjacent to one another, the male and female pronuclei undergo one of two patterns of morphogenesis (Longo, 1973a). (1) In some instances (principally in the echinoids) the nuclear envelopes of the male and female pronuclei fuse and become continuous, thereby forming a single or zygote nucleus. During this process the chromatin within the male and female pronuclei does not appear to be exposed to the surrounding cytoplasm and remains isolated from it until some time later, during the first mitotic division of the zygote. This process is known as pronuclear fusion and was originally referred to as the sea urchin type of fertilization (Wilson, 1925, Longo, 1973a). (2) The second pattern of pronuclear morphogenesis is one in which the chromosomes in each pronucleus condense, with the concomitant breakdown of the pronuclear envelopes. The chromosomes from both pronuclei then intermix and become situated on the metaphase plate of the mitotic spindle, which is formed in anticipation of the first cleavage division of the embryo. This pattern, which was originally referred to as the *Ascaris* type of fertilization (Wilson, 1925), appears to be characteristic of most animals.

III. Control of Pronuclear Development and Activity

The results of a number of investigations have indicated that the state of the cytoplasm of the egg influences the morphogenesis of the incorporated sperm nucleus and the manner in which association of the male and female pronuclei occurs (Wilson, 1925; Longo and Anderson, 1968, 1969d; Longo and Plunkett, 1973; Longo, 1973a, 1976a, 1977). Recent investigations have shown that events involving the metamorphosis of the incorporated sperm nucleus can take place in eggs devoid of maternally derived chromatin (Skoblina, 1974; Longo, 1976a).

Investigations by Yanagimachi and Usui (1972) suggest that there is a component(s) in hamster eggs responsible, at least in part, for the dispersion of the condensed sperm nuclear chromatin. Similar observations have also been made of inseminated rabbit oocytes, having undergone nuclear maturation in culture (Thibault and Gerard, 1970).

Little is known concerning the substance(s) necessary for pronuclear development; it is believed to be a component of the egg that appears at the time of germinal vesicle breakdown. Recent investigations with anurans have demonstrated the failure of pronuclear formation and DNA synthesis by fertilizing or experimentally injected sperm in enucleate toad oocytes (Katagiri, 1974; Skoblina, 1974; Katagiri and Moriya, 1976). The absence of pronuclear development and activity in these instances has been explained in terms of the lack of a suitable cytoplasmic state established after the release or experimental injection of germinal vesicle material. Whether or not this situation is applicable to the eggs of all animals is unknown. Investigations of Iwamatsu (1966) suggest that male pronuclear development may not depend upon on substances derived from the germinal vesicle in all organisms.

Results of studies reinseminating zygotes and two-cell stage embryos indicate that a component(s) disappears or is inactive at later periods of development in the hamster (Yanagimachi and Usui, 1972; Usui and Yanagimachi, 1976). In this case incorporated spermatozoa fail to metamorphase into male pronuclei. On the other hand, Sugiyama (1951) reported that in re-inseminated sea urchin embryos at least a portion of the paternally derived structures incorporated into the embryo undergo a morphogenesis similar to that observed during fertilization. These results are similar to those of Graham (1966), who showed that accessory sperm incorporated into fertilized *Xenopus* eggs at different times after insemination undergo DNA synthesis and mitosis in synchrony with the male and female pronuclei. Graham (1966) concludes that specific signals exist in egg cytoplasm for the induction of DNA synthesis and mitosis (cf. also Graham *et al.*, 1966; Gurdon and Woodland, 1968; Ziegler and Masui, 1973; de Terra, 1969; Johnson and Rao, 1971). Moreover these results also suggest that components required for activation of incorporated spermatozoa are still present for a period after fertilization.

In connection with the above observations, experiments by Sawicki and Koprowski (1971) demonstrated that sperm, incorporated into cultured somatic cells by the technique of Sendai virus-induced cell fusion, fail to form male pronuclei and undergo DNA synthesis (cf. also Bendich *et al.*, 1974; Zelenin *et al.*, 1974; Phillips *et al.*, 1976). In some cases sperm chromatin decondensation in heterokaryons (Gabara *et al.*, 1973) has been described and DNA synthesis has been detected in sperm nuclei pretreated with lysolecithin and incorporated by SV40-transformed Syrian hamster cells (Gledhill *et al.*, 1972). Studies by Phillips *et al.* (1976) of cell hybridization with sperm suspensions have shown that spermatozoa are spontaneously taken up by fibroblasts in tissue culture by phagocytosis. Although sperm readily enter tissue culture cells, it appears unlikely that they make a contribution to the genetic content of the recipient cell. The morphological alterations that take place in sperm after they enter a cell have the character of degenerative changes rather than sperm activation (Phillips *et al.*, 1976).

Studies by Hunter (1967), with polyspermic porcine ova, also indicate the presence of a component(s) within the cytoplasm of eggs that is responsible for a portion of the development of male pronuclei. Light microscopic observations of polyspermic porcine eggs revealed the presence of completed male pronuclei and undeveloped, incorporated sperm nuclei within the same cytoplasm. On the basis of such results Hunter (1967) suggested that an agent responsible for a portion of male pronuclear development was present in egg cytoplasm in a limited quantity. Moreover, Hunter (1967) suggested that the material may have been exhausted or inactivated by the developed male pronuclei and therefore was unable to exert its effect on remaining incorporated sperm nuclei.

Experiments by Longo (1973b) with polyspermic surf clam (Spisula) eggs are consistent with Hunter's (1967) suggestion; however, other possibilities may account for the presence of male pronuclei and incorporated sperm nuclei in the same cytoplasm. For example, Longo and Anderson (1970b) and Longo and Schuel (1973) have observed polyspermic sea urchin eggs in which supernumerary sperm are incorporated into the zygote during the later stages of fertilization; i.e., multiple sperm entry into the egg does not occur at approximately the same time, but rather over a protracted period.

Immature Arbacia eggs, which lack a block to multiple sperm incorporation, can be inseminated and become polyspermic (Longo, 1977). Electron microscopic observations demonstrated that spermatozoa were able to fuse with previtellogenic, vitellogenic, meiotically dividing oocytes and eggs having completed meiosis (pronuclear ova) (Longo, 1978; cf. also, Longo and Plunkett, 1973; Franklin, 1965). Incorporated sperm nuclei exhibited greater differentiation with oocyte maturation (Longo, 1977). Transformation of incorporated sperm nuclei into male pronuclei, i.e., disappearance of the sperm nuclear envelope, chromatin dispersion, and formation of a pronuclear envelope was only observed in inseminated pronuclear eggs. Sperm nuclei that enter meiotically dividing oocytes decondense to a limited extent but not to the same degree as observed in inseminated pronuclear ova. Cisternae do not become associated with the dispersed chromatin and a nuclear envelope is not formed in these specimens. Sperm nuclei incorporated into pre- and vitellogenic oocytes become surrounded by membranous elements of undetermined origin and do not undergo chromatin dispersion (Longo, 1977). The direct relation of sperm nuclear differentiation and egg maturation in sea urchins lends support to the notion that factors or conditions required for pronuclear development appear (are activated) as the egg progresses through meiosis (Thibault, 1973; Delage, 1901; Iwamatsu and Chang, 1971; Skoblina, 1974, 1976; Dettlaff *et al.,* 1964; Katagiri, 1974; Katagiri and Moriya, 1976; Ziegler and Masui, 1973; Smith and Ecker, 1969; Brachet, 1922).

IV. Pronuclear Development and Activity in Cross-Fertilized Eggs

Although a number of investigations employing hybrid embryos have been published (cf. Wilson, 1925; Giudice, 1973), few have considered changes undergone by the sperm nucleus upon its entry into a "foreign" ooplasm. Recent investigations have been carried out in which sea urchin *(Arbacia)* ova have been inseminated with mussel *(Mytilus)* sperm by treating the eggs with trypsin and suspending the gametes in alkaline seawater (Longo, 1976b).

Mytilus sperm become incorporated into *Arbacia* eggs via the coalescence of the membrane outlining the acrosomal process of the spermatozoon and the plasmalemma of the egg (Colwin and Colwin, 1967). Accompanying the sperm nucleus during its entry into the cortex of the egg are the sperm mitochondria and flagellar axoneme. As a result of the disappearance of the nuclear envelope, the condensed chromatin of incorporated *Mytilus* sperm nuclei is placed in direct contact with the cytoplasm of the egg. Dispersion of the condensed sperm chromatin occurs in a manner morphologically similar to that observed for *Mytilus* sperm incorporated into *Mytilus* ova (Longo and Anderson, 1969d) and yields a mass of diffused nucleoplasm. During the latter stages of chromatin dispersion, vesicles aggregate along the periphery of the dispersed chromatin, fuse together, and form a nuclear envelope.

Unlike male pronuclei that form in *Mytilus* zygotes, those that develop in cross-fertilized *Arbacia* eggs are spheroidal and smaller, measuring approximately 6 μm in diameter (Table I). Nucleolus-like bodies consisting of a fine-textured material and structurally similar to those observed in male pronuclei of polyspermic *Arbacia* eggs (Longo and Anderson, 1970a,b) develop in male pronuclei derived from *Mytilus* sperm incorporated into *Arbacia* eggs. Nucleolus-like bodies have not been observed in male or female pronuclei of monospermic *Mytilus* eggs (Longo and Anderson, 1969c,d) and, as far as we are aware, the morphology of male pronuclei of *Mytilus* zygotes under conditions of polyspermy or delayed migration has not been reported. Consequently, the manner in which nucleolus-like bodies are formed in male pronuclei of *Arbacia* ♀ × *Mytilus* ♂ hybrids requires further investigation.

The basis for the structural similarity between *Arbacia* male pronuclei and those that form in *Arbacia* ♀ × *Mytilus* ♂ hybrids was not established. Earlier investigations (Wilson, 1925) have shown that differences in pronuclear morphogenesis exhibited by various organisms

TABLE I

DIAMETER AND VOLUME OF MALE AND FEMALE PRONUCLEI IN *Mytilus*
AND *Arbacia* ZYGOTES AND CROSS-FERTILIZED *Arbacia* EGGS[a]

Site	Nuclear diameter (μm)	Nuclear volume (μm^3)
Mytilus sperm nucleus	2.2 ± 0.16	5.6
Mytilus male pronucleus in *Mytilus* zygote	10.7 ± 1.0	647.7
Arbacia male pronucleus in *Arbacia* zygote	4.5 ± 0.29	48.1
Mytilus male pronucleus in *Arbacia* zygote	5.8 ± 0.61	103.2
Arbacia female pronucleus in fertilized egg	10.9 ± 0.67	684.7
Arbacia female pronucleus in artifically activated egg	11.1 ± 0.48	723.1
Arbacia female pronucleus in cross-fertilized egg	12.2 ± 0.67	960.1

[a] Taken from Longo (1976b).

may be accounted for by the element of time, i.e., the interval between sperm entry and association of the pronuclei. If this period is prolonged in sea urchin zygotes, the male pronucleus, which is normally smaller than the female at the time of their fusion, enlarges, and the later events of fertilization take on characteristics observed in *Mytilus* zygotes (Wilson, 1925). Early investigators demonstrated (cf. Wilson, 1925) that when sperm entry occurs prior to the completion of polar body formation, the male and female pronuclei are approximately equal in volume at the time of their association. If, however, sperm entrance is deferred until after polar body formation the pronuclei are unequal in size, the male being smaller than the female.

Variations in pronuclear morphogenesis may be a reflection of differences in conditions or factors within the egg. The relation of factors that are normally involved in the morphogenesis of homologous sperm nuclei into male pronuclei to those that apparently function in cross-fertilized sea urchin eggs was not determined. If such factors function in cross-fertilized ova, they may affect pronuclear development in several ways. For example, pronuclei may develop characteristics of the species from which the spermatozoon was derived; i.e., conditions within the egg may initiate the morphogenesis of the male pronucleus but not determine its pattern (the latter being indigenous to the sperm itself). Conversely, components of the egg may act in a manner whereby male pronuclei develop that are characteristic of the host species. Results have been presented to show that *Mytilus* sperm nuclei are able to react to conditions within *Arbacia* ova and differentiate into male pronuclei (Longo, 1976b). However, unequivocal evidence that pronuclear morphogenesis follows one or the other of the above proposed schemes has not been obtained.

Morphogenesis of male pronuclei in *Arbacia* ♀ × *Mytilus* ♂ hybrids is similar to that described for studies of nuclear transplantation and somatic cell fusion (cf. Gurdon and Woodland, 1968; Gurdon, 1974; Harris, 1974; Johnson and Rao, 1971). One of the earliest consequences of nuclei transplanted in *Xenopus* egg cytoplasm is their swelling, which may represent a 60-fold increase in volume. The increase in volume of incorporated *Mytilus* sperm nuclei, as they differentiate into male pronuclei in *Mytilus* and *Arbacia* eggs, is approximately 115- and 20-fold, respectively. Although it is uncertain whether or not swelling of transplanted nuclei is necessary for changes in gene function, it is, nevertheless, related to DNA synthesis (Gurdon and Woodland, 1968). Nuclear swelling is also thought to be related to (1) the uptake of essential components (Arms, 1968; Merriam, 1969) and (2) the alteration of nuclear chromatin in such a manner that it can respond to whatever kind of synthesis the cytoplasm is promoting (Gurdon and Woodland, 1968; Johnson and Rao, 1971).

In fertilized eggs of *Mytilus,* the male and female pronuclei migrate centrad but do not fuse in the manner described for *Arbacia* (Longo and Anderson, 1968). Instead, the pronuclei undergo a pattern of morphogenesis characteristic of the *Ascaris* type of fertilization. Direct evidence has not been obtained to indicate whether or not male pronuclei derived from *Mytilus* sperm are able to fuse with the female pronucleus in *Arbacia* ♀ × *Mytilus* ♂ hybrids. However, observations which suggest that pronuclear fusion may occur include the following ones. (1) Many of the female pronuclei examined 60 minutes after insemination were larger than their counterparts in unfertilized eggs and contained regions of condensed chromatin that were distributed in a manner similar to that found in zygote nuclei of polyspermic eggs (Longo and Anderson, 1970a,b). (b) Sperm axonemes were observed within the perinuclear region of such female pronuclei, suggesting that male pronuclei may become closely associated with the female pronucleus. This evidence is at best only circumstantial, since other interpretations of such observations are possible. Furthermore, there is no indication that the concluding events of fertilization as observed in *Mytilus* zygotes occur in cross-fertilized *Arbacia* eggs.

V. Transformations of the Paternally Derived Chromatin

The nucleus of the mature spermatozoon is generally considered to be metabolically inert and having no obvious active role in the mature cell. This impression stems partially from the considerable structural and molecular modification the sperm nucleus undergoes during spermatogenesis, and the failure of the nucleus to participate in the synthesis of nucleic acids (Mazia and Hinegardner, 1963; Loeb *et al.*, 1969; Johnson and Hnilica, 1970; Premkumar and Bhargava, 1972). The timing of DNA synthesis during sperm development has been well characterized in some animals (e.g., rodents) and is usually completed by the primary spermatocyte stage, whereas RNA synthesis ceases soon after the second meiotic division. This period coincides with the beginning of nuclear elongation and fibrillar organization of the spermatid nucleus (Monesi, 1973).

There are numerous reports that under certain circumstances mature sperm nuclei (e.g., bull, rabbit, and sea urchin) may incorporate labeled glycine or adenine (Graves and Salisbury, 1963, 1966; Salisbury and Hart, 1970; Koefed-Johnsen *et al.*, 1968; Malkin, 1953). Hecht (1974) has demonstrated the presence of and characterized a DNA-dependent, DNA polymerase isolated from bovine spermatozoa. Comparison of this polymerase with others isolated from subcellular fractions of bovine and murine cells suggests that it may be of mitochondrial origin. A nuclear DNA-polymerase activity has been detected *in situ* in sectioned mouse spermatozoa by Chevaillier and Philippe (1976). The biological significance of this polymerase activity remains to be elucidated.

Although there is little direct proof for such a contention, the metabolic inactivity of the sperm nucleus has been attributed to the basic nuclear proteins which are complexed with its DNA. Trypsin treatment of sperm chromatin has been shown to digest histone and release template restriction (Johnson and Hnilica, 1970).

The basic proteins in the sperm nuclei of many organisms differ from those of somatic cells (Bloch, 1969). During its development, the sperm nucleus of many animals acquires nuclear proteins that are often more basic than those found in the nuclei of somatic cells. In some organisms, e.g., crustacea, basic proteins are not detected in sperm nuclei (Vaughn and Hinsch, 1972; Chevaillier, 1966). The sperm of animals that undergo a transition in nuclear protein content do not necessarily acquire the same or similar types of basic proteins. Different types of basic nuclear proteins have been found in different groups of animals and have been classified by Bloch (1969).

In addition to the acquisition of new basic nuclear proteins, developing sperm nuclei of some organisms undergo an elimination of all nonhistone proteins (Monesi, 1973) or there is "almost a maximum exclusion of acid proteins from the nucleus" (Goldstein, 1974). The

investigations of Chevaillier and Philippe (1976) and the data discussed below (cf. Kunkle *et al.*, 1977a; O'Brien and Bellvé, 1976) indicate that nonhistone proteins are present in sperm nuclei of some organisms. For example, as much as 20% of the nuclear proteins found in
the sperm nuclei of the sea urchin *Strongylocentrotus* are nonhistone
(Kunkle *et al.*, 1978a). The presence and relative amounts of nonhistone proteins in sperm of other organisms require further examination,
particularly in light of the prevalent notion that nonhistone proteins
participate in the specific regulation of gene transcription (Gilmour,
1974; Stein *et al.*, 1974).

A number of hypotheses have been proposed to account for the basic
nuclear protein changes that occur in sperm nuclei during spermiogenesis, and these are reviewed by (Bloch, 1969). These supposi-
tions include sperm basic proteins (1) permit condensation and stream-
lining of the sperm nucleus (Subirana, 1975), (2) inhibit template activity, (3) have a protective role, (4) permit the sperm nucleus to with-
stand adverse environmental conditions and long periods of storage, (5)
"erase" the developmental history of the cell, thereby affording a
means by which the nucleus of the spermatozoon is made "totipotent,"
and (6) reflect a need of early embryonic development. There is little or
no proof for many of the above suggestions. In fact, evidence exists
contrary to some of the proposals just cited (cf. Bloch, 1969). For example, in some organisms template activity ceases before developing
sperm nuclei acquire distinctive sperm basic proteins (Bloch, 1969).

During spermiogenesis the nuclear chromatin becomes condensed.
In the cricket this is correlated with a disappearance of inter-
chromosomal granules and fibrils and a loss of nohistone proteins as
measured by histochemical and electron microscopic techniques (Kaye
and McMaster-Kaye, 1966). Chromatin fibrils increase in diameter;
the physical basis for this enlargement is not understood. A number of
suggestions, such as aggregation, coiling, folding, have been proposed;
however, none have been substantiated (cf. Kaye, 1969). Chromatin material is seen as a system of thick fibers, granules, or an interconnect-
ing system of lamellae. These become more densely packed until, at the
end of spermiogenesis, the nucleus often appears as a uniformily dense
mass when sectioned specimens are observed by transmission electron
microscopy. Other techniques, however, reveal a definite pattern in the
chromatin of mature sperm of some animals (Koehler, 1966; Inoue and
Sato, 1966). There is relatively little correlative work on changes
in chromatin morphology and protein content of the sperm nucleus
during its development (cf. Kaye, 1969; Kaye and McMaster-Kaye,

1975; Gledhill, 1975; Calvin, 1975). Recent studies by Marushige and Marushige (1975) demonstrated that the acquisition of arginine-rich proteins is intimately involved in the process of chromatin condensation of developing rat spermatozoa.

Bilaminar nuclear envelopes are found in the sperm of most animals studied to date; however, the sperm chromatin of some nematodes and coccid insects is not associated with membrane (Foor, 1970; Moses and Wilson, 1970; cf. Franke and Scheer, 1974; Baccetti and Afzelius, 1976). What function the sperm nuclear envelope may serve is open to question, particularly in light of the fact that the nucleus is supposedly metabolically inert and this bilaminar structure is dismantled rather quickly following gamete fusion (cf. Longo, 1973a). Although pores have been observed in portions of the nuclear envelope of the sperm of some organisms (Fawcett, 1975; Franklin, 1968; Stanley, 1969, 1971a,b; Rattner and Brinkley, 1971; Wooding and O'Donnell, 1971), the regular absence of such fenestrations suggests that the sperm nuclear envelope may be protective.

As previously indicated the sperm nucleus on entering the egg cytoplasm transforms from a dense mass to a highly dispersed aggregation of nuclear protein (Bedford, 1970; Longo, 1973a; Longo and Anderson, 1969d; Yanagimachi and Noda, 1970; Pasteels, 1965; Zamboni, 1971). The mechanism by which this change is brought about is unknown; however, the breakage of disulfide bonds has been implicated in the case of incorporated mammalian sperm (cf. Calvin and Bedford, 1971; Mahi and Yanagimachi, 1975; Heston et al., 1975; see below).

A number of investigators have commented on the fact that the morphology of chromatin dispersion appears the opposite of nuclear condensation during spermiogenesis (Szollosi and Ris, 1961; Bedford, 1970). Comparisons of chromatin dispersion during pronuclear development and condensation during spermatid morphogenesis show little similarity in the species that have been critically examined (Longo and Dornfeld, 1967; Longo and Anderson, 1969a,b). Moreover, there is evidence to indicate that the protein changes the sperm nucleus undergoes during its formation in the testis differ considerably as it metamorphoses into a male pronucleus (Kunkle et al., 1978a).

It is suggested that transformations in chromatin conformation during pronuclear development represent changes in the nuclear protein content of the paternally derived chromatin (Kunkle et al., 1978a). As stated by Goldstein (1974) ". . . when a sperm nucleus is 'transplanted' (by fertilization) to a new cytoplasm it is genetically 'reactivated' in the zygote. This reactivation occurs concomitantly with a marked enlargement of nuclear volume, which undoubtedly occurs by an acquisition of macromolecules from the cytoplasm."

Histochemical studies have shown that most sperm nuclei react with stains specific for basic proteins before fertilization; however, after insemination, the male pronucleus does not show the same staining reaction (Bloch, 1969; Bloch and Hew, 1960; C. C. Das *et al.*, 1964; N. K. Das *et al.*, 1975). Recent investigations, employing radioactively labeled arginine incorporated into sperm indicate that the basic proteins of the paternally derived chromatin are, in fact, lost shortly after sperm incorporation, during development of the male pronucleus (Ecklund and Levine, 1975; Kopečný and Pavlok, 1975a,b). The radioactivity formerly associated with the spermatozoa does not remain within either the male pronucleus or within the zygote cytoplasm. It is suggested that the labeled protein(s) is diluted by the ooplasm or leaves the zygote. Ecklund and Levine (1975) have shown that the labeled protein that is lost after fertilization is a sperm-specific nuclear protein, referred to as Mz, and is not adventitiously bound.

The work of Ecklund and Levine (1975) has some bearing, indirectly at least, on the suggested function of sperm basic nuclear proteins. The sperm specific protein, Mz, is acquired during spermiogenesis when spermatid DNA is being packaged into a condensed form for transmission to the egg. When chromatin condensation is completed the sperm DNA does not synthesize RNA. The behavior of Mz protein, i.e., its acquisition and loss, is temporally associated with the regulation of the form and function of mouse DNA in the spermatozoon and in the fertilized ovum. Although proof to substantiate this claim is lacking, this correlation suggests that Mz protein may play a role in the management of the male genome during genetic transmission and subsequent re-activation.

Hnilica and Johnson (1970) and Johnson and Hnilica (1970, 1971) have also demonstrated that there is an apparent loss of sperm-specific nuclear protein upon fertilization (cf. also, Subirana and Palau, 1968; Subirana, 1970; Easton and Chalkley, 1972). These investigators were able to isolate typical histones from sea urchin sperm but were unable to do so from fertilized eggs. The lack of typical histones in fertilized eggs is also found in other organisms, e.g., the snail (Bloch and Hew, 1960; Bloch, 1963) and the frog (Horn, 1962; Moore, 1963). These findings are in agreement with those of Thaler *et al.* (1970) and Spiegel *et al.* (1970), who have extracted basic proteins from nuclei and chromatin of unfertilized and fertilized sea urchin eggs.

More recent experiments have analyzed the total nuclear protein changes of the paternally derived chromatin upon fertilization by a direct comparative analysis of polyacrylamide gel electrophoretic profiles of proteins from sperm nuclei and male and female pronuclei (Kunkle *et al.*, 1978a). Changes in the nuclear protein content of the paternally derived chromatin were investigated in the following manner: Sperm nuclei and male and female pronuclei were isolated; their nuclear proteins were extracted by increasing salt washes (0.1 to 1.0 M NaCl) and then analyzed by polyacrylamide gel electrophoresis (PAGE).

VI. Nuclear Protein Changes in the Paternally Derived Chromatin at Fertilization

Attempts have been made to isolate pure preparations of male pronuclei from zygotes of sea urchins by sucrose density gradient centrifugation but they have not been successful (Kunkle *et al.*, 1978a). Comparisons, however, were made of nuclear proteins isolated by stepwise salt elution (0.1, 0.25, 0.6, and 1.0 M NaCl) from sperm nuclei, female pronuclei, and those extracted from a population consisting of male and female pronuclei (Kunkle *et al.*, 1978a). A residual protein fraction, those proteins soluble in sodium dodecyl sulfate after the salt washes of the nuclei and pronuclei, was also prepared.

That the nuclear protein of male pronuclei contributes to the polypeptide profiles on polyacrylamide gels of a combination of male and female pronuclei has been demonstrated by the following observations. (1) The male pronuclei outnumbered the females by approximately 2:1 in the pronuclear isolates. (2) Activation of ova had a negligible effect on the quantity of nuclear protein extracted per 100 ml of settled eggs (Table II). (3) The nuclear protein obtained from combined male and female pronuclei per 100 ml of settled zygotes was approximately twice that of unfertilized eggs (Table II), indicating that

TABLE II

Nuclear Protein Extractable from
Isolated Pronuclei[a]

Source of nuclear protein	Milligrams of protein per 100 ml of settled eggs
Female pronuclei (unactivated)	2.6
Female pronuclei (activated)	2.8
Male and female pronuclei	4.8

[a] Taken from Kunkle *et al.* (1978a).

male pronuclei do contribute significantly to the nuclear protein extract.

Contrary to what has been suggested for sperm of other organisms (Monesi, 1973; Dixon, 1972; Kopecný and Pavlok, 1975a), the sperm nucleus of the sea urchin *Strongylocentrotus* contains numerous proteins, the majority of which have molecular weights of less than 80,000 (Kunkle *et al.*, 1978a). This finding is in agreement with investigations by Platz *et al.* (1975), O'Brien and Bellvé (1976), and Gineitis *et al.* (1976), who reported similar results for rat spermatids and mouse and sea urchin spermatozoa.

There is a major change in both the solubility characteristic and polypeptide profiles of the sperm nucleus upon insemination (Table III; Fig. 4). By 15 minutes after insemination, the percentage of protein extracted from combined male and female pronuclei in each salt wash resembled the extracts from female pronuclei (Table III). The most dramatic change following insemination was in the percentage of protein extractable in 1.0 M NaCl. Ninty-three percent of the sperm nuclear protein was soluble in 1.0 M NaCl compared with only 5% in the combined male and female pronuclei. Sperm nuclei had 2% of their protein insoluble in the salt washes compared with 89% from the combined male and female pronuclei. Therefore, it appears that a major reorganization of proteins of both low and high molecular weight occur within the sperm nucleus during its development into a male pronucleus and the means by which this transformation is achieved is unknown.

TABLE III

PERCENTAGE OF EXTRACTABLE PROTEIN IN EACH SALT WASH
OF NUCLEI AND PRONUCLEI[a,b]

Solvent	Male and female pronuclei	Female pronuclei (unactivated ova)	Female pronuclei (activated ova)	Sperm nuclei
NaCl				
0.1M	2	2	3	3
0.25M	1	1	1	1
0.6M	2	3	3	0.8
1.0M	5	5	4	93
SDS	90	89	89	2

[a] Taken from Kunkle *et al.* (1978a).

[b] Percentages were calculated from total extractable protein from each nuclear and pronuclear fraction.

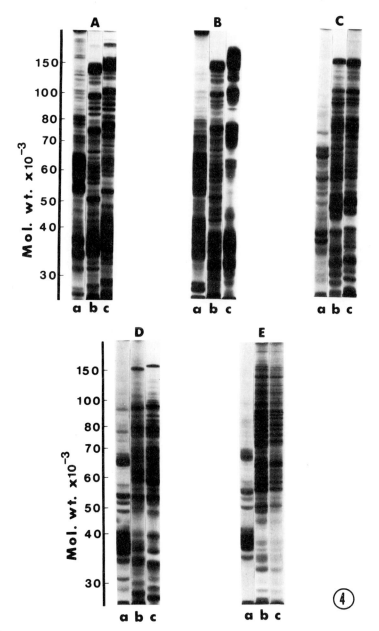

Fig. 4. Polyacrylamide gel electrophoretic profiles of proteins extracted from sperm nuclei (a), combined male and female pronuclei (b), and female pronuclei (c). A to D: 0.1, 0.25, 0.6, and 1.0 M NaCl-soluble proteins; E: sodium dodecyl sulfate-soluble proteins. Taken from Kunkle *et al.* (1978a).

Since separation of male from female pronuclei has not been accomplished a direct analysis of the proteins of the paternally derived chromatin has not been carried out. Nevertheless, the results of Kunkle *et al.* (1978a) indicate the likelihood that the male pronucleus contains the same or similar polypeptide species as the female pronucleus.

Investigations of Gurdon (1974), Harris (1974), and Thompson and McCarthy (1968) demonstrated that the cytoplasm into which a nucleus is placed exerts an effect on its morphology and synthetic activities. The resemblance in morphology and synthetic activities of male and female pronuclei have been demonstrated by Longo and Anderson (1970a,b) and Longo and Plunkett (1973). The similarities in nuclear protein profiles between male and female pronuclei (Kunkle *et al.*, 1977a) is consistent with the morphological and functional similarities of the maternally and paternally derived chromatin.

The proteins that become associated with the paternally derived chromatin shortly after its entry into the egg may function in the structural modification of the condensed chromatin making up the sperm nucleus and in gene activation (cf. Gurdon, 1975; Merriam, 1969; Goto and Ringertz, 1974; Appels *et al.*, 1974, 1975). Although there is a temporal coincidence of the protein changes with other activities of the paternally derived chromatin, it is unknown whether or not they are causally related.

Experiments by Paoletti and Huang (1969) and Johnson and Hnilica (1970) indicate that sperm nuclei are inactive in RNA synthesis even with added *Escherichia coli* RNA polymerase. These results suggest that sea urchin sperm DNA is not available for nucleic acid synthesis. Some investigators (Kaulenas and Fairbairn, 1968; Foor, 1970; Longo and Kunkle, 1977) demonstrated that the paternal genome (male pronucleus) is capable of RNA synthesis soon after its entry into the egg. Furthermore, it has been shown in a number of organisms that both the male and female pronuclei are capable of DNA replication (Simmel and Karnofsky, 1961; Hinegardner *et al.*, 1964; Luthardt and Donahue, 1973; Longo and Plunkett, 1973; Anderson, 1969; Graham, 1966). Thus, during fertilization the paternal genome goes from a state in which it is inactive in nucleic acid synthesis to one whereby it actively engages in these functions. Nonhistone nuclear proteins (NHP) have been shown to be responsible for the regulation of gene activity (cf. Stein *et al.*, 1974). These newly acquired capacities may be initiated and regulated by the NHP which become associated with the paternally derived chromatin during the development of the male pronucleus.

VII. Origin of Nuclear Proteins That Become Associated with Sperm Chromatin

The relatively brief period required for pronuclear development in some organisms (Longo and Anderson, 1968; Longo, 1973a) and the fact that this process occurs when protein synthesis is reduced by 80% suggest that the proteins which become associated with the paternal genome may be present in the egg prior to fertilization (Longo, 1976a; cf. also Hultin, 1961). The presence of proteins that have an affinity for the paternally derived chromatin has been investigated by incubating isolated sperm nuclei in egg cytosol (Kunkle *et al.*, 1978b). In addition, since the sperm chromatin is exposed to the ooplasm at fertilization (Longo, 1973a), the possibility exists that some cytoplasmic proteins have an affinity for DNA. To test for the presence of DNA-binding proteins, egg cytosol was passed through DNA–agaraose columns (Kunkle *et al.*, 1978b).

Isolated sea urchin (Strongylocentrotus) sperm nuclei incubated in egg cytosol undergo nuclear enlargement and spherulation (Fig. 5). This effect was potentiated, i.e., relatively more protein became associated with sperm nuclei when they were treated with 0.25 N HCl to extract basic proteins prior to incubation in egg cytosol (Table IV). Incubation in cytosol from *Physarum*, transformed NRK cells, and Novikoff cells had no effect on the morphology of isolated sperm nuclei. These structural changes mimic the normal morphogenesis of the sperm nucleus into a male pronucleus and indicate that factors responsible for nuclear enlargement may be present in the egg prior to fertilization. Incubation in saturating amounts of cytosol demonstrated that approximately 1% of the cytoplasmic proteins bind to acid-washed

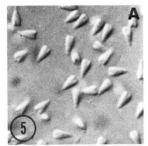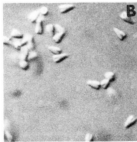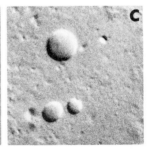

FIG. 5. Photomicrographs of sperm nuclei unincubated and incubated in egg cytosol. (A) Isolated sperm nuclei; (B) isolated sperm nuclei after treatment with 0.25 N HCl; (C) acid-washed sperm nuclei after 75 minutes of incubation in egg cytosol. All ×1200. Taken from Kunkle *et al.* 1978b).

TABLE IV

Change in Extractable Protein from Sperm Nuclei
upon Incubation in Egg Cytosol[a]

Eluent	A	B	B:A
	Protein, μg per 10^8 sperm, unincubated	Protein, μg per 10^8 sperm, incubated[b]	
NaCl *(M)*			
0.1	2.9	19.0	6.8
0.25	0.9	19.0	21.0
0.6	0.7	36.0	51.0
1.0	87.0	57.0	0.7
SDS (5%)	1.9	31.0	16.0
	Protein, μg per 10^8 acid-washed sperm, unincubated	Protein, μg per 10^8 acid-washed sperm, incubated[b]	
NaCl *(M)*			
0.1	1.8	47.0	81.0
0.25	1.0	87.0	87.0
0.6	3.1	66.0	21.0
1.0	2.0	66.0	33.0
SDS (5%)	11.9	300.0	25.0

[a] Taken from Kunkle *et al.* (1978a).

[b] Nuclei incubated in unfertilized egg cytosol.

sperm. Incubation also causes the protein/DNA ratio to increase from 0.11 to 3.7. Hence, there are proteins in the egg cytoplasm that have an affinity for sperm nuclei. Similar results have been reported by Skoblina (1976) and Katagiri and Moriya (1976) who have shown that sperm nuclei microinjected into amphibian eggs behave in a manner similar to that of sperm nuclei during fertilization, i.e., they swell, synthesize DNA, and divide. Uehara and Yanagimachi (1977) demonstrated that testicular and cauda epididymal sperm nuclei injected into hamster eggs by micromanipulation could transform into pronuclei. Furthermore, these results are in agreement with experiments by Sevaljevic (1973) who demonstrated that antibodies made against sea urchin egg cytoplasm were able to precipitate chromatin from nuclei obtained at later stages of development.

Kunkle *et al.* (1978b) have shown that although 93% of the whole sperm nuclear protein is removed with 1.0 *M* NaCl only 10% of the protein remaining after acid treatment is soluble in 1.0 M NaCl (Table IV). It is therefore likely that the acid-soluble proteins are identical to those soluble in 1.0 M NaCl. Upon incubation of whole sperm nuclei in cytosol, about 30% of the proteins of the 1.0 M NaCl fraction are removed and the other fractions show large increases in polypeptides. This phenomenon may be a partial reflection of the *in vivo* loss of basic proteins during the development of the male pronucleus (Bloch and Hew, 1960; Das *et al.*, 1964; Ecklund and Levine, 1975; Kopecny and Pavlok, 1975b), since the pronuclear proteins soluble in 1.0 M NaCl comprise only 5% of the total pronuclear proteins (Kunkle *et al.*, 1978a).

Comparison of PAGE profiles of acid-washed sperm nuclei incubated and unincubated in egg cytosol demonstrate that a large proportion of the proteins associated with incubated nuclei have molecular weights greater than 60,000 (Fig. 6). Moreover, incubation of acid-washed sperm nuclei in egg cytosol results in the binding of many polypeptides that have the same apparent molecular weights as proteins associated with combined and male and female pronuclei. Whether or not these proteins are the same has not been established. Experiments to analyze the function of these proteins are necessary before any conclusive statements concerning their role in pronuclear development can be made.

For the components tested (e.g., NaCl, acidic and basic polymers), the ionic composition of the incubating medium does not induce swelling of sperm nuclei (Kunkle *et al.*, 1978b; cf. also Coffey *et al.*, 1974). Furthermore, incubation of acid-washed sperm nuclei in unsaturating amounts of egg cytosol (up to 36 hours) does not induce enlargement. Thus, some limiting component within the egg cytoplasm may be necessary for sperm nuclear enlargement.

A number of methods have been employed to disperse mammalian sperm nuclei *in vitro* and to isolate and characterize the sperm chromatin and nuclear protein (Borenfreund *et al.*, 1961; Henricks and Mayer, 1965; Lung, 1972; Mahi and Yanagimachi, 1975). Sodium dodecyl sulfate and dithiothreitol have been used to study nuclear stabilization during sperm maturation (Calvin and Bedford, 1971; Calvin *et al.*, 1973; Calvin, 1975). The stabilization of the sperm nucleus by disulfide bonds makes it reasonable to assume that these must be broken before chromatin dispersion and formation of a male pronucleus can occur. Calvin and Bedford (1971) have speculated that the high concentration of protein —SH groups in mammalian ova makes it possible that a thio-disulfide exchange reaction may be involved in the mechanisms of this nuclear expansion. A similar possibility is also proposed by Mahi and Yanagimachi (1975) involving glutathione.

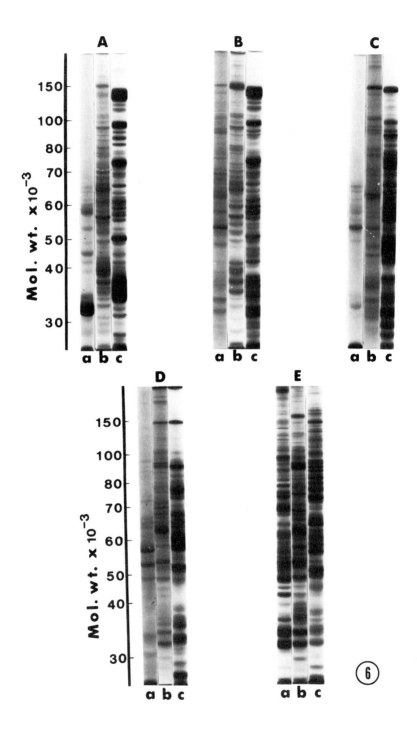

To analyze for the presence of cytoplasmic DNA-binding proteins, the postribosomal supernatant from unfertilized eggs was passed through sequential columns of native and denatured DNA-agarose (Kunkle et al., 1978b). It was found that approximately 1% of the cytoplasmic proteins bound to native DNA and 1% to denatured DNA. Each of the fractions from the native and denatured columns demonstrated a heterogeneous population of polypeptides ranging in molecular weight from 25,000 to over 250,000.

Two polypeptides (270,000 and 260,000 molecular weight) that bind to denatured DNA and are removed with 0.1 M NaCl are of particular interest, since they correspond in molecular weight with major polypeptides associated with sea urchin zygote nuclei but not with combined male and female pronuclei (Kunkle et al., 1978b). It has been suggested that these polypeptides may be transported to the nucleus and play some role in its activity.

Although polypeptides are present in egg cytosol that bind to sperm nuclei and DNA, they do not eliminate the possibility that some may be derived de novo (Longo, 1976a; Kunkle et al., 1978b). Further investigations are necessary to determine the origin of the polypeptides that become associated with the paternally derived chromatin, their role in pronuclear morphogenesis and activation of the embryonic genome. Moreover, the fate of the proteins brought into the egg with the sperm nucleus has not been well established. Continued investigation of this aspect of fertilization may bring to light the role of these polypeptides in the sperm nucleus and in the early development of the embryo.

VIII. Changes in Activity of the Paternally Derived Chromatin

The regulatory mechanism of DNA synthesis in fertilized eggs has recently been reviewed by De Petrocellis et al. (1974). Incorporation of precursors of DNA into male and female pronuclei of sea urchin zygotes may precede or follow pronuclear fusion (Hinegardner et al., 1964; Anderson, 1969; Longo and Plunkett, 1973). In those organisms that do not undergo pronuclear fusion, DNA replication appears to take place in the male and female pronuclei prior to and following their association (Luthardt and Donahue, 1973; Graham, 1966; Oprescu and Thibault, 1965).

There is little doubt that DNA replication is controlled in the pronuclei by some factor activated upon insemination. This is supported

---

FIG. 6. Polyacrylamide gel electrophoretic profiles of proteins extracted from acid-washed sperm nuclei unincubated (a) and incubated (b) in egg cytosol and combined male and female pronuclei (c). A to D: 0.1, 0.25, 0.6, and 1.0 M NaCl-soluble proteins; E: sodium dodecyl sulfate-soluble proteins. Taken from Kunkle et al. (1978b).

by the following observations: (1) There is a time lag between insemination and DNA replication in fertilized *Arbacia* eggs (Longo and Plunkett, 1973). Labeled thymidine is taken up by unfertilized ova but is not phosphorylated. Formation of thymidine triphosphate starts at about 10 minutes after insemination (Longo and Plunkett, 1973; De Petrocellis *et al.*, 1974). (2) When DNA synthesis precedes pronuclear fusion, replication commences at the same time in both pronuclei (Simmel and Karnofsky, 1961). (3) In polyspermic eggs treated to prevent pronuclear fusion, male pronuclei initiate DNA synthesis at the same time and in concert with the female pronucleus (Longo and Plunkett, 1973; cf. Graham, 1966).

These data and results of investigations with other organisms demonstrate that male pronuclei are capable of DNA synthesis. Together these results are of particular importance in light of investigations by Mazia and Hinegardner (1963) and Loeb *et al.* (1969), who claimed that sea urchin sperm lack DNA polymerase activity. [In view of more recent findings (Chevaillier and Philippe, 1976), the presence of DNA polymerase activity in mature sperm nuclei requires further examination.] Thus, it is possible that the male pronucleus of sea urchin zygotes may acquire DNA polymerase activity some time during its morphogenesis, possibly from the cytoplasmic region surrounding the reorganizing sperm nucleus. This possibility is supported by investigations of Fansler and Loeb, 1969), who demonstrated DNA polymerase activity in the cytoplasm of the egg and embryo of *Arbacia*. In the unfertilized egg the enzyme appears to be localized in the cytoplasm, and as development proceeds greater activity becomes associated with the blastomere nuclei (Loeb *et al.*, 1969; Fansler and Loeb, 1969).

Kaulenas and Fairbairn (1968; cf. also Foor, 1970) have shown that at fertilization in *Ascaris* eggs there is a massive burst of RNA synthesis by the male genome, at a time when the maternally derived chromatin is occupied with its meiotic divisions. At the same time, a much smaller amount of DNA-like RNA is synthesized. These authors conclude that in *Ascaris* a large fraction of the ribosomes necessary for embryogenesis are synthesized after insemination rather than before and by the paternally rather than the maternally derived genome.

In the sea urchins *Strongylocentrotus* and *Arbacia* it has been shown that male pronuclei are capable of RNA synthesis (Longo and Kunkle, 1977). This claim is supported by the following evidence. (1) Polyspermic eggs show higher levels of [³H]uridine incorporation than monospermic eggs, which sucrose gradient analysis indicates is heterodisperse RNA (Table V). (2) Monospermic and polyspermic eggs treated with actinomycin D have the same levels of [³H]uridine incor-

TABLE V

INCORPORATION OF [³H]URIDINE INTO ZYGOTES OF *Strongylocentrotus purpuratus* AND *Arbacia punctulata*[a,b]

Zygotes	Sperm concentration	Nicotine, 0.2%	Colchicine, 2.75×10^{-4} M	Actino-mycin D	Cpm/10^5 zygotes	
					Strongylocentrotus	*Arbacia*
Monospermic	Dilute	−	−	−	6203	5369
Polyspermic	Concentrated	−	−	−	10016	7864
Monospermic	Dilute	+	+	−	7376	6611
Polyspermic	Concentrated	+	+	−	16539	21201
Monospermic	Dilute	−	+	+	ND	2500
Polyspermic	Concentrated	−	+	+	ND	2500

[a] Taken from Longo and Kunkle (1977).

[b] Eggs were suspended in seawater containing [³H]uridine at a concentration of 58 μCi/ml. Less than 2% of the radioactivity detected in the specimens was in DNA; the remainder was in RNA. Presence (+) or absence (−) of nicotine, colchicine, or actinomycin D.

poration, which sedimentation analysis indicates to be -CCA turnover of tRNA (Table V). (3) Autoradiographs of sea urchin zygotes show silver grains over male and female pronuclei in monospermic and polyspermic zygotes. Mintz (1964) has also reported labeling of pronuclei in mouse zygotes incubated in [³H]uridine. Perhaps the pronuclei of this organism are also transcriptionally active.

The classes of RNA formed by the pronuclei of *Arbacia* and *Strongylocentrotus* zygotes have not been ascertained. Moreover, it is not known whether the RNA synthesized by the male pronucleus is transported to the cytoplasm and utilized by the embryo. It has been speculated that the nuclear protein changes of the paternally derived chromatin during the development of male pronuclei are responsible for this transformation in transcriptional activity of the paternally derived genome (Longo and Kunkle, 1977).

IX. Derivation of the Membrane That Comprises the Nuclear Envelope of the Male Pronucleus

Development of the nuclear envelope of the male pronucleus (male pronuclear envelope) has been studied in numerous organisms (Pasteels, 1963, 1965; Longo and Anderson, 1968, 1969d, 1970c; Yanagimachi and Noda, 1970; Bedford, 1970). The membrane incorporated into the structure of the pronuclear envelope may be derived from (1) the sperm nuclear envelope, (2) nascent membrane (formed *de novo*), and (3) preexisting membrane derived from the egg cytoplasm. Pasteels (1963, 1965) states that in the mollusc *Barnea* the vesicles that aggregate to form the male pronuclear envelope are derived from endoplasmic reticulum of the egg, although conclusive proof was not provided. It is possible that some of the membranous elements that combine to form the pronuclear envelope in *Barnea* may originate from other sources. Ultrastructural observations have demonstrated that a portion of the pronuclear envelope in the sea urchin *Arbacia* is derived from the sperm nuclear envelope (Longo and Anderson, 1968; Longo, 1976a). Observations by Bedford (1970) with rabbit zygotes suggest that none of the sperm nuclear envelope remains after chromatin dispersion and that the limiting membranes of the male pronucleus arise *de novo*. The possible role of excess nuclear envelope contained within some spermatozoa (redundant nuclear envelope) during pronuclear development has been considered by Potswald (1967), Fawcett (1965), and Franklin (1968). Thus far, redundant sperm nuclear envelope has not been shown to be involved in the formation of the male pronuclear envelope. Furthermore, other membranous elements observed in the eggs of many organisms, e.g., annulate lamellae, have not been shown to be involved in the development of the nuclear envelope of the male pronucleus (Longo, 1973a).

The extent to which the sperm nuclear envelope, the endoplasmic reticulum of the egg, and nascent membrane are involved in the formation of the pronuclear envelope of the male pronucleus has been examined by Longo (1976a). Inhibition of protein synthesis by as much as 80% of control preparations has little or no effect on the development of the male pronuclear envelope. Morphogenesis of the male pronucleus in puromycin-treated zygotes is morphologically similar to and occurs within the same period of time as in untreated specimens. This result differs from studies that demonstrate that protein synthesis is involved in the differentiation of the endoplasmic reticulum (Orrenius et al., 1965; Dallner et al., 1966) and is necessary in late G_1 of Don cells for nuclear reconstruction at telophase (Obara et al., 1975). Obara et al. (1975) suggested that the factors responsible for nuclear envelope formation at telophase are macromolecules that may either be catalytic in nature or become structural components of the nuclear envelope.

Electron microscopic observations of *Arbacia* zygotes have demonstrated that the nuclear envelope lining the apical and basal portions of the sperm nucleus are incorporated into the structure of the male pronuclear envelope (Longo and Anderson, 1968; Longo, 1973a, 1976a). Because of their distinctive morphology, these portions of the male pronuclear envelope may be traced up to and following the fusion of the pronuclei. These investigations demonstrate that remnants of the sperm nuclear envelope do make a contribution to the structure of the male pronuclear envelope. The maximum extent of this contribution has been estimated to be about 15% of the male pronuclear envelope (Longo, 1976a). Additional observations indicate that much of the membrane (85%) making up the nuclear envelope of the male pronucleus is derived from elements of endoplasmic reticulum (Longo, 1976a).

That the endoplasmic reticulum contributes to the structure of the male pronuclear envelope has been demonstrated by an analysis of pronuclear development in fertilized stratified eggs and nucleate and nonnucleate halves. The organelles of centrifuged sea urchin eggs layer into fairly homogeneous strata; continued centrifugation of stratified ova brings about their bisection and yields nucleate and nonnucleate halves. A paucity of endoplasmic reticulum is observed in nonnucleate halves and in the centrifugal region of stratified eggs, whereas abundant endoplasmic reticulum is located in nucleate halves and in the centripetal region of stratified eggs (Anderson, 1970; Longo, 1976a).

The period required for the development of the male pronuclear envelope in stratified eggs is inversely related to the amount of endoplasmic reticulum present in the vicinity of the incorporated sperm nucleus (Table VI). The protraction of the development of the male pronuclear nuclear envelope in the centrifugal region of stratified eggs may be due to a deficiency of endoplasmic reticulum within this region of the fertilized ovum. The accelerated development of the male pronuclear envelope in nucleate halves and in the centripetal region of stratified eggs, both possessing copious amounts of endoplasmic reticulum, and the absence of completed male pronuclei for up to 20 minutes after insemination in nonnucleate halves, which lack these membranous elements, supports this contention. These results, however, do not eliminate the possibility that, during centrifugation, factors (e.g., enzymes, a variety of macromolecules) that may be involved in nuclear envelope formation (cf. Obara *et al.*, 1975; Franke *et al.*, 1975) are concentrated in the centripetal region of stratified eggs and nucleate halves and diluted in the centrifugal region of stratified eggs and in nonnucleate halves.

Further evidence in support of the claim that the endoplasmic reticulum of the egg is utilized for the development of the male pronuclear envelope comes from observation of developing male pronuclei located in the centrifugal region of stratified eggs, near the mitochondrial layer. In these cases formation of the pronuclear envelope is often completed along that region facing the centripetal pole (endoplasmic reticulum-rich area) before development along that region directed to the centrifugal pole (endoplasmic reticulum poor area) is initiated.

In considering results obtained with fertilized centrifuged eggs, one must also take into account what effect packing of organelles may have on pronuclear morphogenesis. This parameter has not been measured. Moreover, although the rate of male pronuclear envelope development in stratified eggs is directly related to the amount of endoplasmic present in the vicinity of the reorganizing sperm nucleus, there is an equally strong inverse correlation between pronuclear envelope formation and the amount of yolk and pigment bodies present. Therefore, the possibility remains that they, not the endoplasmic reticulum, influence the rate of pronuclear formation.

X. Summary and Conclusions

The nucleus of the mature spermatozoon can be considered to be at a zero state of activity, and it, like the egg, is activated upon fertilization. The "inactivity" of the sperm nucleus is believed to be due to the basic proteins associated with its DNA. It has been shown that in

TABLE VI

ESTIMATED AMOUNT OF ENDOPLASMIC RETICULUM PRESENT AND TIME REQUIRED TO COMPLETE THE FORMATION OF THE MALE PRONUCLEAR ENVELOPE[a,b]

| | Stratified egg | | Nucleate half | Non-nucleate half |
Parameter	Centripetal region	Centrifugal region	Nucleate half	Non-nucleate half
Estimated amount of endoplasmic reticulum	Abundant	Sparse	Abundant	Negligible
Time required to complete the formation of the pronuclear envelope (minutes after insemination)	4–6	12[c]	4	—[d]

[a] Taken from Longo (1976a).

[b] Estimated amount of endoplasmic reticulum in stratified eggs and nucleate and nonnucleate halves based on observations from 8–12 specimens for each time period sampled.

[c] Completed male pronuclear envelopes first observed at 12 minutes after insemination.

[d] Male pronuclear envelope not formed as late as 20 minutes after insemination.

addition to basic protein, the sperm nucleus also contains nonbasic proteins. The function of these nuclear proteins in the mature sperm and during sperm development, fertilization and early embryogenesis is unknown.

After its incorporation into the egg, the sperm nucleus undergoes a dramatic metamorphosis, which eventually results in the formation of a male pronucleus. Development of the male pronucleus is a nuclear–cytoplasmic phenomenon, which appears to be initiated and presumably guided by components within the egg. Identification of the factors involved and their mode of action has not been accomplished.

The apparent interplay of cytoplasmic elements and structures paternally derived affect structural and functional changes in the sperm nucleus. For example, electron microscopic investigations have demonstrated that maternally derived organelles (endoplasmic reticulum) are directly involved in the formation of the male pronuclear envelope. Moreover, it has been demonstrated that there is a change in the nuclear protein content of the paternally derived chromatin upon insemination. In the case of the sea urchin, the developing male pronucleus acquires a polypeptide profile similar to that observed in the female pronucleus. Whether or not a similar reorganization of nuclear proteins occurs in other organisms has not been determined. It has been speculated that these changes in nuclear protein content are involved in functional changes of the paternally derived chromatin following insemination.

Transformations of sperm nuclei at fertilization are similar to changes observed in nuclei of nuclear transplantation and cell hybridization experiments. In all three instances there is a significant enlargement of the nucleus and dispersion of chromatin following its introduction into a "new" cytoplasm. This correlation is not surprising, for fertilization is nature's method of transplanting nuclei into "new and different" cytoplasms.

Because of the unique state of the sperm nucleus, i.e., one of a poised genome, primed for activation, study of its transformations during pronuclear development should provide new insights into such phenomena as gene activation and nuclear–cytoplasmic interactions. Future efforts in the potentially fruitful areas of nuclear protein changes upon insemination and of the factors initiating and controlling metamorphosis of the sperm nucleus into a male pronucleus may help to support this optimistic, if not biased, view.

ACKNOWLEDGMENT

Appreciation is expressed to Dr. B. Gledhill and Dr. E. Anderson for their discussions on portions of this review.

REFERENCES

Anderson, E. (1970). *J. Cell Biol.* **47**, 711.

Anderson, W. A. (1969). *J. Ultrastruct. Res.* **26**, 95.

Appels, R., and Ringertz, N. R. (1975). *Curr. Top. Dev. Biol.* **9**, 137.

Appels, R., Bolund, L., Goto, S., and Ringertz, N. R. (1974). *Exp. Cell Res.* **85**, 182.

Appels, R., Tallroth, E., Appels, D. M., and Ringertz, N. R. (1975). *Exp. Cell Res.* **92**, 70.

Arms, K. (1968). *J. Embryol. Exp. Morphol.* **20**, 367.

Baccetti, B., and Afzelius, B. A. (1976). "The Biology of the Sperm Cell." Karger, Basel.

Bedford, J. M. (1970). *In* "Mammalian Reproduction" (H. Gibian and E. J. Plotz, eds.), p. 124. Springer-Verlag, Berlin and New York.

Bendich, A., Borenfreund, E., and Sternberg, S. S. (1974). *Science* **183**, 857.

Bloch, D. P. (1963). *J. Cell. Comp. Physiol.* **62**, Suppl. 1, 87.

Bloch, D. P. (1969). *Genetics, Suppl.* **61**, 13.

Bloch, D. P., and Hew, H. Y. C. (1960). *J. Biophys. Biochem. Cytol.* **8**, 69.

Borenfreund, E., Fitt, E., and Bendich, A. (1961). *Nature (London)* **191**, 1375.

Brachet, A. (1922). *Arch. Biol.* **32**, 205.

Calvin, H. I. (1975). *In* "The Biology of the Male Gamete" (J. G. Duckett and P. A. Racey, eds.), p. 257. Academic Press, New York.

Calvin, H. I., and Bedford, J. M. (1971). *J. Reprod. Fertil., Suppl.* **13**, 65.

Calvin, H. I., Yu, C. C., and Bedford, J. M. (1973). *Exp. Cell Res.* **81**, 333.

Chevaillier, P. (1966). *J. Microsc. (Paris)* **5**, 739.

Chevaillier, P., and Philippe, M. (1976). *Chromosoma* **54**, 33.

Coffey, D. S., Barrock, E. R., and Heston, W. E. W. (1974). *Adv. Enzyme Regul.* **12**, 219.

Colwin, L. H., and Colwin, A. L. (1967). *In* "Fertilization" (C. B. Metz and A. Monroy, eds.), Vol. 1, p. 295. Academic Press, New York.

Dallner, G. P., Siekevitz, P., and Palade, G. E. (1966). *J. Cell Biol.* **30**, 97.

Das, C. C., Kaufmann, B. P., and Gay, H. (1964). *J. Cell Biol.* **23**, 423.

Das, N. K., Micou-Eastwood, J., and Alfert, M. (1975). *Dev. Biol.* **43**, 333.

Delage, Y. (1901). *Arch. Zool. Exp. Gen.* (Ser. 3) **9**, 254.

De Petrocellis, B., Grippo, P., Monroy, A., Parisi, E., and Rossi, M. (1974). *In* "Physiology and Genetics of Reproduction" (E. M. Coutinho and F. Fuchs, eds.), p. 35. Plenum, New York.

Dettlaff, T. A., Nikitina, L. A., and Stroeva, O. G. (1964). *J. Embryol. Exp. Morphol.* **12**, 851.

de Terra, N. (1969). *Int. Rev. Cytol.* **25**, 1.

Dixon, G. H. (1972). *In* "Karolinska Symposia on Research Methods in Reproductive Endocrinology" (E. Diczfalusy, ed.), p. 128. Bogtrykkeriet Forum, Copenhagen.

Easton, D., and Chalkley, R. (1972). *Exp. Cell Res.* **72**, 502.

Ecklund, P. S., and Levine, L. (1975). *J. Cell Biol.* **66**, 251.

Fansler, B., and Loeb, L. A. (1969). *Exp. Cell Res.* **57**, 305.

Fawcett, D. W. (1965). *Z. Zellforsch. Mikrosk. Anat.* **67**, 279.

Fawcett, D. W. (1975). *Dev. Biol.* **44**, 394.

Foor, W. E. (1970). *Biol. Reprod., Suppl.* **2**, 177.

Franke, W. W., and Scheer, U. (1974). *In* "The Cell Nucleus" (H. Busch, ed.), Vol. 1, p. 220. Academic Press, New York.

Franke, W. W., Spring, H., Scheer, U., and Zerban, H. (1975). *J. Cell Biol.* **66**, 681.

Franklin, L. E. (1965). *J. Cell Biol.* **25**, 81.

Franklin, L. E. (1968). *Anat. Rec.* **161**, 149.

Gabara, B., Gledhill, B. L., Croce, C. M., Cesarini, J. P., and Koprowski, H. (1973). *Proc. Soc. Exp. Biol. Med.* **143**, 1120.

Gilmour, R. S. (1974). *In* "Acid Proteins of the Nucleus" (I. L. Cameron and J. R. Jeter, eds.), p. 297. Academic Press, New York.

Gineitis, A. A., Nivinskas, H. H., and Vorobev, V. I. (1976). *Exp. Cell Res.* **98,** 248.

Giudice, G. (1973). "Developmental Biology of the Sea Urchin Embryo." Academic Press, New York.

Gledhill, B. L. (1975). *In* "The Biology of the Male Gamete" (J. G. Duckett and P. A. Racey, eds.), p. 215. Academic Press, New York.

Gledhill, B. L., Sawicki, W., Croce, C. M., and Koprowski, H. (1972). *Exp. Cell Res.* **73,** 33.

Goldstein, L. (1974). *In* "The Cell Nucleus" (H. Busch, ed.), Vol. 1, p. 388. Academic Press, New York.

Goto, S., and Ringertz, N. R. (1974). *Exp. Cell Res.* **85,** 173.

Graham, C. F. (1966). *J. Cell Sci.* **1,** 363.

Graham, C. F., Arms, K., and Gurdon, J. B. (1966). *Dev. Biol.* **14,** 349.

Graves, C. N., and Salisbury, G. W. (1963). *Fed. Proc., Fed. Am. Soc. Exp. Biol.* **22,** 569.

Graves, C. N., and Salisbury, G. W. (1966). *Fed. Proc., Fed. Am. Soc. Exp. Biol.* **25,** 314.

Gurdon, J. B. (1974). "The Control of Gene Expression in Animal Development." Harvard Univ. Press, Cambridge, Massachusetts.

Gurdon, J. B. (1975). *In* "Cell Cycle and Cell Differentiation" (J. Reinert and H. Holtzer, eds.), p. 123. Springer-Verlag, Berlin and New York.

Gurdon, J. B., and Woodland, H. R. (1968). *Biol. Rev. Cambridge Philos. Soc.* **43,** 233.

Harris, H. (1974). "Nucleus and Cytoplasm." Oxford Univ. Press (Clarendon), London and New York.

Hecht, N. B. (1974). *J. Reprod. Fertil.* **41,** 345.

Henricks, D. M., and Mayer, D. T. (1965). *Exp. Cell Res.* **40,** 402.

Heston, W. D. W., Zirkin, B. R., and Coffey, D. S. (1975). *Biochem. Biophys. Res. Commun.* **64,** 612.

Hinegardner, R. T., Rao, B., and Feldman, D. E. (1964). *Exp. Cell Res.* **36,** 53.

Hiramoto, Y. (1962). *Exp. Cell Res.* **27,** 416.

Hnilica, L. S., and Johnson, A. W. (1970). *Exp. Cell Res.* **63,** 261.

Horn, E. C. (1962). *Proc. Natl. Acad. Sci. U.S.A.* **48,** 257.

Hultin, T. (1961). *Experientia* **17,** 410.

Hunter, R. H. F. (1967). *J. Exp. Zool.* **165,** 451.

Inoue, S., and Sato, H. (1966). *In* "Molecular Architecture in Cell Physiology" (T. Hayashi and A. Szent-Györgyi, eds.), p. 209. Prentice-Hall, Englewood Cliffs, New Jersey.

Iwamatsu, T. (1966). *Embryologia* **9,** 205.

Iwamatsu, T., and Chang, M. (1971). *J. Reprod. Fert.* **26,** 197.

Iwamatsu, T., and Chang, M. (1972). *J. Reprod. Fert.* **31,** 237.

Johnson, A. W., and Hnilica, L. S. (1970). *Biochim. Biophys. Acta* **224,** 518.

Johnson, A. W., and Hnilica, L. S. (1971). *Biochim. Biophys. Acta* **246,** 141.

Johnson, R. T., and Rao, P. N. (1971). *Biol. Rev. Cambridge Philos. Soc.* **46,** 97.

Katagiri, C. (1974). *J. Embryol. Exp. Morphol.* **31,** 573.

Katagiri, C., and Moriya, M. (1976). *Dev. Biol.* **50,** 235.

Kaulenas, M. S., and Fairbairn, D. (1968). *Exp. Cell Res.* **52,** 233.

Kaye, J. S. (1969). *In* "Handbook of Molecular Cytology" (A. Lima-de-Faria, ed.), p. 361. Am. Elsevier, New York.

Kaye, J. S., and McMaster-Kaye, R. (1966). *J. Cell Biol.* **31,** 159.

Kaye, J. S., and McMaster-Kaye, R. (1975). *In* "The Biology of the Male Gamete" (J. G. Duckett and P. A. Racey, eds.), p. 227. Academic Press, New York.

Koefed-Johnsen, H. H., Fulka, J., and Kopečný, V. (1968). *Proc. Int. Congr. Anim. Reprod. Artif. Insem., 6th, 1968* Vol. 11, p. 1163.

Koehler, J. K. (1966). *J. Ultrastruct. Res.* **16**, 359.

Kopečný, V., and Pavlok, A. (1975a). *Histochemistry* **45**, 341.

Kopečný, V., and Pavlok, A. (1975b). *J. Exp. Zool.* **191**, 85.

Kunkle, M., Longo, F. J., and Magun, B. E. (1978a). *J. Exp. Zool.* (in press).

Kunkle, M., Magun, B. E., and Longo, F. J. (1978b). *J. Exp. Zool.* (in press).

Loeb, L. A., Fansler, B., Williams, R., and Mazia, D. (1969). *Exp. Cell Res.* **57**, 298.

Longo, F. J. (1973a). *Biol. Reprod.* **9**, 149.

Longo, F. J. (1973b). *J. Exp. Zool.* **183**, 153

Longo, F. J. (1976a). *Dev. Biol.* **49**, 347.

Longo, F. J. (1976b). *J. Cell Biol.* **73**, 14.

Longo, F. J. (1978). *Dev. Biol.* (in press).

Longo, F. J., and Anderson, E. (1968). *J. Cell Biol.* **39**, 339.

Longo, F. J., and Anderson, E. (1969a). *J. Ultrastruct. Res.* **27**, 435.

Longo, F. J., and Anderson, E. (1969b). *J. Ultrastruct. Res.* **27**, 486.

Longo, F. J., and Anderson, E. (1969c). *J. Exp. Zool.* **172**, 69.

Longo, F. J., and Anderson, E. (1969d). *J. Exp. Zool.* **172**, 95.

Longo, F. J., and Anderson, E. (1970a). *J. Cell Biol.* **46**, 308.

Longo, F. J., and Anderson, E. (1970b). *J. Cell Biol.* **47**, 646.

Longo, F. J., and Anderson, E. (1970c). *J. Ultrastruct. Res.* **33**, 515.

Longo, F. J., and Dornfeld, E. J. (1967). *J. Ultrastruct. Res.* **20**, 462.

Longo, F. J., and Kunkle, M. (1977). *J. Exp. Zool.* **201**, 431.

Longo, F. J., and Plunkett, W. (1973). *Dev. Biol.* **30**, 56.

Longo, F. J., and Schuel, H. (1973). *Dev. Biol.* **34**, 187.

Lung, B. (1972). *J. Cell Biol.* **52**, 179.

Luthardt, F. W., and Donahue, R. P. (1973). *Exp. Cell Res.* **82**, 143.

Mahi, C. A., and Yanagimachi, R. (1975). *J. Reprod. Fertil.* **44**, 293.

Malkin, H. M. (1953). *Biochim. Biophys. Acta* **12**, 585.

Marushige, Y., and Marushige, K. (1975). *J. Biol. Chem.* **250**, 39.

Mazia, D., and Hinegardner, R. T. (1963). *Proc. Natl. Acad. Sci. U.S.A.* **50**, 148.

Merriam, R. W. (1969). *J. Cell Sci.* **5**, 333.

Mintz, B. (1964). *J. Exp. Zool.* **157**, 85.

Monesi, V. (1973). *In* "The Regulation of Mammalian Reproduction" (S. J. Segal *et al.*, eds.), p. 100. Thomas, Springfield, Illinois.

Moore, B. C. (1963). *Proc. Natl. Acad. Sci. U.S.A.* **50**, 1018.

Moses, M. J., and Wilson, M. H. (1970). *Chromosoma* **30**, 373.

Obara, Y., Weinfeld, H., and Sandberg, A. (1975). *J. Cell Biol.* **64**, 378.

O'Brien, D. A., and Bellvé, A. R. (1976). *J. Cell Biol.* **70**, 108a.

Oprescu, St., and Thibault, C. (1965). *Ann. Biol. Anim., Biochim., Biophys.* **5**, 151.

Orrenius, S., Ericsson, J. L. E., and Ernster, L. (1965). *J. Cell Biol.* **25**, 627.

Paoletti, R., and Huang, R. C. C. (1969). *Biochemistry* **8**, 1615.

Pasteels, J. J. (1963). *Bull. Cl. Sci., Acad. R. Belg.* **49**, 329.

Pasteels, J. J. (1965). *Bull. Soc. Zool. Fr.* **90**, 195.

Phillips, S. G., Phillips, D. M., Dev, V. G., Miller, D. A., Van Diggelen, O. P., and Miller, O. J. (1976). *Exp. Cell Res.* **98**, 429.

Platz, R. D., Grimes, S. D., Meistrich, M. L., and Hnilica, L. S. (1975). *J. Biol. Chem.* **250**, 5791.

Potswald, H. E. (1967). *Z. Zellforsch. Mikrosk. Anat.* **83**, 231.

Premkumar, E., and Bhargava, P. M. (1972). *Nature (London) New Biol.* **240**, 139.

Rattner, J. B., and Brinkley, B. R. (1971). *J. Ultrastruct. Res.* **36,** 1.

Salisbury, G. W., and Hart, R. G. (1970). *Biol. Reprod., Suppl.* **1,** 1.

Sawicki, W., and Koprowski, H., (1971). *Exp. Cell Res.* **66,** 145.

Sevaljević, L. (1973). *Biochim. Biophys. Acta* **335,** 102.

Simmel, E. B., and Karnofsky, D. A. (1961). *J. Biophys. Biochem. Cytol.* **10,** 59.

Skoblina, M. N. (1974). *Ontogenez* **5,** 334.

Skoblina, M. N. (1976). *J. Embryol. Exp. Morphol.* **36,** 67.

Smith, L. D., and Ecker, R. E. (1969). *Dev. Biol.* **19,** 281.

Spiegel, M., Spiegel, E. S., and Meltzer, P. S. (1970). *Dev. Biol.* **21,** 73.

Stanley, H. P. (1969). *J. Ultrastruct. Res.* **27,** 230.

Stanley, H. P. (1971a). *J. Ultrastruct. Res.* **36,** 86.

Stanley, H. P. (1971b). *J. Ultrastruct. Res.* **36,** 103.

Stein, G. S., Spelsberg, T. C., and Kleinsmith, L. J. (1974). *Science* **183,** 817.

Subirana, J. A. (1970). *Exp. Cell Res.* **63,** 253.

Subirana, J. A. (1975). *In* "The Biology of the Male Gamete" (J. G. Duckett and P. A. Racey, eds.), p. 239. Academic Press, New York.

Subirana, J. A., and Palau, J. (1968). *Exp. Cell Res.* **53,** 471.

Sugiyama, M. (1951). *Biol. Bull. (Woods Hole, Mass.)* **101,** 335.

Szollosi, D., and Ris, H. (1961). *J. Biophys. Biochem. Cytol.* **10,** 275.

Thaler, M. M., Cox, M. C. L., and Villee, C. A. (1970). *J. Biol. Chem.* **245,** 1479.

Thibault, C. (1973). In "The Regulation of Mammalian Reproduction" (S. Segal, R. Crozier, P. Corfman, and P. Condliffe, eds.) p. 231. Thomas, Springfield, Illinois.

Thibault, C., and Gerard, M. (1970). *C. R. Hebd. Seances Acad. Sci.* **270,** 2025.

Thompson, L. R., and McCarthy, B. J. (1968). *Biochem. Biophys. Res. Commun.* **30,** 166.

Uehara, T., and Yanagimachi, R. (1977). *Biol. Reprod.* **16,** 315.

Usui, N., and Yanagimachi, R. (1976). *J. Ultrastr. Res.* **57,** 276.

Vaughn, J. C., and Hinsch, G. W. (1972). *J. Cell Sci.* **11,** 131.

Wilson, E. B. (1925). "The Cell in Development and Heredity." Macmillan, New York.

Wooding, F. B. P., and O'Donnell, J. M. (1971). *J. Ultrastruct. Res.* **35,** 71.

Yanagimachi, R., and Noda, Y. D. (1970). *J. Ultrastruct. Res.* **31,** 465.

Yanagimachi, R., and Usui, N. (1972). *J. Cell Biol.* **55,** 293a.

Zamboni, L. (1971). "Fine Morphology of Mammalian Fertilization." Harper, New York.

Zelenin, A. V., Shapiro, I. M., Kolesnikov, V. A., and Senin, V. M. (1974). *Cell Differ.* **3,** 95.

Ziegler, D., and Masui, Y. (1973). *Dev. Biol.* **35,** 283.

CHAPTER 7

MECHANISMS OF ACTIVATION OF SPERM AND EGG DURING FERTILIZATION OF SEA URCHIN GAMETES

David Epel

HOPKINS MARINE STATION
DEPARTMENT OF BIOLOGICAL SCIENCES
STANFORD UNIVERSITY
PACIFIC GROVE, CALIFORNIA

I. Introduction

A series of events occurs at fertilization which catapults the metabolism of the previously quiescent egg into pathways leading to differentiation and the formation of a new adult. The changes that occur at this time do not require immediate gene action; for example, enucleated eggs can be activated by irradiated sperm or by various chemical or physical treatments (see Harvey, 1956). This implies that the genetic activity required for setting up the fertilization responses occurs at some earlier period, as during oogenesis and egg maturation. However, the consequences of fertilization do affect later gene expression in that the changes evoked by fertilization ultimately result in specific events leading to determination, new gene action, and differentiation.

Recent work has provided important insights into the causal chain of events that occur during the activation of the egg at fertilization. These insights begin to reveal the nature of the changes that accompany sperm–egg attachment and fusion and how these surface events are transmitted to the cytoplasm. A sequence or program of events is initiated, and it is now becoming clear how some of these changes are linked to each other. It is an exciting saga in developmental biology, since fertilization is perhaps one of the best understood sequences in which the reception of a signal at the cell surface leads to the turning on of new synthetic activities and initiation of new developmental programs. These principles for "turning on" cell activities at fertilization might also apply to the turning on of other developmental programs, such as occur following hormonal stimulation or embryonic induction.

In this chapter I shall primarily focus on work from our laboratory on the fertilization of the sea urchin egg. The metabolic and morphological changes of sea urchin gametes during fertilization are the best characterized of all embryos, and the interested reader is especially referred to four recent and comprehensive reviews on the metabolism and development of these eggs (Giudice, 1973; Horstadius, 1973; Stearns, 1974; Czihak, 1975). In organization, this chapter will examine the activation of both gametes, first considering the activation of the sperm upon its contact with egg jelly and the resultant cascade of events leading to sperm–egg attachment and sperm–egg fusion. We shall then examine the consequences of sperm fusion with the egg, which lead (1) to responses excluding other sperm from fusing with the egg, and (2) to responses that result in the activation of embryonic development. I shall especially emphasize our recent analysis of these latter responses, concentrating on the important roles played by intracellular calcium and cytoplasmic pH in turning on cell metabolism.

II. Activation of Sperm

Although most recent research has emphasized the activation of the egg by the sperm, there is a prior activation of the sperm by the egg which is a prerequisite for successful fertilization. This first activation occurs when the sperm contacts an outermost mucopolysaccharide coat of the egg, known as the jelly layer, or possibly other substances released by the egg. Two responses generally occur as a consequence of this contact. The first is the acrosome reaction, which results from the exocytosis of the acrosomal granule at the apical end of the sperm (see Summers et al., 1975, for recent review). This exocytosis releases enzymes facilitating the passage of the sperm through the jelly layer (Isaka et al., 1966) and the vitelline layer (Levine et al., 1977). Substances are also exposed at the end of the newly formed acrosomal process that allow the sperm to adhere to the egg surface (Summers et al., 1975; Vacquier and Moy, 1977).

The second response to egg jelly is a behavioral response referred to as isoagglutination or the "fertilizin–antifertilizin" reaction. This response is seen as an aggregation or "agglutination" of the sperm in huge clusters for variable amounts of time and a subsequent falling apart or disaggregation of the clumps (see Metz, 1967, for a comprehensive review).

A. THE ACROSOME REACTION

As noted, the acrosome reaction results from the exocytosis of the acrosomal granule at the apical end of the sperm. This results in a radical reorganization of the cell. The new membrane that is exposed, referred to as the acrosomal process, is extended in front of the sperm by an internal polymerization of actin (Tilney *et al.*, 1973). Also exposed at the sides and end of this acrosomal process is a ruthenium red-staining substance, probably involved in sperm–egg adhesion since the initial attachment of the sperm to the egg surface occurs between this substance and the vitelline layer (Summers *et al.*, 1975; Collins, 1976; Vacquier and Moy, 1977; also see later).

The natural trigger of the acrosome reaction is either a relatively permanent component of the egg jelly or some substance secreted by the egg but having only a transient residence in the jelly. Most workers have assumed that the trigger is an integral jelly constituent, since the acrosome reaction of most species is elicited during passage through the intact jelly layer (e.g., Summers and Hylander, 1976) or by jelly in solution (e.g., Collins, 1976). However, recent work of Aketa and Ohta (1977) and Decker *et al.* (1976) indicate that the reaction may be more complex. Aketa and Ohta (1977) isolated jelly hulls from eggs of *Pseudocentrotus depressus* and "fertilized" them with sperm; the sperm which passed through these hulls had not undergone an acrosome reaction. This finding is also consistent with the observations of Decker *et al.* (1976) that the solubilized jelly layer from *Arbacia punctulata* eggs does not induce an acrosome reaction in *Arbacia* sperm at physiological pH. These recent results, suggesting that egg jelly may not be the inducer, might represent species differences or might indicate that in these two species the acrosome-inducing activity is either loosely associated with the jelly, is unstable and continuously secreted by the egg, or that the acrosomal trigger is not in the jelly layer but resides on the egg surface itself.

The triggering of the acrosome reaction by egg or egg jelly components appears to be through increasing calcium permeability of the sperm plasma membrane. This hypothesis was first suggested by J. C. Dan, who observed an absolute calcium requirement for the induction of the acrosome reaction by jelly (Dan *et al.*, 1965), and further evidence for this hypothesis has come from the recent work of Collins (1976), Collins and Epel (1977), Decker *et al.* (1976), and Summers *et al.*

(1976). These workers realized that use of the ionophorous antibiotic A23187 would allow a critical testing of the Dan hypothesis. This drug abolishes the selective permeability of the cell's plasma membrane to divalent cations, such as calcium and magnesium (see Reed and Lardy, 1972). If the hypothesis were correct, then increasing the calcium content of the cell by exposure to A23187 should induce an acrosome reaction.

All three groups found that micromolar amounts of this drug would induce an acrosome reaction morphologically identical to that induced by egg jelly. The reaction, however, would occur only in the presence of exogenous calcium. These results strongly support the hypothesis that elevation of the intracellular calcium level will induce an acrosome reaction and suggests that the normal effect of jelly is to alter the plasma membrane so that calcium enters the cell. Additional evidence in support of this hypothesis is that simply increasing the Ca^{2+} concentration (or its analogs Ba^{2+} and Sr^{2+}) will induce an acrosome reaction in the absence of jelly (Collins and Epel, 1977). Finally, the action of jelly is blocked by anesthetics, such as procaine or lidocaine, which compete for Ca^{2+}-binding sites (Collins and Epel, 1977) and by calcium antagonists, such as La^{3+} (Decker et al., 1976; Collins and Epel, 1977).

Collins and Epel (1977) and Decker et al. (1976) triggered a calcium-dependent acrosome reaction by simply increasing the external pH. They also found that the pH dependence was considerably lowered in the presence of egg jelly (Fig. 1). These results support the concept that binding of jelly alters the calcium channel so that calcium enters at physiological pH. As high pH by itself can induce an acrosome reaction (in the presence of Ca^{2+}), increased alkalinity may act by altering calcium permeability channels directly. The high pH requirement might also relate to the necessity for intracellular pH changes as a part of the acrosome reaction. Sperm (Collins and Epel, 1977; Tilney et al., 1977) and eggs (Johnson et al., 1976) release acid when activated by jelly (in case of sperm) or fertilization (in the case of eggs). In eggs, this reflects an alkalinization of the cytoplasm which is a prerequisite for many of the morphological and biochemical consequences of fertilization (Johnson et al., 1976). Recent important work of Tilney et al. (1978) has shown a similar requirement for sperm activation.

Tilney and his colleagues (1978), studying the acrosome reaction in starfish, have found that both divalent and monovalent ionophores will initiate the internal polymerization of actin. The only apparent common denominator of all these agents is that they also induce the

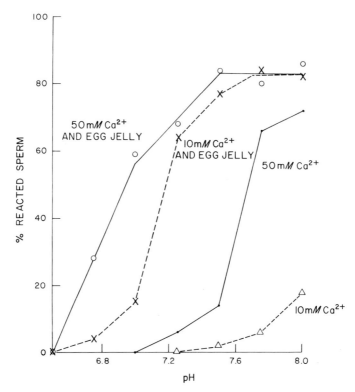

Fig. 1. Interrelationship between pH and Ca^{2+} in the induction of the acrosome reaction of *Lytechinus pictus* sperm. Sperm were incubated in the indicated concentrations of Ca^{2+} in the presence or in the absence of egg jelly. As seen, high pH and high Ca^{2+} by themselves will induce the reaction; jelly shifts the pH requirement downward toward a more physiological pH.

aforementioned acid release from the sperm. The important question is whether this acid release has anything to do with the actin polymerization.

Previously, Tilney (1976) had found that the unpolymerized actin was associated with a protein that appeared to prevent the spontaneous polymerization of actin. *In vitro,* this protein could be dissociated, with the concomitant polymerization of actin, by increasing the pH from 6.5 to 8.0. This suggests the hypothesis that jelly also acts to induce acid release from the sperm, which then raises the internal pH so that the inhibitory protein dissociates from the actin, with resultant actin polymerization.

Another important observation of Tilney *et al.* (1978) was that the membrane fusion could be separated from the actin polymerization and that the fusion could be shown to require Ca^{2+}. For example, ionophore A23187 could induce H^+ release and the actin polymerization in the presence of NaCl. In the absence of any Ca^{2+} ion, however, there was no membrane fusion. The subsequent addition of Ca^{2+} ion resulted in fusion. Besides providing strong evidence that Ca^{2+} ion is required for membrane fusion, this result suggests that jelly or ionophore effect fusion by increasing Ca^{2+} levels or making Ca^{2+} available to the plasma membrane.

An important question is whether jelly induces both Ca^{2+} influx and H^+ release or whether the Ca^{2+} change is first and the H^+ release a secondary consequence. An observation of Collins and Epel (1977) suggests the Ca^{2+} release is first. They examined sea urchin sperm with the transmission electron microscope following exposure of the sperm to jelly in the absence of extracellular Ca^{2+} ion. There were no signs of membrane fusion or any other components of the acrosome reaction. This suggests that the primary action of jelly is to increase Ca^{2+} levels, which then initiates membrane fusion. Acid extrusion might occur simultaneously as a Ca^{2+}/H^+ exchange, or follow Ca^{2+} release as a consequence of the Ca^{2+} effect on plasma membrane permeability or as a direct consequence of membrane fusion and extrusion of H^+ ion down a concentration gradient. Irrespective of mechanism, membrane fusion and actin polymerization would expose adhesive substances and release acrosomal enzymes necessary for the subsequent steps of fertilization.

B. SPERM BEHAVIOR

The second change induced by egg jelly is a profound alteration in sperm behavior. This new behavior is referred to as an aggregation, clumping, or "agglutination," in which sperm come together in macroscopic clumps, which last for a few minutes and then fall apart. The phenomenon is apparent without even a light microscope, and its discovery preceded the description of the acrosome reaction (reviewed by Metz, 1967).

Because the clumping response is often (but not always) species specific and results in an apparent agglutination, it was referred to as an isoagglutination in analogy to the agglutination of antigens by antibodies, and the hypothetical components in the reaction were named fertilizin (antibody of jelly) and antifertilizin (antigen of the sperm). It was suggested that the agglutination was through multivalent jelly molecules (fertilizin) bound to antifertilizin molecules on the sperm surface. Additional evidence consistent with an antigen–antibody hypothesis was that one could extract a fraction from sperm that interacted with egg jelly similar to an antigen–antibody precipitate (reviewed by Tyler, 1949; Metz, 1967).

The realization that the isoagglutination phenomena, at least in *Strongylocentrotus purpuratus* sperm, was not really an agglutination but a behavioral response resulting in aggregation has come from the recent work of Collins (1976). He became dissatisfied with the agglutination hypothesis when he attempted to fix jelly-induced sperm clusters for electron microscope examination; all fixatives caused an immediate disappearance of clumps except for a small percentage of head-to-head aggregates. Similar results were obtained when inhibitors of energy metabolism, such as azide or cyanide, were added to the sperm; as soon as motility ceased, the clumps dispersed. Additional evidence contradicting the idea of agglutination were that sperm, if rendered immotile by any one of a variety of unrelated treatments, would not agglutinate when jelly was added. Also, under conditions of low pH or low Ca^{2+}, one can disperse the clusters by simply shaking the tube; when the shaking is stopped, the clusters reform (Collins, 1976).

An important control in all these experiments was the demonstration that aggregation resulting from exposure to known cross-linking molecules did not require motility. If sperm were agglutinated by addition of an agglutinating antibody or a lectin, the resultant sperm clusters were not affected by cyanide or other inhibitors of motility. Similarly, the sperm clusters resulting from these treatments were retained after fixation (Collins, 1976). All these observations suggest that the jelly-induced "agglutination" is in reality a behavioral response best classified as an aggregation behavior.

The aggregation response is not simply a consequence of the induction of the acrosome reaction by jelly, since the aggregation behavior is not seen when the acrosome reaction is induced by elevated pH or by ionophore. Conversely, jelly can induce aggregation when the acrosome reaction is prevented by low Ca^{2+} concentrations (Collins, 1976).

In sum, the work of Collins suggests that the different components of jelly may have different functions. One component may be involved in inducing the acrosome reaction, another in inducing the aggregative behavior. Since the aggregation behavior is often species specific, one would predict that the former component would have species specificity, while the latter component would induce the acrosome reaction with little or no species specificity (Summers and Hylander, 1976).

If separate components of jelly are involved in these distinct sperm responses, it is reasonable to assume that there are also specific receptors on the sperm membrane for these jelly components. Perhaps one of these receptors corresponds to the antifertilizin molecule described by

Tyler and his collaborators. As noted earlier, this is a component that can be extracted from sperm and that interacts with jelly in a manner similar to an antigen–antibody precipitate. Could this actually be the membrane receptor of the sperm for a specific jelly molecule?

C. ROLE OF SPERM AGGREGATION IN FERTILIZATION

A major question raised by Collins' observations is what role, if any, does the transient aggregation behavior have in fertilization? Although the aggregation behavior can be induced by egg jelly in solution, sperm also exhibit the same behavior in the vicinity of the egg during normal fertilization and can be seen clustering around each egg. These sperm clusters are transient and disappear soon after elevation of the fertilization membrane. One possibility is that the aggregation behavior is a form of chemotaxis initiated by the first sperm to contact the jelly coat of the egg. The resultant production of chemotactic molecules and subsequent aggregation would ensure that sufficient sperm are attracted to the egg to effect its fertilization. Since a large number of sperm are required to fertilize the egg (see, e.g., Glaser, 1915; Decker et al., 1976), it may be necessary to call forth many sperm to elicit activation. If so, the transient nature of the aggregation response could then be a protective mechanism to ensure that an individual egg does not attract "too many" sperm to it. The protection may be not so much related to preventing polyspermy as to preventing a group of already fertilized eggs from attracting all the available sperm to it.

This idea of chemotaxis of animal sperm has been continually referred to and also continually refuted (for example, see the book by Rothschild, 1956) except for gametes of certain coelenterates and tunicates (R. Miller, 1973; R. L. Miller, 1975). However, if chemotaxis in other forms is transient, as is the aggregation behavior of sea urchin sperm, then a chemotactic response might be impossible to assess by current procedures. It might, therefore, be worthwhile to ascertain whether transient behavioral changes of sperm are evoked by eggs or egg secretions in other species. Some evidence for egg substances affecting sperm binding has been seen in mammals (Hartmann and Hutchison, 1974).

A second question raised by Collins' observations is how sperm can maintain aggregates in a uniform solution of jelly. One possibility is that the aggregation response of sperm is similar to that seen during aggregation of slime mold amoebae. Here "founder" cells send out large pulses of low-molecular-weight compounds, which act as chemotactic substances, to attract other cells toward the aggregating centers. In the slime mold *Dictyostelium discoideum*, the chemotactic substance is cyclic AMP (cAMP) (see Cohen and Robertson, 1971, for review).

If a similar mechanism were operative in sperm aggregation, a particular sperm or group of sperm, upon contact with jelly, might put out large amounts of a chemotactic substance, which then attracts other sperm. The amount of substance and duration of production would then be a function of the jelly concentration.

The nature of such chemotactic molecules—if any—involved in sea urchin sperm behavior remains unknown. These sperm possess high levels of nucleotide cyclases and both cAMP and cGMP increase in the presence of egg jelly (Garber and Hardman, 1975). However, sperm of *S. purpuratus* maintain normal aggregating behavior in the presence of large amounts of cGMP or cAMP, suggesting that neither nucleotide is involved in the aggregation behavior (F. D. Collins, unpublished observations).

III. Sperm–Egg Attachment and Fusion

Sperm attach to eggs up to the time of the cortical reaction. The question of major interest is the morphological and molecular nature of attachment. Are there specific receptors on the surface of the two gametes which function in binding and ultimately fusion? Are the egg receptors attached to or integrated with other membrane components such that their interaction leads to changes in the egg that prevent polyspermy and/or start the cascade of events that initiates development?

A. SPERM RECEPTORS ON THE EGG

At the fine-structural level, it can be seen that numerous sperm attach to the vitelline layer, and quantitative studies of sperm binding indicate 1300–1800 binding sites per egg (Vacquier and Payne, 1973). As there is space for many more sperm to attach to the surface, an important question is whether the maximum number of bound sperm corresponds to some morphological structure on the egg. Transmission electron microscope (EM) studies on fertilization of *S. purpuratus* eggs (D. Chase, personal communication; F. D. Collins, unpublished) indicate that sperm–egg attachment and fusion tends to be at microvillar tips. However, there are many more microvilli than sperm-binding sites (Tegner and Epel, 1976). Scanning EM studies indicate no obvious morphological differentiations of the egg surface, and these studies also show no obvious patterns of sperm attachment. One possible interpretation of the limited binding sites, therefore, is that the number of bound sperm is sterically limited by the movement of the attached sperm.

Since sperm attach to eggs in a species-specific manner, it is most probable that this limited attachment is through binding to specific receptor molecules. These molecules might reside on either or both the vitelline layer and the plasma membrane, but so far only vitelline layer receptor molecules have been described. Veron and Shapiro (1977) have carefully studied the inhibition of fertilization by concanavalin A (Con A). Two classes of binding sites were found, a low-affinity ($K_a = 4 \times 10^{-6} M$) site on the plasma membrane and a high-affinity ($K_a = 8 \times 10^{-7} M$) site on the vitelline layer. The loss of fertilizability was associated with lectin binding to the high-affinity site (i.e., the vitelline layer). Several workers have attempted to isolate and characterize the sperm receptors of the vitelline layer. Aketa (1967) and Aketa et al. (1972) noted that both sperm–egg binding and fertilizability were considerably reduced if the eggs were pretreated with trypsin. This suggested the presence of a trypsin-sensitive sperm-binding site on the egg surface. Other work from Aketa's laboratory showed that a proteinaceous substance could be isolated from the vitelline layer and that sperm would bind to bubbles coated with these proteins. If antibodies are prepared to this protein fraction, fertilizability of eggs was considerably reduced (Aketa and Onitake, 1969).

Schmell et al. (1977) have recently isolated a soluble protein from a membrane fraction of Arbacia eggs which binds to sperm and prevents fertilization of eggs. This protein binds to the lectin Con A, and Con A also prevents fertilization. Neither Aketa nor Schmell et al. have yet purified these receptors, and there is little information on their molecular nature.

Although the above results and observations all point to the vitelline layer as the site of sperm binding, it should be emphasized that this layer is not essential for fertilization. For example, if the vitelline layer is removed by a sequential protease–dithothreitol treatment, fertilizability is considerably reduced but can be restored by pretreating the sperm with egg jelly (Carroll et al., 1977).

Studies on interspecies cross-fertilization suggest that the role of vitelline layer sperm receptors is as barriers to interspecies hybridization. In crosses between species that are difficult to hybridize, the heterologous sperm do not bind to the vitelline layer (Summers et al., 1976), but fertilizability can be considerably improved by pretreating the eggs with proteases (reviewed by Giudice, 1973). The enzyme action removes most of the vitelline layer but increases fertilizability. An alternative viewpoint may be to look at the vitelline layer as a blocking agent to fertilization, analogous to a condom covering the egg surface and protecting it from sperm, especially sperm of other species. In order for fertilization to be successful, the sperm must be able to attach to the vitelline layer, penetrate the layer, and then fuse with the plasma membrane. If this view is correct, attachment can be viewed simply as a prerequisite for anchoring the sperm so that the hydrolytic enzymes associated with the acrosomal process can digest through the vitelline layer in order for the sperm to fuse with the plasma membrane.

A question not yet answered is the nature of sperm receptors on the plasma membrane. Are there any? Is it possible, for example, that the plasma membrane per se is extremely fusible and that binding receptors are not needed? Sperm could fuse with such a membrane without a preliminary attachment phase.

Finally, it should be noted that additional receptors might form in response to sperm attachment. As discussed in Section III, C, fine filaments are released from the egg surface and might function in either sperm binding or in the incorporation of sperm into the egg.

B. EGG RECEPTORS ON THE SPERM

As noted earlier, the acrosome reaction exposes a new ruthenium-red staining component attached to the apical end of the acrosomal process. This substance attaches directly to the egg surface in what is probably the initial phase of sperm–egg adhesion. The substance appears to be of a generally sticky nature, as sperm will stick to glass cover slips or slides. Also, if an acrosome reaction occurs in a concentrated suspension of sperm, a small percentage of these sperm will adhere to each other through the ruthenium-red staining substance. This adhesion also occurs with heterologous sperm (Collins, 1976).

Vacquier and Moy (1977) have recently purified the vesicle containing this adhesive substance. As isolated, the vesicle contains only highly insoluble protein but no carbohydrate. When solubilized and run on a sodium dodecyl sulfate (SDS)–gel electrophoresis system, only a single protein of 30,500 molecular weight is seen. Studies with specific antibody to the protein show that the protein corresponds to the substance that attaches sperm to egg. Additional evidence for a role in binding is that the insoluble vesicles will bind to vitelline layers of eggs in a species-specific manner. Although the receptor for this protein has not been isolated, it probably corresponds to the sperm receptor of the vitelline layer. As this receptor is probably a glycoprotein (see the Con A result), the binding protein of the sperm probably interacts with this glycoprotein in a lectinlike manner.

C. SPERM–EGG FUSION AND SPERM ENTRY INTO THE EGG

Motion picture and scanning electron microscope analyses of fertilization have provided important insights into the mechanisms of sperm incorporation into the egg (Tegner and Epel, 1976; Epel *et al.*, 1977). In those motion picture sequences where the "fertilizing sperm" (i.e., that sperm which will later fuse with the egg) can be seen, one can follow the sequence back and study the behavior of this fertilizing sperm in relation to its less successful "brothers." It is seen that the fertilizing sperm is almost always one of the first to attach to the egg surface. However, the fertilizing sperm, and indeed all sperm that attach to the egg, cannot initially be differentiated on the basis of their behavior. All sperm gyrate around the point of their attachment. About 20 seconds after attachment, the fertilizing sperm undergoes a radical change in behavior. It suddenly stops moving and literally "stands up," perpendicular to the egg's surface, with an almost complete cessation of flagellar motion. Within a second or two the first responses of the egg are seen: the beginnings of the cortical reaction and the elevation of the fertilization membrane. The fertilization membrane elevates around the upright fertilizing sperm and this sperm remains attached to the egg plasma membrane. However, the elevating fertilization membrane carries away from the egg surface all the other unsuccessful sperm. During the next 30–40 seconds, the fertilizing sperm moves into the egg at a linear rate of 5 μm per minute (Epel *et al.*, 1977).

These observations indicate that motility of the sperm per se is not required for its incorporation into the egg and suggests that the motive force for incorporating the sperm might reside in the egg itself. The egg surface contracts in response to fertilization (see, e.g., Fig. 1 in Epel *et al.*, 1977). It is reasonable to assume that this contraction, as well as the force for sperm incorporation, is attributable to actin or myosin of the egg cortex. This hypothesis is also supported by the observation that low concentrations of cytochalasin B (CB) will prevent incorporation of the sperm into the egg (G. Perry and E. W. Byrd, unpublished observation). A similar effect has also been observed for the echiuroid *Urechis caupo* (Gould-Somero *et al.*, 1977).

In both the echinoid and the echiuroid, sperm attach to the egg and elicit a normal activation response, but the sperm is not incorporated into the egg. In the case of the sea urchin, it seems as if the "activating" sperm is cast off from the egg during the ensuing cortical reaction and elevation of the fertilization membrane (G. Perry and E. W. Byrd, unpublished observations). In *Urechis,* CB prevents the development of the fertilization cone, suggesting that the cone is involved in sperm entry (Gould-Somero *et al.,* 1977). So far, there has been no evidence for an alignment of microfilaments at or near the site of the sperm entry in eggs from either species.

It should be noted that a CB-sensitive incorporation mechanism might not be operative in eggs from all species. In eggs of the bivalve clam *Spisula solidissima*, there is an apparent *enhancement* of sperm incorporation in the presence of CB, and it appears that CB prevents development of the block to polyspermy (Ziomek and Epel, 1975). One possible explanation of these apparently divergent findings is that the block to polyspermy is affected by CB in eggs of all species, but that in eggs of sea urchins and *Urechis* the sperm incorporation mechanism is much more sensitive to CB than the development of the polyspermy block.

An alternative mechanism for incorporating the sperm into the egg, which might still be CB sensitive, is that sperm incorporation is facilitated by "extracellular filaments." These filaments (about 0.05 μm in diameter), seen in scanning electron microscope studies of sea urchin fertilization (Tegner and Epel, 1976), appear to emanate from the microvilli and surround the attached sperm (Fig. 2). The structures are not consistently seen and hence cannot be systematically studied. It is unclear whether they are associated with only the fertilizing sperm, with all sperm or with only the supernumerary sperm. If associated solely with the fertilizing sperm, these structures may be involved in the actual incorporation of that sperm into the egg. If involved with all sperm, it might be involved in anchoring or attaching sperm to the egg surface. Finally, if involved with only supernumerary sperm, it could be part of the egg's response to prevent polyspermy. Alternatively, the filaments might be an artifact produced during the preparation of the eggs for viewing with the scanning microscope.

Incorporation of the sperm also involves a localized "creeping," phagocytosis, or engulfment of the attached sperm by the egg plasma membrane and associated cytoplasm. At the microscopic level, this is visualized as the formation of the fertilization cone around the sperm. The scanning electron micrograph shown in Fig. 3 indicates that the egg plasma membrane and associated microvilli completely covers the cone and underlying sperm by 180 seconds. Incorporation of the sperm

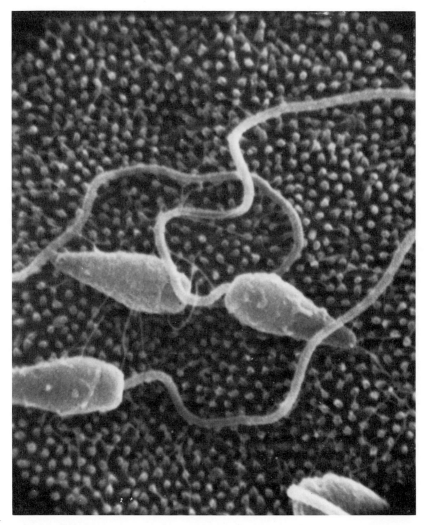

FIG. 2. Thin filaments, probably emanating from the vitelline layer, become associated with sperm and may be a part of the mechanism by which sperm are attached to the egg or are incorporated into the egg. From Tegner and Epel (1976); reprinted with permission of the *Journal of Experimental Zoology*.

therefore involves an initial fusion phase followed by an engulfment or phagocytic phase. The relative role of fusion vs engulfment has been a subject of controversy, but both processes may be involved (see, e.g., Colwin and Colwin, 1967; Tyler, 1963).

Fig. 3. Fertilization cone seen 3 minutes after insemination. The pattern and shape of microvilli over the cone are similar to those of the egg, suggesting that the egg plasma membrane has enveloped the sperm, akin to a phagocytotic process. ×12,500. From Tegner (1974).

IV. Experimental Analysis of Egg Activation

A. APPROACHES

The structural and metabolic changes that are evoked by fertilization superficially appear overwhelming and almost unamenable to experimental analysis. Two experimental approaches, however, have allowed meaningful dissection and understanding of the events at fertilization. The first approach is taxonomic and temporal, in which the various changes are described and their timing after fertilization is determined. Since one does not necessarily know in advance what changes to look for, a large "luck" or "chance" factor is encompassed in this approach. The second approach is a dissection of causal relationships between the various changes and uses *in vivo* (experimental) and *in vitro* (analytical) analyses. This approach has been considerably simplified by techniques for separating the various fertilization responses from each other.

The current results of the first approach are summarized in Fig. 4, which depicts the nature and timing of the various changes that accompany fertilization of the eggs of *S. purpuratus* at 17°C. This temporal schedule allows one to assign potential causal relations; an early event might trigger a later one, but not vice versa.

The schedule or program suggests two separate causal webs. The first centers around a series of *early changes,* all initiated within the

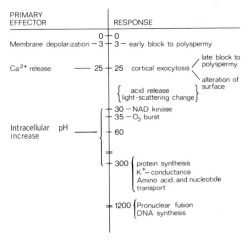

Fig. 4. A program or schedule of the major postfertilization changes in the egg of *Strongylocentrotus purpuratus* at 17°C. Factors on the left appear to be primary effectors; those on the right appear to be responses to these effectors.

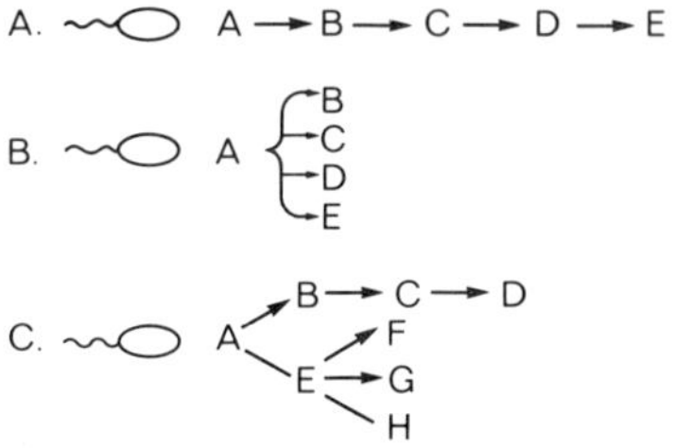

FIG. 5. Three possible relationships to account for the activation of development at fertilization. (A) *Simple linear dependence* scheme, in which each change is dependent on an immediately prior change. (B) *Pervasive* scheme, in which a single generalized change results in the turning on of many changes. (C) *Mixed linear-pervasive* scheme, in which both types of changes are involved.

first 60 seconds, which might, therefore, be causally related. These include an increase in membrane potential, increased free Ca^{2+}, the cortical exocytosis, activation of the enzyme NAD kinase, a change in light-scattering properties of the egg, release of acid or protons from the egg, and a large increase in respiration.

This is followed, after a "dark" period of about 4 minutes, by a constellation of *late changes* including increased conductance of potassium by the plasma membrane (seen as a decreased membrane potential), activation or insertion of various transport systems for nucleosides, phosphate, and amino acids, and a large increase in the rate of protein synthesis. The temporal coincidence in initiation of these changes suggests that these late events might also be causally linked to each other, presumably from some linkage to an earlier event or events.

The major objective of the second approach is to assign causal connections to the various postfertilization changes. For example, does fertilization initiate a series of linked, dependent events (as in Fig. 5A)? Or a single generalized or pervasive change in the cell, from which all changes emanate (Fig. 5B)? Or, as is most likely, a combination of linked changes and generalized changes (Fig. 5C)? Some of these questions can be asked *in vivo*. For example, if Ca^{2+} normally increases, its role can be assessed by artificially increasing the Ca^{2+} level with ionophore A23187 or by direct injection. If protein synthesis increases, its role can be assessed by inhibiting synthesis with puromycin.

These approaches might generate further questions. What induces an increase in Ca^{2+}? If increased respiration is a consequence of the Ca^{2+} increase, how is this accomplished and is this related to subsequent steps? *In vitro* analysis might be helpful, as by assessing the effects of Ca^{2+} addition to egg homogenates.

B. CONCLUSIONS AND OVERVIEW OF EGG ACTIVATION

The above types of analysis, described in detail in the subsequent sections of this article, reveal that the activation of development by fertilization results from massive alterations in plasma membrane permeability and consequent changes in the content of intracellular ions. The three primary effectors are indicated on the left part of Fig. 4. So far the primary response to fertilization appears to be a large change in membrane potential beginning at 3 seconds after sperm addition. The second effector, from 20 to 140 seconds, ensues from an increased level of intracellular Ca^{2+} and results in the cortical reaction, the respiratory burst, and probably other undescribed changes. This leads to the third effector, which is the activation of a Na^+–H^+ exchange system with a resultant influx of Na^+ and efflux of H^+ between 60 and 300 seconds after fertilization. The consequence is an increase in intracellular pH.

The initial membrane potential change seems to be related to establishing the block to polyspermy. The two later changes are involved in activating the metabolism of the egg.

V. Primary Response of the Egg to Fertilization—Membrane Potential Changes

A. IS SPERM ATTACHMENT OR SPERM FUSION A PRIMARY TRIGGER?

The responses of the egg to fertilization presumably result from the attachment of sperm to egg or from the fusion of the plasma membranes of sperm and egg during the first few seconds after sperm attachment. The events during this brief interval have barely been studied; numerous questions remain to be answered about this critical time.

A most important question is whether it is sperm–egg fusion or some prior event that activates the egg. As noted, the sperm does not noticeably change its behavior for about 20 seconds after attachment. Yet, as described below, there is a rapid change in membrane potential of the egg by 3 seconds after addition of sperm to an egg suspension. This indicates that a significant interaction occurs within 3 seconds; yet this interaction has no effect on sperm behavior, which is not altered until 20 seconds later (Section III, C).

It would be interesting to determine by transmission electron microscopy whether this early event is sperm–egg fusion. An alternative explanation, for example, might be that the fertilizing sperm (which is generally one of the first sperm to attach to the egg) passes through a preliminary to fusion (see, e.g., Baker and Presley, 1969; Presley and Baker, 1970), and this early event then triggers the membrane potential changes. Sperm behavior is not altered until actual cytoplasmic continuity occurs 20 seconds later.

A second question, related to the above, is whether there are receptors on the egg plasma membrane which respond in a specific way to sperm attachment. Such a response would lead to subsequent incorporation of sperm and activation of the egg. These receptors would thus be analogous to hormone or mitogen receptors, with their specific responses. If this hypothesis were correct, one should be able to isolate sperm fractions which by themselves would activate the egg. Such fractions have not been reported (for review of problems, see Epel *et al.*, 1977), but antibodies to eggs do act as parthenogenic agents (Baxandall *et al.*, 1964). This suggests that pertubation of surface receptors might indeed lead to egg activation.

Irrespective of which alternative is correct, the problem is how sperm–egg contact (or fusion) is transduced to activate development. The area of contact or fusion is extremely small, only 0.0002% of the egg surface; yet this minute pertubation is somehow transduced into the massive or global response of egg activation.

B. MEMBRANE POTENTIAL CHANGES DURING FERTILIZATION

As noted, the earliest detectable response to fertilization is a large change in the membrane potential, which is seen within 3 seconds after sperm addition. These early changes have been studied by electrophysiological methods in which microelectrodes are inserted into eggs and the changes in the membrane potential and membrane resistance determined. In some species (notably *Lytechinus pictus*) the membrane potential slowly increases from about −10 to approximately +20 mV; the potential peaks around the time of the cortical reaction and then declines to around −10 mV for the next 4 minutes (Fig. 6). Beginning at 5 minutes after fertilization, the potential drops to −60 mV over a 20-minute period (Steinhardt *et al.*, 1971).

A different type of response is seen in the eggs of *Stronglylocentrotus purpuratus*. Here, the initial membrane potential is already low, −60 to −80 mV. Fertilization results in an extremely rapid increase in the membrane potential, with a rise time of less than a second, to about −10 to +10 mV (Fig. 6). The potential remains high for 60 seconds and then drops back to the −60-mV level (Jaffe, 1976). It is unclear whether these differences relate to species variation or represent differences in

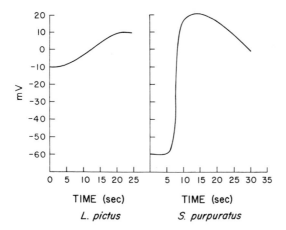

FIG. 6. Pattern of membrane potential changes after fertilization, in two species of sea urchin eggs (*Lytechinus pictus*, derived from Steinhardt *et al.*, 1971; *Strongylocentrotus purpuratus*, derived from Jaffe, 1976).

the wound-healing ability of the two types of eggs in response to electrode insertion.

The ionic basis of the membrane potential in the unfertilized egg has been studied by Steinhardt *et al.* (1971) in the eggs of *L. pictus* and by Jaffe and Robinson (1977) in the eggs of *S. purpuratus*. From ion substitution experiments, the membrane of the unfertilized *L. pictus* egg appears to be impermeable to all cations tested but has a slight permeability to anions, such as chloride, suggesting the potential is an anion potential. In *Stronglylocentrotus,* tracer and electrophysiological studies support the idea that the unactivated egg is permeable to potassium and that the -60-mV membrane potential seen in the unfertilized egg results from potassium permeability.

The nature of the membrane potential changes following fertilization has been thoroughly investigated in *Lytechinus* (Steinhardt *et al.*, 1971). The initial changes in these eggs appear to result from increased Na^+ permeability. The absolute amount of Na^+ influx is probably small, however, relative to the major increase in Na^+ permeability beginning at 60 seconds after fertilization. [Results of ^{22}Na influx measurements; see Johnson *et al.* (1976).]

The question of major interest is the significance of this earliest membrane change to activation of development. The potential may be related to one or more of the following events: (1) the block to polyspermy, (2) incorporation of the sperm, (3) the cortical reaction, or

(4) subsequent activation of the egg. So far, the only role for the conductance changes seems to be as part of a fast block to polyspermy.

C. Membrane Potential Changes and Block to Polyspermy

The idea of a rapid change in the egg which leads to a loss in sperm receptivity is patently obvious when one looks at sea urchin fertilization under the microscope. Numerous sperm can be seen around the egg, but normally only one sperm fuses with it. To be sure, polyspermy does occur, but the degree of multiple sperm fusion is low relative to the number of sperm that might attach to the egg during the first few seconds after insemination.

Rothschild and Swann (1954) on the basis of a kinetic analysis of fertilization of sea urchin eggs, suggested there must be a rapid decrease in sperm receptivity between 1 and 5 seconds after insemination. Similar kinetics and interpretations were reported by Presley and Baker (1970), Paul (1975a), and Ziomek and Epel (1975) in eggs from three separate phyla.

Byrd and Collins (1975) have recently reexamined the kinetics of sperm fusion in sea urchin eggs under conditions where the sperm : egg ratio is extremely high and polyspermy takes place. These authors stopped sperm–egg interactions by adding dilute detergent or formaldehyde at various times after sperm addition. They then examined the eggs for sperm nuclei to determine the number of sperm that had entered at the various times. The results, summarized in Fig. 7, indicate that sperm entry ceases when the cortical reaction begins (see also

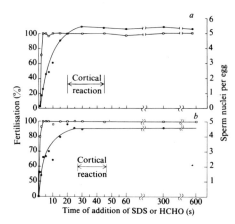

Fig. 7. Time sperm–egg fusion under conditions of heavy insemination, where many sperm fuse with the egg. Sperm–egg fusion (filled circles) ceases at the time of the cortical reaction. From Byrd and Collins (1975); reprinted with permission of *Nature*.

Presley and Baker, 1970). However, between insemination and the beginning of the cortical reaction at 20 seconds, there is a continuous entry of sperm into the egg. The rate of incorporation is linear and proportional to the number of sperm in the insemination mixture. Since the rate of sperm entry was the same *before* and *after* the first sperm had entered the egg, their data would seem to indicate that there is no early response of the egg to exclude an additional sperm until the beginning of the cortical reaction (about 20 seconds). Even with a ratio of 10^6 sperm per egg, there was relatively little sperm incorporation. Taken as a whole, their results suggested the alternative hypothesis that, instead of a specific egg response to prevent polyspermy, there might be a general resistance to fertilization; for instance, the structure of the egg surface might limit the entry of sperm, or all sperm might not be capable of fertilizing the egg, or both.

There is some evidence suggesting that the egg surface is not uniformly receptive to sperm (Schuel *et al.*, 1976) or that not all sperm are equivalent (Timourian and Watchmaker, 1970). Also, the various extracellular egg coats might modulate sperm entry (Runnstrom and Manelli, 1964). However, a recent experimental approach of F. D. Collins (unpublished results) suggests that over a limited range of sperm concentrations there may be a rapid alteration in egg receptivity that prevents polyspermy. If the sperm concentration is above this concentration, polyspermy will take place.

Collins found that if sufficiently dilute sperm suspensions are added to eggs, sperm attach to and fertilize the eggs over a range of times such that the eggs undergo the cortical reaction asynchronously. As the sperm concentration is increased, more eggs exhibit a cortical reaction soon after sperm addition, until a sperm concentration is reached at which 100% of the fertilizable eggs begin the cortical reaction simultaneously and in the minimum possible time after sperm addition (about 20 seconds in *S. purpuratus*). At this sperm concentration the eggs may still be monospermic or slightly polyspermic. Therefore, any increase in the sperm concentration should produce polyspermy, if there really is no change in receptivity to sperm before the cortical reaction (i.e., no fast block). However, Collins (1978) found that the sperm concentration which just gave 100% cortical reactions in the minimum possible time could be increased by at least a factor of 20 without inducing polyspermy. This result is also consistent with the plateau seen in Fig. 1 from the original work of Byrd and Collins (1975). These results suggest that there may indeed be a rapid alteration in sperm receptivity, but that this alteration or "block to polyspermy" can be overcome at high sperm–egg ratios.

An important insight into how eggs might alter their sperm receptivity has come from recent experiments of Jaffe (1976), which suggest that the loss of sperm receptivity in S. purpuratus eggs is related to the rapid increase in membrane potential. As noted, the potential of these eggs increases rapidly from −60 to +10 mV within a few seconds after insemination (Jaffe, 1976). The rapidity of the increase varied from egg to egg, and Jaffe noted that "fast" eggs were never polyspermic, whereas "slow" eggs were polyspermic. This suggested the hypothesis that the fast alteration in potential might alter the egg surface so that sperm could no longer fuse with it. This was tested by applying a crude "voltage block" to individual eggs such that the potential was increased to +10 mV. Many sperm attached to such eggs, but none fused. However, as soon as the potential was dropped below −10 mV, sperm–egg fusion took place and a fertilization response ensued.

The hypothesis generated by Jaffe's observation is that the initial interaction of the fertilizing sperm with the egg results in a rapid change in membrane potential. The increased membrane potential, if above +10 mV, then excludes other sperm from interacting "successfully" with the egg. The nature of this successful interaction, which is so sensitive to membrane potential, is unclear. One possibility is membrane fusion. However, as noted earlier, it is unclear that fusion occurs by 3 seconds, especially since the fertilizing sperm does not alter its behavior until just before the cortical reaction.

An alternative hypothesis is that there are multiple steps leading to fusion (Baker and Presley, 1969; Presley and Baker, 1970) and that the critical step is the initial binding of sperm to an electrically sensitive membrane receptor. This binding, by itself, initiates steps leading to the completion of the fusion process 20 seconds later. The binding also triggers a membrane depolarization. This depolarization results in the other sperm receptors being placed in a "nonpermissive" state as regards their ability to initiate a subsequent fusion.

There are precedents from other systems for at least parts of the above model. Hormone binding to the plasma membrane of hormone-sensitive cells results in a membrane depolarization (Peterson, 1974). For other macromolecules the extent of their binding to cells is sensitive to membrane potential; for example, scorpion venom binding is a function of this potential (Catteral et al., 1976).

Irrespective of exact mechanism, the idea that a rapid increase in membrane potential causes decreased sperm receptivity is attractive. It would account for the general difficulty in making eggs polyspermic. It would also explain the relative ease of making L. pictus eggs polyspermic (slow rise in membrane potential) as compared to S. purpuratus eggs (rapid rise in membrane potential).

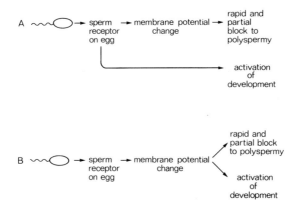

FIG. 8. Two possible causal relationships between the membrane potential changes and the subsequent events of fertilization. One possibility (A) is that the membrane potential change is solely involved in the block to polyspermy and some other change is involved in activation of development. An alternative possibility (B) is that the potential change is responsible for both the block to polyspermy and the activation of development.

A bothersome aspect of the membrane potential hypothesis, however, is that only *one-third* of the eggs in any given egg population exhibit the rapid membrane potential increase (Jaffe and Robinson, 1977); the remaining eggs would therefore be more prone to polyspermy. Also, it is hard to understand how this polyspermy-preventing mechanism can be saturated in the presence of high sperm concentrations. Perhaps, as Byrd and Collins (1975) rightly noted, other factors such as the presence of extracellular coats are also important in preventing polyspermy at high sperm : egg ratios.

D. MEMBRANE POTENTIAL CHANGES AND ACTIVATION OF DEVELOPMENT

Since the rise in membrane potential is one of the earliest postfertilization responses, an important question is whether this change has any role in inducing or regulating later events, such as sperm incorporation, the cortical exocytosis or the activation of development (Fig. 8B). An alternative possibility, for example, is that sperm–egg attachment or fusion triggers two separate events: (1) an Na^+-dependent potential change involved only in preventing polyspermy, and (2) some other unknown or unappreciated consequence of sperm–egg binding or fusion inducing the subsequent steps (Fig. 8A).

A direct test of the role of the membrane potential change in egg activation is to voltage-clamp the egg and ascertain whether such eggs undergo a cortical reaction. When this was done, no cortical reaction was observed (Jaffe, 1976, and personal communication). Therefore, the situation appears to be as depicted in Fig. 8A in which the membrane potential change is involved only in preventing polyspermy and some other, presumably later, step is involved in egg activation.

The inability to elicit the cortical reaction of eggs by increasing their membrane potential is also consistent with the finding that a cortical reaction can be induced in the absence of Na^+ ion or in low Na^+ in the extracellular medium (increased permeability of this ion is responsible for the membrane potential). Eggs can be fertilized in low Na^+ media (1–2 mM) and will still exhibit a cortical exocytosis; it is aberrant, but at least some exocytosis occurs. As will be described later, eggs can be activated with the calcium ionophore A23187 in regular seawater. Eggs can also be activated by ionophore in sodium-free media (Steinhardt and Epel, 1974), but again there is impairment of the cortical reaction (Paul and Epel, 1975). Even if some sodium were still present, as from egg leakage, the net Na^+ transport would be an efflux from eggs and the membrane would have hyperpolarized rather than depolarized. These observations suggest that the Na^+ influx and membrane depolarization do not induce the cortical exocytosis. As there are some inhibitory effects in Na^+-free media, small amounts of Na^+ may be required, perhaps specifically as the Na^+ ion or for a permissive ionic strength. As will be described later, Na^+ is needed for the activation of subsequent steps in the developmental program, but the requirement in these later events is for a Na^+-H^+ exchange (Section XI).

VI. Primary–Secondary Responses of the Egg to Fertilization—Calcium

Although the sperm–egg interaction that activates the egg is not known, it is now clear that the important consequence of this interaction leads to an increase in cytoplasmic or free calcium. As detailed below, a number of the early changes can be directly related to this increase. These include the cortical granule exocytosis, the consequent elevation of the fertilization membrane, establishment of the complete block to polyspermy, a large burst in respiration, and possibly the activation of the enzyme NAD kinase.

A. Evidence for Increased Cytoplasmic Calcium

The concept that increased free calcium might be related to activation has had a long history. This view was especially championed by Heilbrun and his students, and in 1937 Mazia reported a doubling in the amount of free calcium after fertilization of *Arbacia* eggs. Circumstantial evidence supporting a similar increase has been more recently provided by Nakamura and Yasumasu (1974) who used equilibrium dialysis techniques to examine calcium changes after fertilization. Both Mazia (1937) and Nakamura and Yasumasu (1974) detected about 0.5 mM in unfertilized eggs and about 1 mM free Ca^{2+} in fertilized eggs.

More direct and dramatic evidence for an increase in calcium after fertilization has come from the elegant experiments of Ridgeway et al. (1977) on fertilization of fish eggs. They have used the calcium-dependent luminescent protein, aequorin, which emits light only in the presence of calcium ion. When this protein was injected into the large transparent egg of the fish *Oryzias latipes*, there was very little luminescence detected with a photomultiplier or image intensifier. When the eggs were fertilized, however, there was a 10,000-fold increase in luminescence beginning about the time of the cortical reactions and ending about the time the cortical reaction terminated (Ridgeway et al., 1977). Observation of these eggs with an image intensifier reveals that the luminescence begins at the animal pole, under the micropyle, and travels down the egg as a peripheral band of light (L. Jaffe, personal communication). This suggests that calcium is released in the cortical region of the egg and that the release is propagated just beneath the egg surface. Of extreme interest is that the luminescence, i.e., calcium content, does not remain elevated. As the decrease in luminescence does not result from a depletion of available aequorin (Ridgeway et al., 1977) the released calcium is either resequestered in some cell compartment or is extruded from the egg.

A similar approach has been used by Steinhardt et al. (1977) to study calcium changes in sea urchin eggs. Since these eggs are much smaller than the fish eggs it was necessary to inject a number of eggs and measure the luminescence of the entire egg population during fertilization or activation. The results showed an increase in free calcium beginning at the time of the cortical reaction and lasting for an additional 100 seconds. Calibration of the luminescence, combined with determinations of the minimal Ca^{2+} needed to obtain cortical granule exocytosis in a cell-free cortical granule system (see Section VIII, A) suggest the level of Ca^{2+} is elevated to 10^{-5} M in the region of the egg cortex.

B. Does the Increase in Calcium Activate the Egg?

An important question raised by these results is whether the Ca^{2+} increase is a causal change or simply a result of the activation process. This question can be approached by using agents that increase the divalent ion content of cells, such as ionophore A23187. As noted earlier, this drug dissolves in the plasma membrane or intracellular membranes of cells and abolishes their selective permeability to cations such as calcium and magnesium (see Reed and Lardy, 1972).

If an increase in calcium (or other divalent cations) is causally related to fertilization, then these ionophores should be potent parthenogenetic agents. This was found to be the case. Micromolar amounts of A23187 resulted in activation of eggs of sea urchins (Steinhardt and Epel, 1974; Chambers *et al.*, 1974) as well as eggs from a wide variety of animals in different phyla (Steinhardt *et al.*, 1974). The sequence of postfertilization events was carefully analyzed in the A23187-activated sea urchin embryo and found to be identical to that accompanying normal activation by sperm (Steinhardt and Epel, 1974).

Use of the ionophore also allowed, asking whether the increase in divalent cation results from transport of extracellular cations into the egg or from the release of such cations from intracellular stores. The latter hypothesis would be consistent with the earlier results of Mazia (1937) showing no increase in total calcium after fertilization. Eggs were therefore activated in various ion-substituted media. The results showed that sea-urchin eggs could be activated in the absence of exogenous calcium or magnesium (Steinhardt and Epel, 1974). Indeed, activation was even faster in magnesium or calcium-free media (Steinhardt and Epel, 1974), and one can even obtain at least cortical granule discharge in isotonic (0.33 M) sodium citrate (D. Epel, unpublished results). These results, which were confirmed with amphibian and mammalian eggs, suggest that the ionophore activation occurs through the release of calcium or magnesium from intracellular stores (Steinhardt *et al.*, 1974).

One might argue that ionophore activation in Ca^{2+}-free media shows what *can* happen, but not what *does* happen normally. In other words, the drug might release Ca^{2+} from intracellular stores whereas fertilization normally involves transport of Ca^{2+} from the surrounding medium. Two experiments show that this is not the case. First, normal activation can be attained following fertilization in Ca^{2+}-free seawater. This experiment can be done if the calcium-requiring acrosome reaction is induced in the presence of calcium and the reacted sperm are then added to eggs in calcium-free seawater (Takahashi and Sugiyama, 1973). Second, one can directly measure an increase in intracellular calcium in Ca^{2+}-free seawater. Using the aequorin procedure, Steinhardt *et al.* (1977) fertilized eggs in regular seawater and then quickly washed the calcium away with Ca^{2+}-free seawater. These eggs showed a typical release of Ca^{2+} presumably from intracellular stores.

These results, however, do not distinguish between activation of eggs through increased intracellular calcium or through increased intracellular magnesium. Although both the A23187 and aequorin data indicate an increase in calcium as being causal, there could be a similar increase in the magnesium content. [Indeed, there is a magnesium requirement for fertilization, but it appears to be related to sperm fusion (Sano and Mohri, 1976).] Perhaps the best evidence implicating calcium comes from the analysis of Schuetz (1975) on the A23187-activation of the eggs of the mollusc *Spisula.* These eggs are activated only in the presence of exogenous calcium. Thus, in this exception to the rule, activation by ionophore involves bringing in calcium from an external source.

Although such results, especially those with *Spisula,* suggest that increased intracellular calcium results in activation, there are data to suggest that getting rid of calcium is also a concomitant of fertilization and may also be important. First, calcium is released by eggs after fertilization, as shown from studies of eggs preloaded with $^{45}Ca^{2+}$ (Steinhardt and Epel, 1974). Direct analysis of calcium levels by Azarnia and Chambers (1976) shows an immediate and sharp increase of 20%, followed by a variable decrease to the unfertilized level. However, if these fertilized eggs are washed in Ca^{2+}-free seawater, up to 50% of the total calcium is lost; unfertilized eggs do not lose Ca^{2+}.

One possible interpretation of these results is that after fertilization there is a large and permanent increase in cytosol calcium. When eggs are placed in calcium-free seawater this increased calcium pool simply diffuses from the eggs. This possibility, however, is not supported by the aequorin analysis (Steinhardt *et al.,* 1977).

The other possibility, which Azarnia and Chambers (1976) especially advocate, is that most of the calcium measured in fertilized eggs is associated with the extracellular hyaline layer that appears on the egg surface after fertilization. The 20% increase in Ca^{2+} after fertilization is assumed to reflect Ca^{2+} binding to the hyaline layer, as is the 50% loss in Ca^{2+} ion when eggs are placed in Ca^{2+}-free seawater. If Azarnia and Chambers' (1976) interpretation is correct and 70% of the total calcium ends up in the hyaline layer, then there must be a considerable decrease in total cellular Ca^{2+} after fertilization.

If there is such a large loss of calcium, an interesting hypothesis is that calcium actually inhibits certain functions in the egg by avidly binding to regulatory molecules. Fertilization results in changes that lead to less efficient binding, and the level of free Ca^{2+} increases (consistent with the analysis using aequorin). This calcium must now be removed from the cell. Ionophore A23187 might then activate by increasing plasma membrane permeability to calcium, disturb the equilibrium, and thus decrease calcium-binding to the putative regulator. This is consistent with the more efficacious activation by A23187 in Ca^{2+}-free media (although other interpretations, such as increased A23187 solubility in Ca^{2+}-free media are also valid). This unorthodox hypothesis could also explain why mammalian eggs can be activated simply by incubation in calcium-free media (Surani and Kaufman, 1977).

C. Is Calcium Release a Primary or Secondary Response?

Regardless of whether increased cytoplasmic calcium or loss of calcium is critical for activation, it is imperative to ascertain whether the calcium change is a direct (primary) or indirect (secondary) response to fertilization. Several lines of evidence suggest that the calcium change is later than the membrane potential change that begins at 3 seconds.

First, the calcium increase as determined by aequorin luminescence does not appear to begin until the onset of the cortical reaction, around 20–30 seconds. A problem with this measurement, however, is that the sensitivity in the sea urchin system is poor; a small increase in Ca^{2+} could occur early and not be detected until sufficient Ca^{2+} levels had occurred.

A second line of evidence is based on the finding that calcium is involved in two later phases of fertilization, the cortical exocytosis and a calcium-induced increase in respiration (see below). Both of these changes are not seen until 20–30 seconds after insemination (17–27 seconds after the membrane potential change), suggesting that the increase in free calcium is indeed late relative to the initial Na^+ influx. A problem with all these arguments, however, is that the Ca^{2+} increase could begin immediately, and the lag period could represent the time required for the Ca^{2+} concentration to increase sufficiently to initiate subsequent calcium-dependent responses. This idea is consistent with kinetic analyses of aequorin luminescence in the fish egg after fertilization, which has been interpreted as showing an autocatalytic increase in Ca^{2+} (Gilkey et al., 1977).

If one assumes that Ca^{2+} release is indeed late, then a parsimonious hypothesis is that the Na^+ influx and membrane depolarization are primary and that the resultant increase in Na^+ then displaces Ca^{2+} from some Ca^{2+}-binding system. This hypothesis can be tested by fertilizing eggs in low Na^+ or Na^+-free seawater; as noted, however, activation of at least the cortical reaction occurs in low Na^+ seawater.

An alternative hypothesis is that the membrane potential change and the Ca^{2+} change are *both* primary responses. Referring to Fig. 8, we can imagine the membrane potential change as resulting from contact of a sperm protein with an electrically sensitive sperm receptor on the egg surface. This contact then triggers the potential change and resultant block to additional sperm–egg fusion. However, no further activation results from this change. Some intermediate step between sperm–egg binding and sperm–egg membrane fusion might then lead directly to an increase in free calcium and the resultant cascade of events.

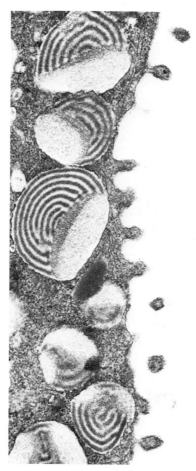

Fig. 9. Electron micrograph of an *Stronglylocentrotus purpuratus* egg, depicting the extensive reticulum of the cortex. This reticulum might function in the transmission of a signal from the site of sperm–egg fusion through the cortex, perhaps as a part of the block of polyspermy or as a part of the propagated Ca^{2+} release.

One would also like to know how sperm–egg binding/fusion is transduced into the propagated wave of Ca^{2+} release. One possibility is that a specialized reticulum is involved. Campanella and Andreucetti (1977) have described extensive ramifications of endoplasmic or vesiculated reticulum near the surface of an amphibian egg. A similar reticulum has been seen by Carroll *et al.* (1977) in transmission electron micrographs of sea urchin eggs (Fig. 9), and Vacquier (1975) has described similar structures in scanning electron micrographs of the egg cortex. Perhaps this system is analogous to the T-system of muscle, which conducts surface impulses to the muscle fibers for rapid communication with the Ca^{2+}-regulating sarcoplasmic reticulum. Alternatively, the actual propagating mechanism for Ca^{2+} release may reside within the cortical granules themselves (see Section VIII, A; also Vacquier, 1975).

VII. Consequences of Increased Calcium in the Activation of Development

Since transient increase in intracellular Ca^{2+} will activate the egg to begin development, a major problem is to understand the chain of events between Ca^{2+} release and activation. In the following two sections, I will describe the known consequences of increased Ca^{2+} and attempt to point out areas of greatest ignorance. In Section VIII, I will describe the role of Ca^{2+} in the cortical exocytosis and then digress slightly to examine the consequences of the cortical exocytosis, especially the role of the cortical granule proteases in elevating the vitelline layer and establishing the block to polyspermy. In Section IX, I shall examine the role of Ca^{2+} in two cytoplasmic changes, a burst in respiration and activation of NAD kinase.

The calcium increase must also induce the third effector of fertilization, an increased intracellular pH, which is required for turning on various synthetic and permeability changes. This effector is examined in Sections X–XIII.

VIII. The Cortical Reaction as a Consequence of the Ca^{2+} Increase

A. DIRECT EFFECTS ON EXOCYTOSIS

The cortical reaction or cortical exocytosis is a secretory event in which cortical granules 1 μm in diameter, closely apposed to the plasma membrane, are discharged into the extracellular space. In *S. purpuratus* eggs, this secretion begins 20–30 seconds after fertilization and propagates around the 80 μm in diameter egg in an additional 20 seconds (Paul and Epel, 1971).

This exocytosis is probably a direct result of the increase in cytoplasmic calcium. Vacquier (1975) has prepared fragments of plasma membrane containing the cortical granules and found that when calcium is added to these membrane "lawns," the granules fuse with each other and their contents are released. The sequence is not exactly like the normal secretion, since the granules fuse with each other rather than with the overlying plasma membrane. Nevertheless, these results indicate that the increase in cytoplasmic calcium can account for the cortical exocytosis.

Vacquier (1975) has also made the important observation that the exocytosis induced by Ca^{2+} can be self-propagating in this *in vitro* system. This suggests that a localized release of Ca^{2+} around the site of sperm–egg fusion could account for the initial exocytosis; subsequent release of Ca^{2+} from the granules or the surrounding membrane complex could then initiate the observed propagated response around the egg.

The source of this initial Ca^{2+} release is still unknown. It would not appear to originate from localized entry from the seawater since, as noted above, eggs can be fertilized in Ca^{2+}-free seawater if acrosome-reacted sperm are used (Takahashi and Sugiyama, 1973). It would also not appear to come from the lysis of cortical granules at the site of sperm entry, since preliminary electron micrograph observations in our laboratory indicate that the site of sperm–egg fusion is actually one where granules do *not* undergo exocytosis. An alternative possibility, therefore, is calcium release from some membrane protein or membrane–reticulum complex.

B. ROLE OF THE EXOCYTOSIS IN DEVELOPMENT

The cortical reaction also results in a cascade of events yielding considerable modification of the egg surface. Most dramatic is the elevation of the vitelline layer and its transformation into the fertilization membrane. Structural proteins (Bryan, 1970) and enzymes of the cortical granules are involved in both elevation of the vitelline layer (Carroll and Epel, 1975a,b) and the structuralization or hardening of the resultant fertilization membrane (Lallier, 1970; Foerder *et al.*, 1977). Another structural protein, hyalin, contributes to the formation of the hyaline layer that is required for early cell adhesion (Citkowitz, 1972; Kane, 1974). The cortical exocytosis also results in the formation of a new mosaic membrane in which at least 50% of the plasma membrane is now derived from the inner surface of the cortical granules. Finally, there occurs a considerable elongation of microvilli (Tegner, 1974; Eddy and Shapiro, 1976), but this does not appear to require the prior cortical exocytosis (Mazia *et al.*, 1975).

The role of the cortical exocytosis for later development is probably minimal. Its major functions appear to be in establishing the late or complete block to polyspermy (Section VIII, C). Although the hyaline layer is important for early cell adhesion, it is not essential. This is shown in experiments in which eggs are fertilized in the presence of drugs that prevent the cortical exocytosis and hence formation of the hyaline layer. The blastomeres do not adhere well initially. Eventually, however, the poorly adhering blastomeres come together and develop into normal plutei (at least in *S. purpuratus* embryos) (M. Garavito and D. Epel, unpublished observations). As hyaline is continually secreted during cleavage (Kane, 1974), sufficient concentrations might accumulate and enable reaggregation to occur.

The exocytosis is also required for turning on several amino acid transport systems after fertilization (Epel and Johnson, 1976). Since development proceeds if eggs are fertilized under conditions where the cortical exocytosis does not occur, such transport would also not appear to be essential. Some transport capability eventually develops, however, and perhaps this residual activity is adequate (Epel and Johnson, 1976; D. Epel, unpublished results). Alternatively, the amino acid transport is not needed for early nutrition, since the yolk reserves should be quite adequate.

C. PROTEASE ACTIVITY OF THE CORTICAL GRANULES

1. Elevation of the Vitelline Layer

There have been recent important insights into how the exocytosis results in the transformation of the vitelline layer into the fertilization membrane with a resultant block to polyspermy. The earlier work of Lundblad (1954), showing that proteases are released at the time of the cortical reaction, has been considerably extended by the finding that proteases are actually contained in the cortical granules and are released outward during the secretion phase (Vacquier *et al.*, 1972a,b; Schuel *et al.*, 1973). The proteolytic activity, which is trypsinlike in nature, has been partially purified by Carroll and Epel (1975b). They find two activities that can be separated by isoelectric focusing or by elution from affinity chromatographic columns.

One activity, referred to as vitelline delaminase, is involved in hydrolyzing linkages between the vitelline layer and the plasma membrane (Carroll and Epel, 1975b). If one fertilizes eggs in the presence of soybean trypsin inhibitor (a potent inhibitor of the enzyme), the vitelline layer does not elevate properly but remains attached to the egg plasma membrane at many foci. However, if one first treats the egg with the partially purified delaminase, and then activates in the presence of the trypsin inhibitor, a normal fertilization membrane arises. This indicates that the previous incubation of the egg in the protease hydrolyzed protease-sensitive linkages between vitelline layer and egg surface. Other evidence is that if an unfertilized egg is treated with the protease and the egg is then "shrunk" by placing it in hypertonic seawater, one can see a thin shell around the egg corresponding to the vitelline layer. The visualization of this shell requires prior treatment with the protease.

Simple hydrolysis of these linkages is not, by itself, sufficient to elevate the layer. Rather, a subsequent cortical reaction is required suggesting that other components of the cortical granules are needed to elevate the detached layer. This second component may be mucopolysaccharides contained within the granules. If these are hydrophilic, their hydration upon contact with seawater could result in the elevation of the layer once it has been detached by the action of the delaminase.

Subsequent alterations in the vitelline layer result in a structuralization or hardening of the fertilization membrane. This change can be visualized as a loss of mercaptan solubility. Up to 3 minutes after fertilization, the membrane is soluble in dithiothreitol or mercaptoethanol; thereafter it is insoluble in these compounds (Paul and Epel, 1971; Lallier, 1970). The change is not catalyzed by the soluble components released from the cortical granules (Carroll and Epel, 1975a); it probably requires insoluble proteins contained within the granules which normally become incorporated into the fertilization membrane (Bryan, 1970). Lallier (1971) suggested that protein cross-linking reactions are involved, and Veron et al. (1977) have recently found that glycine ethyl ester, an inhibitor of cross-linking, prevents one of the major structural changes in the hardening process. These workers have also found that a peroxidatic cross-linking of tyrosine residues is an important part of the hardening process (Foerder et al., 1977).

2. Destruction of Sperm Receptors of the Vitelline Layer

The second proteolytic activity present in the cortical granules, referred to as sperm-receptor hydrolase, specifically alters sperm binding to the vitelline layer surface (Carroll and Epel, 1975b); it is important to note that the layer itself is not removed by this enzyme (see later). If unfertilized eggs are incubated in partially purified sperm-receptor hydrolase, sperm will not attach to these eggs, and the eggs are not capable of being fertilized. Apparently the sperm-receptor hydrolase alters vitelline layer receptors, but not plasma membrane receptors, since after the removal of the vitelline layer with Pronase or dithiothreitol, eggs can be fertilized.

The simplest interpretation of this observation is that the receptor hydrolase activity has somehow altered the vitelline layer such that sperm cannot bind to it. This contrasts with the effects of trypsin, Pronase, etc., which simply digest the entire layer but apparently leave available sperm receptors on the plasma membrane or expose a highly fusible plasma membrane surface. The receptor hydrolase activity does not appreciably digest the vitelline layer (Carroll et al., 1977), which remains as a physical barrier over the egg surface. Sperm do not bind to this layer and thus do not pass through it to fuse with the egg.

3. Protease Specificity

The specificity of the delaminase and hydrolase are remarkable, and studies of these two enzymes could provide experimental models for understanding specific proteolysis. Although trypsinlike in some respects, their action is radically different from bovine pancreatic trypsin. Incubation of unfertilized eggs in an equivalent proteolytic or esterolytic activity of pancreatic trypsin simply digests the vitelline layer away. If the egg surface is first labeled with the [^{125}I]lactoperoxidase procedure, more than 90% of the ^{125}I counts are removed during incubation in trypsin (Johnson and Epel, 1975; Carroll et al., 1977). This contrasts markedly with the situation where the eggs are incubated in a mixture of the cortical granule proteases; there is no visible digestion of the vitelline layer and almost no release of ^{125}I (Carroll et al., 1977). Thus, these proteases are acting in an extremely specific manner; digestion of the vitelline layer into soluble fragments is minimal, but the proteolysis results in large changes in function.

How might this specificity be attained? One insight has come from the interesting observation that if one "ages" the crude proteolytic fraction at 0°C, the specificity is lost. Instead of solely altering the vitelline layer to prevent sperm binding, this aged preparation now acts like pancreatic trypsin and digests the vitelline layer away (Carroll and Epel, 1975b). One explanation for this behavior is that during the aging process some modulating protein is lost from the enzyme. This idea is supported by the data of Fodor et al. (1975) who have extensively purified a trypsinlike activity from unfertilized sea urchin eggs. This enzyme is initially present in large-molecular-weight aggregates. After treatment with butanol, however, the activity is confined to a molecule similar in molecular weight to standard bovine trypsin. It is thus possible that the specificity of action is attained by modulating proteins and that during the aging process these modulating proteins are lost (recent unpublished data of V. D. Vacquier suggest that aging does not occur with the protease fraction obtained from ionophore-activated eggs. Either the ionophore-induced secretion is incomplete, or some factor causing the loss of specificity during aging is derived from the sperm).

4. Other Effects of the Proteases on Exocytosis and the Cell Surface

A third function for these proteases may be for processing or solubilizing the contents of the cortical granules or for destroying the perigranular membrane–plasma membrane junction as part of exocytosis. These ideas are suggested by an electron microscope analysis of Longo and Schuel (1973) of eggs fertilized in the presence of various trypsin inhibitors. A percentage of the granules does not initially break down, and these then fuse slowly with the plasma membrane. Although it is bothersome that there is no complete inhibition of the exocytosis, incomplete effects of inhibitor could result if the inhibition had to occur inside the granule or very quickly during the actual exocytosis. However, these dramatic effects of trypsin inhibitors on exocytosis are apparent only in the eggs of *Arbacia punctulata;* there appears to be little effect on the cortical reaction in the eggs of *S. purpuratus* (D. Epel, unpublished results).

The protease activities also result in a limited proteolysis of cell surface components, presumably proteins of both the plasma membrane and fertilization membrane (Shapiro, 1975). These modified proteins are retained on the egg surface at least through the larval stage. It is not clear whether this modification has developmental significance, since, as noted earlier, embryos whose cortical reaction has been prevented will develop into apparently normal larvae (Section VIII, B).

5. Role in Late Block to Polyspermy

Several observations indicate that the delaminase and receptor hydrolase may alter the vitelline layer to establish the late and complete block to polyspermy. This block is important since, as noted earlier, the fast block associated with the membrane depolarization can be overcome by high sperm concentrations. One line of evidence is from kinetic analyses that show that the complete block to polyspermy is established simultaneously with the cortical reaction (Presley and

Baker, 1970; Byrd and Collins, 1975; Collins and Byrd, 1978). Second, sperm detachment from the vitelline layer normally occurs just as the vitelline layer elevates (Tegner and Epel, 1973; Vacquier and Payne, 1973); however, when eggs are fertilized in the presence of trypsin inhibitors, sperm detachment does not occur and vitelline layer elevation is severely impaired (Vacquier *et al.*, 1972b, 1973). These eggs become polyspermic and sperm continue to fuse with these eggs for some time after the cortical reaction (Vacquier *et al.*, 1973; Schuel *et al.*, 1973; Longo *et al.*, 1974). Electron micrographs of Longo *et al.* (1974) indicate that the supernumerary sperm fuse with the egg at areas of the surface where the vitelline layer is still attached to the plasma membrane.

These results indicate that these two proteolytic enzymes prevent polyspermy by (1) detaching the connectives between the vitelline layer and plasma membrane as a part of the elevation process and (2) destroying sperm receptors on the vitelline layer. In the absence of these two events, sperm remain attached to the vitelline layer and fuse with the egg at sites where the vitelline layer is still apposed to the plasma membrane (Schuel *et al.*, 1976). This latter observation suggests that apposition of the vitelline layer and plasma membrane promotes sperm–egg fusion (although the presence of the vitelline layer is not essential, it could enhance fertilizability). An alternative possibility is that the presence of the hyaline layer prevents polyspermy and the development of this layer is slower in areas where cortical granules have not broken down (see, e.g., Tyler *et al.*, 1956). As eggs without vitelline layers also develop a block to polyspermy, other factors such as hyaline secretion, may be involved (Collins and Byrd, 1978).

IX. Oxidations and NAD Kinase Activation as Consequences of the Ca^{2+} Increase

Although Ca^{2+} probably induces the cortical exocytosis, this exocytosis does not appear to be a prerequisite for development. Increased Ca^{2+} does induce at least one cytoplasmic change, and possibly two, and these may be essential for development.

A. RESPIRATORY OR OXIDATIVE BURST

The calcium release is probably the direct cause of the increase in oxygen consumption that follows fertilization of sea urchin eggs. This respiratory burst is not coupled to changes in ADP or ATP levels of the cell (Epel, 1969). An important clue to the nature of the respiration came from the observation of Hultin (1950) that the O_2 consumption of homogenates increased upon addition of calcium. This might result from uncoupling of mitochondrial respiration by calcium. An alternative possibility is that calcium induces the lysis of cortical granules in the homogenate, which then releases and activates oxidases involved in the hardening of the fertilization membrane (e.g., Foerder et al., 1977). However, this alternative was eliminated by isolating cortices and measuring their respiration during calcium-induced cortical granule lysis. There was no O_2 consumption either before or after the addition of calcium (unpublished experiments of D. Epel, J. Schatten, and R. Steinhardt).

Perry and Epel (1977, and unpublished observations) have further analyzed the calcium induction of respiration in homogenates of S. purpuratus eggs and found this respiration to be nonmitochondrial and insensitive to cyanide. It appears to ensue from a Ca^{2+} requirement for unsaturated fatty acid oxidation. Addition of arachidonic acid to homogenates stimulates cyanide-insensitive respiration, and experiments with ^{14}C-labeled arachidonic acid show that this fatty acid is oxidized only in the presence of calcium. There appears to be a large conversion of arachidonic acid to several products, the primary one being hydroxyarachidonic acid. There is also some synthesis of prostaglandins, but the amount is small relative to oxygen consumption.

Arachidonic acid oxidation is also activated after fertilization. If one preloads unfertilized eggs with radioactive arachidonic acid, little or no conversion to other compounds is seen. After fertilization, however, considerable conversion occurs. Additional evidence for the occurrence of this respiration in vivo is that 30–50% of the embryo's respiration is cyanide insensitive, and this respiration can be stimulated by calcium. This is seen in experiments in which ionophore A23187 is added to embryos whose respiration has been previously inhibited with cyanide; addition of ionophore results in a large increase in O_2 consumption (Fig. 10).

These results suggest that the respiration rate may be limited by the calcium level in the cell and that increasing the Ca^{2+} level directly increases oxidations. The Ca^{2+}-sensitive enzyme is presumably a lipoxygenase.

A similar oxidation can be induced in Arbacia punctulata eggs which is also Ca^{2+} stimulated and cyanide insensitive. This resemblance is only superficial, however, since the bulk of this respiration can be attributed to the oxidation of the naphthoquinone pigment, echinochrome (Perry and Epel, 1975; Perry, 1976). It is doubtful that this pigment oxidation occurs in vivo since the affinity for Ca^{2+} ion is in

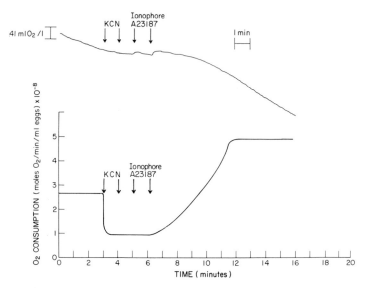

FIG. 10. Ca^{2+}-stimulated cyanide-insensitive respiration in embryos of *Strongylocentrotus purpuratus*. The respiration of embryos was measured with an O_2 electrode (upper part of figure), and rate was derived from the slope of the curve (lower part of figure). When KCN is added, respiration is two-thirds inhibited; when A23187 is added, respiration is stimulated to a rate even greater than the original rate. This suggests the existence of a Ca^{2+}-stimulated, cyanide-insensitive respiratory system in these embryos. Unpublished results of George Perry and D. Epel.

the millimolar range and the Ca^{2+} ion levels in the egg probably reach only 0.1 mM (Steinhardt *et al.*, 1977).

The role of this calcium-induced oxidation for later development is completely unknown. It is not necessary for the postfertilization increase in protein and DNA synthesis, since these latter events occur when eggs are incubated in ammonia, which bypasses the earlier respiratory change (Section XI). However, these ammonia-activated eggs do not divide, so perhaps the calcium-linked oxidation is required for some aspect of mitosis. Alternatively, this oxidation may represent the first steps in catabolism of fatty acids, which might represent the major pathway for energy production in the sea urchin embryo, as opposed to the catabolism of carbohydrate (see, e.g., Isono and Yasumasu, 1968; Yasumasu *et al.*, 1973b).

B. NAD KINASE

Another major change that occurs shortly after the cortical reaction and respiratory burst is the activation of the enzyme NAD kinase. This enzyme is transiently active during the interval between 40 seconds and 90 seconds after insemination of *S. purpuratus* eggs and results in a conversion of half the cell's NAD into NADP and NADPH (Epel, 1964). So far, no one has succeeded in extracting an inactive form of this enzyme from unfertilized eggs (Epel and Iverson, 1966; Blomquist, 1973). This suggests that the enzyme is either activated during the extraction process or the assay procedure is activating the enzyme, perhaps by providing cofactors, or that the enzyme or substrate are compartmentalized and released during cell disruption.

It is disconcerting not to be able to account for the inactivity of this enzyme in the unfertilized egg and its precipitous turn-on shortly after fertilization. One possibility, of course, is that the activation of the enzyme is related to the increase in free calcium. The enzyme requires calcium or magnesium (Epel, 1967; Blomquist, 1973), and it is intriguing to suppose that the postfertilization change in calcium might somehow be related to its activation. The effect could be directly upon the enzyme or on some structure associated with the enzyme. Indeed, given the association of actin with many cytoplasmic enzymes, it is possible that an increase in calcium might lead to events dissociating this enzyme from a structural protein, such as actin.

The role of NAD kinase in development is also unclear. Its activity results in a profound change in the redox potential of the cell (Epel, 1964), which would tend to make egg metabolism much more reductive (Lowenstein, 1960). This could be required for deoxyribonucleotide synthesis as well as for reductive phases possibly associated with microtubule polymerization (see Nath and Rebhun, 1976). However, there is no change in reduced glutathione levels after fertilization (Fahey *et al.*, 1976). It is not yet known whether the kinase is activated during incubation in ammonia (see below). If it is not, and since ammonia-activated eggs cannot divide, the NADP(H) changes and the respiratory burst might both be related to some aspect of mitosis.

X. Separation of Early and Late Events of Fertilization

The above analysis indicates that an increase in cytoplasmic calcium is close to the primary event of fertilization and that this increase by itself can result in the cascade of events leading to activation of development. Is Ca^{2+} acting directly to promote development? Or is Ca^{2+} acting indirectly, causing some change, which then secondarily acts on cell enzymes or structures to promote development? The latter situation appears to be the case, since one can experimentally separate or dissect the early Ca^{2+}-requiring events from the later events of activation. These experiments indicate that although Ca^{2+} is a critical link in the cascade of postfertilization events, Ca^{2+} does not act directly to activate the egg.

A. Experimental Dissection by Incubation in Ammonia

The first dissection came from the observation of Steinhardt and Mazia (1972) that when eggs were incubated in dilute solutions of ammonium hydroxide or ammonium chloride at pH 9, late events such as potassium conductance and DNA synthesis were induced in the absence of such earlier events as the cortical exocytosis and membrane depolarization. Further analyses of the ammonia activation showed that another early response, the respiratory burst, did not occur (Epel *et al.*, 1974), but that other late responses, such as increased protein synthesis (Epel *et al.*, 1974) chromosome condensation (Mazia, 1974; Mazia and Ruby, 1974), and polyadenylation of mRNA (Wilt and Mazia, 1974), were all activated. This activation of development is incomplete, as the activated eggs will not divide. Additional factors are necessary, and their nature will be discussed later (Section XII).

Experimental analysis showed that low concentrations of ammonia could turn on protein synthesis but would not initiate chromosome condensation; a slightly higher concentration would not increase the bulk rate of protein synthesis but would now turn on chromosome condensation (Epel *et al.*, 1974). Thus, the ammonia effect was almost akin to "titrating" the metabolism of the egg (Epel *et al.*, 1974).

Further analysis of the changes induced by ammonia revealed that all of these were independent of one another (Epel *et al.*, 1974). For example, one could prevent potassium conductance, but still get synthesis of DNA and protein. Earlier work had shown that one could stop protein synthesis and still obtain DNA synthesis (Black *et al.*, 1967). Thus, the many changes induced by ammonia are independent of each other. This suggested that ammonia induces a single primary or pervasive change, which then turns on all the subsequent events independently of one another (Epel *et al.*, 1974).

B. Experimental Dissection by Removal of Sodium

The second means for dissecting the early from late events of fertilization came from the important discovery of Chambers (1975, 1976) that small amounts of sodium ion were required for metabolic activation. This Na^+ requirement existed between 30 seconds and 10 minutes after fertilization of *Lytechinus variegatus* eggs. In its absence, the sperm nucleus would enter the egg but would not decondense, a sperm aster with associated microtubules did not form, the nucleus did not swell, and there were no signs of cytoplasmic activation. These "fertilized" eggs could be kept for at least 2 hours in this suspended animation with no further development. If small amounts of sodium (as little as 3 mM) were added, however, the eggs would begin to develop. As noted, this sodium requirement existed only at the beginning of development; after 10 minutes, there was no sodium requirement and eggs could even cleave in sodium-free seawater (Chambers, 1975, 1976).

This dissection of the fertilization process by provision of ammonia or deletion of sodium provided the first tangible evidence that activation of development at fertilization might result from two separate events (see also Uto and Sugiyama, 1969). This separation also corresponded to the previously proposed temporal separation of the fertilization events into early and late phases (Section IV; Epel et al., 1969). The early phases (0–60 seconds) seemed to be linked to the membrane depolarization and Ca^{2+} release; the late changes (beginning at 300 seconds) could be prevented by removing sodium from the medium or could be induced independently of the early changes by incubation of the eggs in ammonia. The potential of these dissections for understanding development was obvious, and a large amount of work has been directed to the question of how ammonia and sodium are involved in the activation of the egg.

XI. Intracellular pH as a Regulator of the Late Changes

A. RELATIONSHIP BETWEEN AMMONIA, NA$^+$, AND H$^+$ IN EGG ACTIVATION

The first important clue to the site of action of ammonia came from the finding of Paul et al. (1976) that ammonia induced one of the early changes, a release of protons known as the "fertilization acid." It had previously been thought that this proton release was related to the cortical exocytosis. However, when eggs are incubated in ammonia and release acid, there is no cortical reaction. If these eggs are now fertilized, a cortical reaction occurs, but there is no additional acid release (Paul et al., 1976). Thus, the acid release is not correlated to exocytosis, but seems to be related to the turning on of egg metabolism by ammonia.

Also consistent with this hypothesis was the finding that the amount of acid release by ammonia is dependent on the ammonia concentration. This corresponds with the "titration" of egg metabolism by ammonia (see above; also Epel et al., 1974). Also, a number of amines and amine anesthetics had been reported to activate egg metabolism, in a manner similar to ammonia (Vacquier, 1975; Johnson and Epel, 1975). These amine compounds also result in acid release (Paul *et al.*, 1976).

A second important clue was the discovery of a sodium requirement for acid release. Paul and Epel (1975) had previously investigated the ionic requirements for acid release, using ionophore A23187 to activate eggs in various ion-substituted media. The only ion affecting acid release was sodium; in its absence, there was a 75% reduction in acid release. At that time, we had attributed this inhibition to the impairment of cortical exocytosis resulting from lack of sodium. However, this explanation was now not tenable, since our subsequent work showed that the acid release did not result from the cortical granule exocytosis (above results with ammonia of Paul *et al.*, 1976). Instead, the results suggested that sodium might be directly required for acid release.

B. NA⁺–H⁺ EXCHANGE

The above studies on acid release, combined with the observation of Chambers that Na⁺ was required for metabolic activation, suggested a relationship between the Na⁺ requirement for metabolic activation and the Na⁺ requirement for acid release. This relationship was studied by Johnson *et al.* (1976) in experiments in which eggs were resuspended in sodium-free seawater 45 seconds after fertilization and the sodium dependence of acid release was monitored. When the pH of this egg suspension was measured with a glass electrode, no hydrogen ions were being released into the medium. When small amounts of sodium were added, however, hydrogen ions began to be released and the rate of release was proportional to the concentration of sodium that

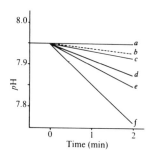

FIG. 11. Acid efflux from eggs is dependent on the Na⁺ concentration. Eggs were fertilized and resuspended in Na⁺-free seawater beginning 60 seconds after insemination. The pH of the suspension was then monitored and varying amounts of NaCl were added: a, 0.1 mM NaCl; b, 100 mM LiCl; c, 3 mM NaCl; d, 10 mM NaCl; e, 20 mM NaCl; f, 40 mM NaCl. The inset shows the linear relationship between Na⁺ and H⁺ efflux at these low Na⁺ concentrations and over short time intervals. From Johnson *et al.* (1976); reprinted with permission of *Nature*.

was present (Fig. 11) (although not shown in the figure, the efflux of hydrogen ion would continue until the egg had released approximately the amount that would have been discharged during the normal fertilization process).

One explanation for these results was an equimolar exchange of sodium ions for protons. Experiments with [22]Na confirmed this hypothesis, i.e., the ratio sodium in : hydrogen out was 1 : 1 to 1.0 : 1.4. Further evidence came from experiments with the drug amiloride. This is a diuretic drug that blocks certain types of sodium channels. When applied to eggs at 1×10^{-4} M in 25 mM Na$^+$ in choline-substituted seawater, it prevented both the sodium influx and hydrogen efflux [Johnson *et al.* (1976); my recent experiments indicate that higher amiloride concentrations, of the order of 2 to 4×10^{-4} M amiloride in 25 mM Na$^+$ are necessary to inhibit activation].

C. MECHANISM OF PROTON RELEASE BY AMMONIA

The induction of acid release by ammonia, amines, and the amine anesthetics appears to be by a different mechanism. First, the release of acid is extremely rapid in ammonia and amine anesthetics, almost as though the channels are opened immediately and completely. Second, the release of acid by ammonia does not require sodium. One possible mechanism is that ammonia enters the cell as undissociated NH$_3$. Since the cell pH is 6.5 (see below), the NH$_3$ would absorb protons and tend to make the cell more alkaline (which does occur, as described below). This explanation, however, does not account for the concomitant efflux of H$^+$ *outside* the cell. An alternative possibility, suggested by Bertil Hille (personal communication) is that ammonia and the amine anesthetics are acting as proton ionophores, exchanging protons for some other cation at the cell membrane. A second possibility is that ammonia and the amine compounds are simply triggering an already primed egg to release H$^+$ ion along with a balancing anion, such as chloride. A final possibility, suggested by Winkler and Grainger (1978); W. F. Boron, A. Roos, and P. DeWeer (personal communication), is that the acid "release" results from the change in equilibrium when undissociated NH$_3$ enters the cell. As the NH$_3$ enters, the equilibrium NH$_4^+ \rightleftharpoons$ NH$_3$ + H$^+$ is shifted and a proton is produced outside the cell.

D. INTRACELLULAR pH

Because a large amount of protons are exported from the cell (5 μmol/ml of packed cells), it seemed plausible that the acid release resulted in a rise in cytoplasmic alkalinity that activates development. We tested the first part of this hypothesis—that the pH of the cytoplasm increases—by measuring the pH of egg homogenates of *S. pur-*

puratus. The pH of homogenates increased from pH 6.5 to pH 6.8 over a time period corresponding to that of acid release. Reassuringly, the homogenate can be titrated back from pH 6.8 to pH 6.5 by an amount of alkali equivalent to the calculated amount of protons released by eggs (Johnson *et al.,* 1976). Similar findings have been reported by Shen and Steinhardt (1978) using intracellular pH microelectrodes.

These pH measurements on egg homogenates indicate that a cytoplasmic pH change accompanies the hydrogen ion efflux. The critical question is whether it is the pH change (resulting from hydrogen efflux) or the sodium influx which is critical for activation. The following experiment was designed to decide between these alternatives. Development of fertilized eggs was arrested by placing them in sodium-free seawater at 60 seconds after fertilization. To one group of eggs was added sodium to elicit sodium influx and hydrogen efflux, and to the other group of eggs was added ammonium chloride to elicit only the hydrogen efflux without sodium influx. Both groups of eggs divided. Therefore hydrogen efflux and the consequent intracellular pH change are the critical factors in activating the egg (Johnson *et al.,* 1976).

Additional evidence that intracellular pH is the critical factor is that agents that cause acid efflux also activate egg metabolism. These include ammonia, the amine anesthetics, and nicotine (Steinhardt and Mazia, 1972; Vacquier and Brandriffe, 1975; Johnson and Epel, 1975; Paul *et al.,* 1976; Johnson *et al.,* 1976). Finally, David Nishioka (unpublished results) has found that the arrest of fertilized eggs that have been placed in Na^+-free seawater can be reversed by simply increasing the extracellular pH. When the extracellular pH is 9, the intracellular pH increases above 6.8 and the eggs will divide. If the extracellular pH is below 9, the intracellular pH remains below pH 6.8 and the eggs remain arrested and do not divide.

An important question is whether the pH must remain high for new cellular events, or whether only a pulse of high pH is needed to start these new cellular activates. Using the homogenate procedure, Nishioka and Epel (1977) and Lopo and Vacquier (1977) have found that the pH begins to decrease 10 to 20 minutes after fertilization. This fall in intracellular pH has not been seen with the microelectrode measurements (Shen and Steinhardt, 1978). Although these differences must be reconciled, they raise the possibility that pH needs to remain high for only a few minutes to irreversibly activate the egg (see Section XII, B for a discussion of the reversibility problem).

E. Regulation of Na^+–H^+ "Exchange" or Counter Transport

The first unresolved question about the Na^+–H^+ exchange is whether it is a true exchange using a common carrier or whether the

1 : 1 stoichiometry actually represents some sort of counter transport in which the two ions move through separate channels, their net flux being determined by electroneutrality requirements. Since amiloride appears to bind to Na^+ channels (Lindemann and Van Driessche, 1977), it is most probable that the latter mechanism is operative. For this reason I shall refer to the Na^+ and H^+ fluxes as counter transport.

The second and most important question is how the Na^+–H^+ counter transport is activated. Several changes precede the activation of counter transport, and one of these changes may be responsible for the activation. A strong possibility is that the increased level of cytoplasmic calcium directly alters membrane permeability. This possibility is suggested by a study on nerve and gland cells, in which a prior increase in cell Ca^{2+} increases permeability of the membrane to potassium ion (Meech, 1976; Berridge, 1976).

Another temporally related change is the exocytosis, which could activate previously inactive Na^+–H^+ transport systems through conformational changes of the surface. If so, one would predict that fertilization under conditions where the cortical reaction is prevented should also prevent sodium–hydrogen counter transport. It may be impossible to test this prediction, however, since the best-described inhibitors of the cortical reaction are amine anesthetics (Vacquier and Brandriffe, 1975); as noted, these independently initiate acid release.

A third change which just precedes Na^+–H^+ exchange is a large alteration in the light-scattering properties of the eggs (Epel et al., 1969; Paul and Epel, 1971). This change begins at the time of the cortical reactions and is temporally coincident with the exocytosis. Although it may seem to be related to exocytosis, a similar light-scattering change occurs after fertilization of Urechis eggs, where there is no exocytosis but there is acid release (Paul, 1975b). Thus, the behavior of the light-scattering change correlates best with a role in acid release. It could represent a contractile change in the cell cortex that could alter the cell surface and activate counter transport independently of the exocytosis.

A final possibility is that there are inhibitory proteins on the cell surface that prevent sodium-hydrogen counter transport and that these proteins are somehow removed after fertilization. Evidence suggesting this hypothesis comes from the earlier experiments of Johnson and Epel (1975) and Mazia et al. (1975), showing that activation of eggs results in alteration of the egg surface and loss of a surface glycoprotein. The best evidence for a role of surface components is the finding of Mazia et al. (1975) that physical perturbation of the egg surface would activate the egg similarly to activation seen with ammonia and the amine compounds. Their procedure is to coat glass fibers or glass rods with a polycation, such as protamine sulfate. If the cell

surface is now perturbed, as by pulling on the rod, the eggs are activated. One interpretation of this finding is that anionic cell surface
proteins are acting as regulators of Na^+–H^+ counter transport, perhaps
as corks or plugs. Removal or perturbation of these proteins then permits counter transport and elevation of cell pH.

Strong evidence that cell surface proteins were regulators of cell
metabolism came from the report of Johnson and Epel (1975) that
concentrated solutions of the cell surface proteins released by activated
eggs would depress protein synthesis of eggs. I have not been able to
repeat these experiments and therefore do not believe that this particular experiment is valid (Fig. 3 of the paper of Johnson and Epel, 1975).

F. REGULATION OF CELL METABOLISM BY pH

1. Statement of the Problem

Does the realization that pH is a regulatory factor help us focus on
the critical pH-sensitive events? In one sense the answer is no, since
one might just modify previously existing hypotheses to take into account the pH concept. For example, if a preexisting model involved
proteolytic conversion of inactive enzymes into active enzymes, the
modified model would simply say that the protease would have to be
extremely sensitive to pHs between 6.5 and 6.8.

In another sense, the realization that pH is involved does help in
that it forces us to concentrate on pH-sensitive steps that would result
in considerable amplification and highly generalized effects. A mechanism is necessary that can account for such unrelated effects as increased permeability of the plasma membrane to K^+, amino acids, and
nucleosides, increased translation of mRNA, initiation of DNA synthesis, and formation of a microtubule-containing sperm aster. Also, there
occur not only increases in ongoing syntheses (as protein synthesis),
but initiation of new activities (as DNA synthesis). The problem, as
modified by the above discussion, is to explain how a 0.3 pH unit increase yields such generalized effects on so many processes, both at the
level of increasing rates of ongoing activities and at the level of initiating new activities.

2. Antagonistic Enzyme Models

Two mechanisms seem worth considering. The first is based on the
relationship between pH and activity, which occurs in many biological
processes. If only one pH-sensitive species of molecule, as an enzyme,
were involved, slight changes in pH would have little effect (perhaps

doubling or tripling in rate). However, if two antagonistic enzymes or "enzyme couples" were involved and if their activity varied oppositely to pH, then slight variations in pH would have much greater effects on cell activity. (Fig. 12). A particularly good enzyme couple is protein kinase *vs* protein phosphatase. It is easy to see how varying the degree of protein phosphorylation could have profound effects on many diverse cell processes.

Another enzyme couple could be the adenyl cyclase–phosphodiesterase. Earlier work from two laboratories indicated that no large changes in cAMP occurred in the first 5–10 minutes of fertilization (Yasumasu *et al.*, 1973a; Rebhun *et al.*, 1973). However, this work did not eliminate the possibility of a large transient increase in this nucleotide, perhaps paralleling the early changes in Ca^{+2} or pH. Unpublished work from my laboratory, done in collaboration with Dr Milton Saier, indicates that there are also no transient changes in cAMP.

3. *Structural Protein Models*

A second mechanism, which would also have pervasive effects on cell structure and metabolism, could come from the aggregation of structural or enzymic macromolecules, whose aggregation is pH- or salt-sensitive and which exhibits high cooperativity. Such aggregation is seen in tobacco mosaic virus assembly. The aggregation is extremely sensitive to pH, and studies on this aggregation show the *extent* and *type* of aggregate varies with pH and also as the exponent of the number of monomers in the aggregate. Thus the larger the size of the aggregate, the greater is the pH sensitivity. A difference of just a few

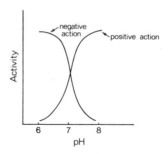

FIG. 12. Antagonistic enzyme model to account for sensitivity of metabolism to pH. We assume that two enzymes with opposite or antagonistic effects are regulating critical processes and that their pH dependence is poised as shown. The effects of slight changes in pH would therefore be doubled, since the activity of one enzyme is decreased while that of the other enzyme is increased to the same extent. As noted in the text, a model of this type of enzyme couple could be protein kinase–protein phosphatase activities.

tenths of a pH unit can shift the aggregate from one form to another (Durham *et al.,* 1971; Butler *et al.,* 1972).

Could similar pH-sensitive aggregation phenomena exist in the egg? We do not yet know, but it is intriguing that the two major structural proteins of the cell are actin and tubulin. Their state of aggregation probably affects cell structure and cell activity, and if this aggregation were pH sensitive at the particular ionic concentrations in the egg, then a slight change in pH could radically shift the monomer–multimer balance with profound effects on the cell (see especially the earlier discussion on actin polymerization, Section II, B). An actin effect could be mediated by the association of actin to cytoplasmic enzymes (see, e.g., Arnold and Pette, 1970). Several enzymes do change their subcellular location after fertilization (see Isono and Yasumasu, 1968). Could this change ensue from changes in the state of actin in the cell?

This aggregation hypothesis is especially stimulating since the pH-sensitive target suggested by this analysis is identical to that being suggested in other activation systems, but for completely different reasons. Studies on the regulation of mitosis in mammalian cells using colchicine and cytochalasin indicate that the state of microtubules and microfilaments is important in the initial steps leading to DNA synthesis (e.g., see Edelman, 1976). It is most provocative that regulation in both systems, the differentiated mammalian cell and the unfertilized sea urchin egg, may be related to the status of their structural proteins.

XII. Additional Factors Regulating the Egg

A. Statement of the Problem

The preceding results suggest that the following three sequential changes result in egg activation: (1) the increased membrane potential, (2) Ca^{2+} release, and (3) increased intracellular pH. So far, the demonstrated roles for these changes, are, respectively: (1) preventing polyspermy, (2) initiating the cortical exocytosis and a Ca^{2+}-linked oxidative system, and (3) initiating a number of diverse changes, including K^+ conductance of the plasma membrane, protein synthesis, DNA synthesis, and chromosome condensation. The change of major impact seems to be the pH change with its pervasive consequences on cell synthesis. The problem I wish to consider in this section is whether this last stage in the sequence is sufficient to activate the egg? Will induction of only this last step lead to embryonic development? Or are some products of the two earlier changes also required?

B. IRREVERSIBLE ACTIVATING FACTOR(S)

Fertilization results in an *irreversible* activation of the egg, but reversible activation can be attained with such parthenogenetic agents as ammonia and the amine anesthetics. Vacquier and Brandriffe (1975) first noted the reversibility of DNA synthesis in eggs activated by procaine. When procaine was removed, further cycles of DNA synthesis stopped, but protein synthesis remained elevated. When procaine was added back, DNA synthesis resumed. D. Nishioka (unpublished re- sults) has found an even greater reversibility in eggs activated with 10 mM ammonia at pH 8. When ammonia is removed, DNA synthesis ceases and the rate of protein synthesis decreases to the level of the unfertilized egg. Addition of ammonia reactivates both syntheses. This reversible behavior is not seen when eggs are activated in 1–2 mM ammonia at pH 9; when the ammonia is removed, cell synthesis remains turned on.

These results suggest that after fertilization an additional factor must come into play that locks in the activation of metabolism, and that this locking in does not occur in eggs activated by procaine or ammonia at pH 8. One possibility is that this factor locks in the *consequences* of the pH change so that the cell is no longer very sensitive to pH. This hypothesis is suggested by observations on cell pH following fertilization and the reversible and irreversible activation by ammonia. In normal fertilization, the pH eventually decreases to a level 0.1 pH above the unfertilized eggs, but the egg is irreversibly activated (Section XI, D). In reversibly activated eggs (10 mM ammonia, pH 8) cell pH decreases when ammonia is removed, but the cell's synthetic activity is turned off. In irreversibly activated eggs (1–2 mM ammonia, pH 9) cell pH does not decrease appreciably when ammonia is removed, and the cell's synthetic activity remains on. This suggests the hypothesis that high pH activates the eggs but normally some other factor then comes into play that locks the synthetic activity of the egg into the "on" position in a manner that synthetic activity is no longer sensitive to pH. The observations on amine-activated eggs would suggest that this factor is not formed in ammonia and that synthesis continues only when the cell pH remains high.

This factor could be the loss of cell surface proteins, which are released after normal fertilization but are released only slowly in ammonia-activated cells (Johnson and Epel, 1975). Alternative candidates for this irreversible activating factor could be some product of the Ca^{2+} increase, such as the NADPH from NAD kinase activation or the products of the Ca^{2+}-dependent respiratory system.

C. CELL-DIVISION FACTOR(S)

Ammonia-activated eggs do not divide, again indicating that some additional factor(s) is needed. Cytological observations show that the mitotic apparatus does not form properly. Rather, a clear nonfibrous area appears in the center of the cell with highly condensed metaphase chromosomes randomly dispersed within the clear area (Mazia, 1974; Mazia and Ruby, 1974). This contrasts with the normal fibrous and highly organized mitotic apparatus. This inability to form a mitotic apparatus does not result from toxic effects of ammonia, since eggs fertilized in the presence of ammonia can divide.

These observations suggest that another lesion in ammonia-activated eggs is in the formation of a mitotic apparatus. The most probable missing factor is the centriole, which is normally provided by the fertilizing sperm. Alternatively, as noted above, the factor could be some consequence of the Ca^{2+} increase, such as NADPH or Ca^{2+} stimulated respiration. Either or all of these might be needed to form a mitotic apparatus.

This requirement for multiple factors was also seen by Loeb (1913) in his classic studies on artificial parthenogenesis; he found that most single treatments did not result in good activation. His best procedure was a double treatment, involving an initial exposure to butyric acid followed by a subsequent incubation in hypertonic seawater. This latter treatment was essential to get cytasters (and presumably centrioles) used for the subsequent mitosis.

This double method, therefore, is truly an artificial procedure that contrasts with the concept of many workers that experimental parthenogenesis is the triggering of an already primed cell. This is partially true, but the second treatment, which results in mitosis, might now be seen as inducing synthesis of structures that the egg does not normally have to make. Normally, the sperm brings in the centriole that is required for organizing the mitotic apparatus; the second treatment might thus be a substitute for this other component of the sperm.

Today we realize that there are at least three, and possibly five, separate effectors involved in fertilization; the described ones are the membrane potential change, Ca^{2+} release, and intracellular pH change. From the above considerations, it appears that no one of these is sufficient to completely activate development and that irreversible activating factors and mitosis-inducing factors should also be looked for.

XII. Do the Principles of Activation at Fertilization Apply to Other Cellular and Developmental Activities?

As we have seen, the early changes of fertilization center around alterations in cation distributions within the cell. The result is a pervasive change in the cell, which goes from a relatively inactive stage into a synthetically active state and embarks on a program leading to development and differentiation. Do similar changes apply in other, more differentiated cells, or are these regulatory processes unique to fertilization, literally a "once in a lifetime event"?

Examination of many cell/developmental processes reveal that changes of state are constantly occurring and result from some triggering event that is probably analogous in principle to the triggering at fertilization. Examples include (1) the triggering of developmental programs by light (as in plants), by hormones, and by inducers and (2) the stimulation of cell division in previously quiescent cells. In all cases a cascade of contingent events is initiated, and in all cases that have been closely analyzed the earliest events appear to be changes in cation permeability.

Four examples are particularly worth examining. The first is the photoinduction of developmental programs in plants. The photoeffector is a pigment known as phytochrome, and photoconversion of this pigment eventually leads to new gene action (see review by Briggs and Rice, 1972). However, the primary events involve extremely rapid changes in membrane potential (Newman and Briggs, 1972) and possibly alterations in NADP levels (Tezuko and Yamamoto, 1972). The parallels to fertilization are remarkable.

A second example is the induction of chromosomal puffs in insect salivary glands by the hormone ecdysone. Studies on the action of this hormone reveal that it causes marked changes in membrane potential (Ito and Loewenstein, 1965) and membrane permeability, particularly in the transport of potassium and sodium ion (Kroeger, 1966). The ion permeability seems to be critical, since simply altering the sodium content of isolated salivary gland cells will induce changes in puffing patterns that mimic those induced by the hormone *in vivo* (Kroeger *et al.*, 1973; but see Rensing and Lansing, 1975).

A third example is seen in the stimulation of mitotically quiescent cells to divide. Lymphocytes and various tissue culture cells can be stimulated to enter DNA synthesis and mitosis by simply increasing the Ca^{2+} or Mg^{2+} content, either with ionophore A23187 or even by increasing the cation content of the medium (Dulbecco and Elkington, 1975; Kamine and Rubin, 1976; Luckasen *et al.,* 1974). The earliest known changes that follow activation of quiescent cells also involve changes in membrane transport (Rozengurt and Heppel, 1975).

A fourth and even more dramatic example is the stimulation of cells that normally never divide to enter another round of cell division. The cells are nerve cells, and they can be induced to divide by various treatments that raise their sodium content (Cone and Cone, 1976).

Given that changes in ions might be causal links in initiating cellular and developmental events, the major problem for future research is to understand how such seemingly nonspecific changes can have such profound effects on the cell. However, if we treat this problem as two separate issues, one of mechanism and one of specificity, the question does appear to be resolvable. As regards *mechanism,* I have noted several possible means by which a change in H^+ ion can have pervasive consequences on cell activity (Section XI, F). In principle, these arguments could also apply to other ions, such as Na^+. As regards *specificity,* the unique response of the cell to a change in ionic composition would result if the particular cell were already programmed or determined (and in a sense differentiated) to respond to a stimulus by changing its intracellular milieu.

It is useful, in this context, to visualize the unfertilized egg as a differentiated cell in which a developmental program has been set up, but the program is "off." The first part of this program, which is triggered by the sperm, results in ionic changes that alter the activity of the entire cell through the pervasive consequences of increased cell pH.

Similar determinations might occur throughout development, in which the next step or steps, which will lead to differentiation, are held in check until a specific developmental signal is received. This specific stimulus, which might be some surface effector, such as a hormone or inducer, evokes a characteristic response in the determined cell that leads to differentiation. In some systems, as chicken muscle differentiation, this characteristic response is an increase in cyclic AMP (cAMP) and this compound by itself is a sufficient stimulus for differentiation (see, e.g., Zalin, 1976; Deshpande and Siddiqui, 1976). Although the exact mechanism is unclear, this involvement of cAMP seems reasonable since these compounds can alter the activity of enzymes, as through protein phosphorylation. Modulating cAMP levels as a means of effecting differentiation would be seemingly impossible, however, since these compounds are probably present in all cells and their levels vary during the cell cycle, etc. Specificity can be attained if, as noted above, the cell has been programmed or determined to respond to the cyclic nucleotides in a manner that specifically leads to the observed differentiation.

Another means of regulating cell activity, which the work on fertilization emphasizes, is for the developmental signal to alter the ionic milieu, with the resultant pervasive changes then triggering new developmental pathways. In both cases, regulation of the cell by cAMP or by ions, the effector is nonspecific. However, the requisite specificity can be achieved if the cell has been previously programmed to respond in a specific way to the altered concentrations of these effectors.

XIV. Summary

My intent in this review has been to concentrate on the major effectors involved in the activation of sperm and egg. In this sense I have perhaps not been comprehensive enough in neglecting such well studied (but poorly understood) events as the activation of protein synthesis at fertilization. My premise, however, is that comprehension of the various responses to fertilization must await the description of their primary regulators. In this context, the studies reviewed in this article show that the sperm and egg are differentiated cells programmed to interact with specific surface receptors, that the interaction leads to sequential changes in cytoplasmic ions, and that it is these ionic changes that result in "activation."

In sperm (Fig. 13) plasma membrane receptors interact with some component of the egg jelly or egg surface. This leads to increased Ca^{2+} content, and the induction of membrane fusion and the acrosomal exocytosis. At the same time, there is an acid efflux, polymerization of internal actin, and exposure of sperm lysins and sperm bindins, which

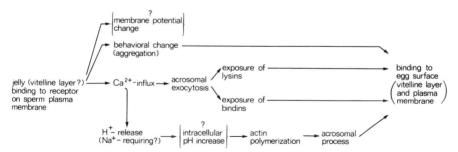

FIG. 13. The sequence of changes emanating from contact of the sperm plasma membrane with egg jelly (or vitelline layer). Unknown changes are indicated by question mark/brackets. This is to be compared with Fig. 14, which shows the similar changes evoked in the egg upon contact with the sperm. See further details in the text.

are attached to the newly formed membrane of the acrosomal process. Simultaneously, the behavior of the sperm is altered so that sperm aggregate around the individual eggs as well as with each other.

Sperm attach to a receptor of the egg's vitelline layer and/or plasma membrane (Fig. 14), and this contact or the subsequent fusion initiates a rapid membrane depolarization that precludes most sperm from fusing with the egg as part of the incomplete early block to polyspermy. Several undescribed steps follow, one of which requires Mg^{2+}, with the resultant fusion of sperm and egg membrane and the release of Ca^{2+} from some cortical or cytoplasmic store. The Ca^{2+} increase appears to trigger the cortical granule exocytosis and resultant release of structural proteins and enzymes, which raise and harden the vitelline layer as it transforms into the fertilization membrane. The fertilization membrane forms a structural barrier to sperm and is the basis of the complete block to polyspermy.

The increase in calcium normally leads to the next major effector of fertilization, the activation of a sodium–hydrogen counter-transport system with a resultant increase in intracellular pH. This increased pH is a prerequisite for activation of numerous syntheses and transport changes. However, the pH change is an inadequate stimulus by itself. Other changes, possibly related to the earlier calcium increase and the burst in nonmitochondrial oxidations, result in an irreversible locking in of egg activation and the formation of a mitotic apparatus.

A general unresolved question is: How similar are the activation of sperm and egg? In both, the primary trigger is an interaction with a surface receptor. There is an initial membrane depolarization in eggs; it is not known whether one occurs in sperm. In both gametes a critical

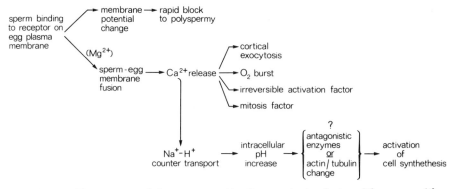

FIG. 14. The sequence of changes emanating from contact or fusion of the sperm with the egg. This is to be compared with Fig. 13, which shows the similar changes evoked in the sperm upon contact with egg jelly. See further details in the text.

response resulting from interaction with the receptor is an increase in cytoplasmic calcium; a difference is that in sperm the source of Ca^{2+} is extracellular whereas in eggs the source is intracellular. In both there is also a release of protons. In eggs this increases cell pH and is critical for activation; in sperm, the proton release may be related to actin polymerization. Changes in egg cortex actin or in sperm acrosomal actin are probably involved in sperm entry into the egg; it is unknown, however, whether changes in egg actin are involved in the turning on of egg metabolism in response to increased pH.

As regards sperm activation, the most important unresolved questions are (1) the nature of receptors of the sperm membrane that bind to egg jelly/vitelline layer and lead to the Ca^{2+} influx, (2) the role of the Ca^{2+} influx and H^+ efflux in exocytosis and actin polymerization, and (3) the role and mechanism of the aggregation response. Is this aggregation critical for fertilization? How is the behavioral change effected?

There are many more questions about egg activation, reflecting in part our greater knowledge about this phenomenon. A major question concerns the role of receptors of the egg surface in activation. Are there receptors only on the vitelline layer? If so, do they function only to prevent interspecies hybridization? Are there receptors on the plasma membrane also? If so, does their interaction with the sperm lead to the membrane depolarization and resultant block to polyspermy? Or is the egg a highly fusible cell in which sperm–egg contact with the plasma membrane leads immediately to fusion, the membrane potential change, and activation of development?

As regards activation, some of the limited questions that can probably be answered in the near future concern (1) the site of calcium in the egg and the mechanism of its release. Is Ca^{2+} in the cortical granules? or in some other cortical vesicle? or as part of some membrane complex? Is release from these stores enzymic? or autocatalytic and ensuing directly from the Ca^{2+} increase? (2) How does Ca^{2+} activate the egg? We know of the O_2-consuming reaction. What is its role? We have hints of an irreversible-activation factor and a cell-division factor. How do these factors work? Are there other undescribed and important consequences of Ca^{2+} release? (3) How is cell pH regulated? What turns on Na^+–H^+ counter transport? Is Ca^{2+} a direct effector? or is Ca^{2+} acting secondarily through its effects on submembranous components, as tubulin? Or through some other messenger, as some product of the Ca^{2+}-stimulated respiration? How does the cell turn off Na^+–H^+ transport? Is there a cellular pH stat?

Finally, one would like to know how the cytoplasmic pH change activates or turns on egg metabolism. Is it through effects on some antagonistic enzyme couple, as protein kinase–protein phosphatase? Or is it through a pH-dependent binding to an inhibitor? Or is it through effects on cell structural proteins, such as actin or tubulin? Answers to many of these questions should be forthcoming in the next few years and will provide new insights into the activation of development at fertilization as well as provide clues to the triggering of programs in the later stages of development.

ACKNOWLEDGMENTS

This article was written while I was a Fellow of the John Simon Guggenheim Foundation, and I thank them for their kind support. I also thank Dr. John Gurdon, in whose laboratory this article was written, for his hospitality and many stimulating discussions. I am also grateful to Drs. William Byrd, Frank Collins, Nicholas Cross, Michael Edidin, Martin Johnson, and Ronald Laskey for their critical comments and to Dr. P. Joseph Butler for sharing with me his ideas on pH and protein aggregation. Finally, especial thanks are due to Mrs. Barbara Rodbard for her help in preparing this manuscript for publication.

REFERENCES

Aketa, K. (1967). *Embryologia* **9,** 238.
Aketa, K., and Ohta, K. (1977). *Dev. Biol.,* (in press).
Aketa, K., and Onitake, K. (1969). *Exp. Cell Res.* **56,** 84.
Aketa, K., Onitake, K., and Tsuzuki, H. (1972). *Exp. Cell Res.* **71,** 27–32.
Arnold, H., and Pette, D. (1970). *Eur. J. Biochem.* **15,** 360.
Azarnia, R., and Chambers, E. L. (1976). *J. Exp. Zool.* **198,** 65.
Baker, P. F., and Presley, R. (1969). *Nature (London)* **221,** 488.
Baxandall, J., Perlman, P., and Afzelius, B. A. (1964). *J. Cell Biol.* **23,** 609.
Berridge, M. J. (1976). *Symp. Soc. Exp. Biol.* **30,** 219–232.
Black, R. E., Baptist, E., and Piland, J. (1967). *Exp. Cell Res.* **48,** 439.
Blomquist, C. H. (1973). *J. Biol. Chem.* **248,** 7044.
Briggs, W., and Rice, H. V. (1972). *Annu. Rev. Plant. Physiol.* **23,** 293.
Bryan, J. (1970). *J. Cell Biol.* **44,** 635.
Butler, P. J. B., Durham, A. C. H., and Klug, A. (1972). *J. Mol. Biol.* **72,** 1.
Byrd, E. W., and Collins, F. D. (1975). *Nature (London)* **257,** 675.
Campanella, C., and Andreucetti, P. (1977). *Dev. Biol.* **56,** 1.
Carroll, E. J., and Epel, D. (1975a). *Exp. Cell Res.* **90,** 429.
Carroll, E. J., and Epel, D. (1975b). *Dev. Biol.* **44,** 22.
Carroll, E. J., Byrd, E. W., and Epel, D. (1977). *Exp. Cell Res.* **108,** 365.
Catteral, W. A., Ray, R., and Morrow, C. S. (1976). *Proc. Natl. Acad. Sci. U.S.A.* **73,** 2682.
Chambers, E. L. (1975). *J. Cell Biol.* **67,** 60a.
Chambers, E. L. (1976). *J. Exp. Zool.* **197,** 149.
Chambers, E. L., Pressman, B. C., and Rose, B. (1974). *Biochem. Biophys. Res. Commun.* **60,** 126.
Citkowitz, E. (1972). *Dev. Biol.* **27,** 494.
Cohen, M. H., and Robertson, A. H. (1971). *J. Theor. Biol.* **31,** 119.
Collins, F. D. (1976). *Dev. Biol.* **49,** 381.
Collins, F. D. (1978). In preparation.

Collins, F. D., and Byrd, E. W. (1977). In preparation.

Collins, F. D., and Epel, D. (1977). *Exp. Cell Res.* **106,** 211.

Colwin, L. H., and Colwin, A. L. (1967). *In* "Fertilization: Comparative Morphology, Biochemistry and Immunology" (C. B. Metz and A. Monroy, eds.), Vol. 1, pp. 295–367. Academic Press, New York.

Cone, C. D. and Cone, C. M. (1976). *Science* **192,** 155.

Czihak, G. (1975). "The Sea Urchin Embryo: Biochemistry and Morphogenesis." Springer-Verlag, Berlin and New York.

Dan, J. C., Ohori, Y., and Kushida, H. (1965). *J. Ultrastruct. Res.* **11,** 508.

Decker, G. L., Joseph, D. B., and Lennarz, W. J. (1976). *Dev. Biol.* **53,** 115.

Deshpande, A. K., and Siddiqui, M. A. Q. (1976). *Nature (London)* **263,** 588.

Dulbecco, R., and Elkington, J. (1975). *Proc. Natl. Acad. Sci. U.S.A.* **72,** 1584.

Durham, A. C. H., Finch, J. T., and Klug, A. (1971). *Nature (London), New Biol.* **229,** 37.

Eddy, E. M., and Shapiro, B. M. (1976). *J. Cell Biol.* **71,** 35.

Edelman, G. M. (1976). *Science* **192,** 218.

Epel, D. (1964). *Biochem. Biophys. Res. Commun.* **17,** 62.

Epel, D. (1967). *In* "The Molecular Aspects of Development" (R. Deering and M. Trask, eds.), NASA Publ. CR-673. Clearinghouse for Federal Information, Springfield, Virginia.

Epel, D. (1969). *Exp. Cell Res.* **58,** 312.

Epel, D., and Iverson, R. M. (1966). *In* "Control of Energy Metabolism" (B. Chance, R. W. Estabrook, and J. R. Williamson, eds.), p. 267. Academic Press, New York.

Epel, D., and Johnson, J. D. (1976). *In* "Biogenesis and Turnover of Membrane Macromolecules" (J. S. Cook, ed.), pp. 105–120. Raven, New York.

Epel, D., Pressman, B. C., Elsaesser, S., and Weaver, A. M. (1969). *In* "The Cell Cycle: Gene-Enzyme Interactions" (G. Padilla, G. L. Whitson, and I. Cameron, eds.), pp. 278–298. Academic Press, New York.

Epel, D., Steinhardt, R. A., Humphreys, T., and Mazia, D. (1974). *Dev. Biol.* **40,** 245.

Epel, D., Cross, N., and Epel, N. (1977). *Dev., Growth & Differ.* **19,** 15.

Fahey, R. C., Mikolajczyk, S. D., Meier, G. P., Epel, D., and Carroll, E. J. (1976). *Biochim. Biophys. Acta* **437,** 445.

Fodor, E. J. B., Ako, H., and Walsh, K. A. (1975). *Biochemistry* **14,** 4923.

Foerder, C., Eddy, E. M., and Shapiro, B. M. (1977). *Fed. Proc., Fed. Am. Soc. Exp. Biol.* **36,** 926.

Garbers, D. L., and Hardman, S. (1975). *Nature (London)* **257,** 677.

Gilkey, J. C., Ridgeway, E. B., Jaffe, L. F., and Reynolds, G. T. (1977). *Biophys. J.* **17,** 277A.

Giudice, G. (1973). "Developmental Biology of the Sea Urchin Embryo." Academic Press, New York.

Glaser, O. (1915). *Biol. Bull.* **28,** 149.

Gould-Somero, M., Holland, L. Z., and Paul, M. (1977). *Dev. Biol.* **58,** 111.

Hartmann, J. F., and Hutchison, C. F. (1974). *J. Reprod. Fertil.* **37,** 443.

Harvey, E. B. (1956). "The American *Arbacia* and Other Sea Urchins." Princeton Univ. Press, Princeton, New Jersey.

Hörstadius, S. (1973). "Experimental Embryology of Echinoderms." Oxford Univ. Press, London and New York.

Hultin, T. (1950). *Exp. Cell Res.* **1,** 159.

Isaka, S., Kanatani, H., and Suzaki, N. (1966). *Exp. Cell Res.* **44,** 66.

Isono, N., and Yasumasu, I. (1968). *Exp. Cell Res.* **50,** 616.

Ito, S., and Loewenstein, W. R. (1965). *Science* **150,** 909.

Jaffe, L. A. (1976). *Nature (London)* **261,** 68.

Jaffe, L. A., and Robinson, K. (1977). *Dev. Biol.* (in press).

Johnson, J. D., and Epel, D. (1975). *Proc. Natl. Acad. Sci. U.S.A.* **72,** 4474.

Johnson, J. D., Epel, D., and Paul, M. (1976). *Nature (London)* **262,** 661.

Kamine, J., and Rubin, H. (1976). *Nature (London)* **263,** 143.

Kane, R. (1974). *Exp. Cell Res.* **81,** 301.

Kroeger, H. (1966). *Exp. Cell Res.* **41,** 64.

Kroeger, H., Trosch, W., and Muller, G. (1973). *Exp. Cell Res.* **80,** 329.

Lallier, R. (1970). *Exp. Cell Res.* **63,** 460.

Lallier, R. (1971). *Experientia* **27,** 1323.

Levine, A. E., Fodor, E. J. B., and Walsh, K. A. (1977). *Fed. Proc. Fed. Am. Soc. Exp. Biol.* **36,** 811.

Lindemann, B., and Van Driessche, W. (1977). *Science* **195,** 292.

Loeb, J. (1913). "Artificial Parthenogenesis and Fertilization." Univ. of Chicago Press, Chicago, Illinois.

Longo, F. G., and Schuel, H. (1973). *Dev. Biol.* **34,** 187.

Longo, F. G., Schuel, H., and Wilson, W. L. (1974). *Dev. Biol.* **41,** 192.

Lopo, A. and Vacquier, V. D. (1977). *Nature (London)* **269,** 590.

Lowenstein, J. M. (1960). *J. Theor. Biol.* **1,** 98.

Luckasen, J. R., White, J. G., and Kersey, J. H. (1974). *Proc. Natl. Acad. Sci. U.S.A.* **71,** 5088.

Lundblad, G. (1954). "Proteolytic Activity in Sea Urchin Gametes." Almqvist & Wiksell, Stockholm.

Mazia, D. (1937). *J. Cell. Comp. Physiol.* **10,** 291.

Mazia, D. (1974). *Proc. Natl. Acad. Sci. U.S.A.* **71,** 690.

Mazia, D., and Ruby, A. (1974). *Exp. Cell Res.* **85,** 167.

Mazia, D., Schatten, G., and Steinhardt, R. A. (1975). *Proc. Natl. Acad. Sci. U.S.A.* **72,** 4469.

Meech, R. A. (1976). *Symp. Soc. Exp. Biol.* **30,** 161–192.

Metz, C. B. (1967). *In* "Fertilization: Comparative Morphology, Biochemistry and Immunology" (C. B. Metz and A. Monroy, eds.), Vol. 1, pp. 163–236. Academic Press, New York.

Miller, R. (1973). *In* "Behavior of Microorganisms" (A. Pery-Miravete, ed.), pp. 31–47. Plenum, New York.

Miller, R. L. (1975). *Nature (London)* **254,** 244.

Nakamura, M., and Yasumasu, I. (1974). *J. Gen. Physiol.* **63,** 374.

Nakashima, S. K., and Sugiyama, M. (1969). *Dev. Growth Differ.* **11,** 115.

Nath, J., and Rebhun, L. I. (1976). *J. Cell Biol.* **68,** 440.

Newman, I. A., and Briggs, W. R. (1972). *Plant Physiol.* **50,** 687.

Nishioka, D., and Epel, D. (1977). *J. Cell Biol.* **75,** 40A.

Paul, M. (1975a). *Exp. Cell Res.* **90,** 137.

Paul, M. (1975b). *Dev. Biol.* **43,** 299.

Paul, M., and Epel, D. (1971). *Exp. Cell Res.* **65,** 281.

Paul, M., and Epel, D. (1975). *Exp. Cell Res.* **94,** 1–6.

Paul, M., Johnson, J. D., and Epel, D. (1976). *J. Exp. Zool.* **197,** 127.

Perry, G. (1976). *Biol. Bull.* **151,** 423.

Perry, G., and Epel, D. (1975). *Biol. Bull.* **149,** 441.

Perry, G., and Epel, D. (1977). *J. Cell Biol.* **75,** 40a.

Peterson, O. H. (1974). *J. Physiol. (London)* **239,** 674.

Poste, G., and Allison, A. C. (1973). *Biochim. Biophys. Acta* **300,** 421.

Presley, R., and Baker, P. F. (1970). *J. Exp. Biol.* **52,** 455.

Rebhun, L. I., White, D., Sander, G., and Ivy, N. (1973). *Exp. Cell Res.* **77,** 312.

Reed, P., and Lardy, H. (1972). *In* "The Role of Membranes in Metabolic Regulations" (M. A. Mehlman and R. W. Hanson, eds.), pp. 111–131. Academic Press, New York.

Rensing, L., and Fischer, M. (1975). *Cell Differ.* **4,** 209.

Ridgeway, E. B., Gilkey, J. C., and Jaffe, L. F. (1977). *Proc. Natl. Acad. Sci. U.S.A.* **74,** 623.

Rothschild, Lord, (1956). "Fertilization." Methuen, London.

Rothschild, Lord, and Swann, M. M. (1954). *J. Exp. Biol.* **29,** 469.

Rozengurt, E., and Heppel, L. A. (1975). *Proc. Natl. Acad. Sci. U.S.A.* **72,** 4492.

Runnstrom, J., and Manelli, H. (1964). *Exp. Cell Res.* **35,** 157.

Sano, K., and Mohri, H. (1976). *Science* **192,** 1339.

Schmell, E., Earles, B. J., Breux, C., and Lennarz, W. J. (1977). *J. Cell Biol.* **72,** 35.

Schuel, H., Wilson, W. L., Chen, K., and Lorand, L. (1973). *Dev. Biol.* **34,** 175.

Schuel, H., Longo, F. J., Wilson, W. L., and Troll, W. (1976). *Dev. Biol.* **49,** 178.

Schuetz, A. W. (1975). *J. Exp. Zool.* **191,** 443.

Shapiro, B. M. (1975). *Dev. Biol.* **46,** 88.

Shen, S. S., and Steinhardt, R. A. (1978). *Nature (London)* (in press).

Stearns, L. W. (1974). "Sea Urchin Development. Cellular and Molecular Aspects." Dowden, Hutchinson & Ross, Stroudsville, Pennsylvania.

Steinhardt, R. A., and Epel, D. (1974). *Proc. Natl. Acad. Sci. U.S.A.* **71,** 1915.

Steinhardt, R. A., and Mazia, D. (1972). *Nature (London)* **241,** 400.

Steinhardt, R. A., Lundin, L., and Mazia, D. (1971). *Proc. Natl. Acad. Sci. U.S.A.* **68,** 2426.

Steinhardt, R. A., Epel, D., Carroll, E. J., and Yanagimachi, R. (1974). *Nature (London)* **252,** 41.

Steinhardt, R. A., Zucker, R., and Schatten, G. (1977). *Dev. Biol.* (in press).

Summers, R. G., and Hylander, B. L. (1976). *Exp. Cell Res.* **100,** 190.

Summers, R. G., Hylander, B. L., Colwin, L. H., and Colwin, A. L. (1975). *Am. Zool.* **15,** 523.

Summers, R. G., Talbot, P., Klough, E. M., Hylander, B. L., and Franklin, L. E. (1976). *J. Exp. Zool.* **196,** 381.

Surani, A., and Kaufman, M. H. (1977). *Dev. Biol.* (in press).

Takahashi, Y. M., and Sugiyama, M. (1973). *Dev., Growth & Differ.* **15,** 261.

Tegner, M. J. (1974). Ph.D. Thesis, University of California, San Diego.

Tegner, M. J., and Epel, D. (1973). *Science* **179,** 685.

Tegner, M. J., and Epel, D. (1976). *J. Exp. Zool.* **197,** 31.

Tezuko, T., and Yamamoto, Y. (1972). *Plant Physiol.* **50,** 458.

Tilney, L. G. (1976). *J. Cell Biol.* **69,** 73.

Tilney, L. G., Hatano, S., Ishikawa, H., and Mooseker, M. S. (1973). *J. Cell Biol.* **59,** 109.

Tilney, L. G., Kiehart, D. P., Sardet, C., and Tilney, M. (1977). *J. Cell Biol.* (in press).

Timourian, H., and Watchmaker, G. (1970).

Tyler, A. (1949). *Am. Nat.* **83,** 195.

Tyler, A. (1963). *Am. Zool.* **3,** 109.

Tyler, A., Monroy, A., and Metz, C. B. (1956). *Biol. Bull.* **110,** 184.

Uto, N., and Sugiyama, M. (1969). *Dev., Growth & Differ.* **11,** 123.

Vacquier, V. D. (1975). *Dev. Biol.* **43,** 62.

Vacquier, V. D., and Brandriffe, B. (1975). *Dev. Biol.* **47,** 12.

Vacquier, V. D., and Moy, G. W. (1977). *Proc. Natl. Acad. Sci. U.S.A.* **74,** 2456.

Vacquier, V. D., and Payne, J. E. (1973). *Exp. Cell Res.* **82,** 227.

Vacquier, V. D., Epel, D., and Douglas, L. A. (1972a). *Nature (London)* **237,** 34.

Vacquier, V. D., Tegner, M. J., and Epel, D. (1972b). *Nature (London)* **240,** 352.

Vacquier, V. D., Tegner, M. J., and Epel, D. (1973). *Exp. Cell Res.* **80,** 111.

Veron, M., and Shapiro, B. M. (1977). *J. Biol. Chem.* **252,** 1286.

Veron, M., Foerder, C., Eddy, E. M., and Shapiro, B. M. (1977). *Cell* **10,** 321.

Wilt, F. H., and Mazia, D. (1974). *Dev. Biol.* **37,** 422.

Winkler, M. M., and Grainger, J. L. (1978). *Nature (London)* (in press).

Yasumasu, I., Fujiwara, I., and Ishida, K. (1973a). *Biochem. Biophys. Res. Commun.* **54,** 628.

Yasumasu, I., Asami, K., Shoger, R. L., and Fujiwara, A. (1973b). *Exp. Cell Res.* **80,** 361.

Zalin, R. J. (1976). *Dev. Biol.* **53,** 1.

Ziomek, C. A., and Epel, D. (1975). *Science* **189,** 139.

SUBJECT INDEX

A

Acrosome reaction
  description of, 118–123
  in sea urchin fertilization, 188–190
Activation
  of sperm and egg, in fertilization, 185–246
  diagrams, 239, 240
Agglutinins, of sperm, 112–118
Ammonia, eggs incubated in, fertilization studies on, 226, 229
Antibodies, as fertilization inhibitors, 132–139
Arbacia, sperm nuclei transformations in, 149–184
Autogamy, in ciliates, initiation mechanism, 73–75

B

Blepharisma
  conjugation signals in, 40–43
  gamone induction of cell union in, 54–55
Blepharismone, formula of, 41
BWW medium, composition of, 85

C

Calcium
  in activation of development, 216
  cortical reaction and increase of, 216–222
  in egg fertilization, 210–216
  mechanism, 222–227
Cell metabolism, pH regulation of, 232
Cells
  communication and union of, in ciliate conjugation, 37–82
    continuous stimulation in, 55
    hypothetical mechanism, 66–67
    protein synthesis, 58–61
    subliminal stimuli, 56–58
    ultrastructural changes, 61–66

Chemotaxis
  in ciliate conjugation, 46–47
  in fertilization, 109–111
Chromatin
  paternally derived
    activity changes in, 173–176
    nuclear protein changes in, 165–168
    transformations of, 160–165
Ciliates
  conjugation mechanisms in, 37–82
  meiosis initiation in, 67–75
  nuclear systems and sexual reproduction in, 67
Conjugation
  in ciliates, 37–82
    cell communication, 46
    chemotactic communication, 46–47
    signals, 43–46
Cortical granules, protease activity in, 218–222

E

Egg(s)
  activation of, 129–132, 234–237
    cell-division factors, 236–237
    experimental analysis, 201–203
    irreversible factors, 235–236
    in sea urchin gamete fertilization, 185–246
  cross-fertilized, pronuclear development and activity in, 158–160
  cytoplasm, sperm nucleus interaction with, 95–100
  Fab antibody effects on, 134–137
  jelly, sperm attachment to, 124–125
  lectin effects on, 137–139
  membrane potential changes in, in fertilization, 203–210
  receptors for sperm on, 194–197
    role in fertilization, 107–147
  sperm attachment and binding to, 123–132
  sperm entry into, 197–200
  sperm fusion with, 197–200

247

CONTENTS OF PREVIOUS VOLUMES

A
B   8
C   9
D   0
E   1
F   2
G   3
H   4
I   5
J   6